PROGRESS IN

Nucleic Acid Research and Molecular Biology

Volume 27

PROGRESS IN

Nucleic Acid Research and Molecular Biology

edited by

WALDO E. COHN

Biology Division
Oak Ridge National Laboratory
Oak Ridge, Tennessee

Volume 27

1982

ACADEMIC PRESS

A Subsidiary of Harcourt Brace Jovanovich, Publishers

New York London
Paris San Diego San Francisco São Paulo Tokyo Toronto

ACADEMIC PRESS, INC.
111 Fifth Avenue, New York, New York 10003

United Kingdom Edition published by
ACADEMIC PRESS, INC. (LONDON) LTD.
24/28 Oval Road, London NW1 7DX

LIBRARY OF CONGRESS CATALOG CARD NUMBER: 63–15847

ISBN 0–12–540027–6

PRINTED IN THE UNITED STATES OF AMERICA

82 83 84 85   9 8 7 6 5 4 3 2 1

Contents

Poly(adenosine diphosphate ribose)

Paul Mandel, Hideo Okazaki, and Claude Niedergang

The Regulatory Function of Poly(A) and Adjacent 3' Sequences in Translated RNA

Uriel Z. Littauer and Hermona Soreq

tRNA-like Structures in the Genomes of RNA Viruses

Anne-Lise Haenni, Sadhna Joshi, and François Chapeville

Mechanism of Interferon Action: Progress toward Its Understanding

Ganes C. Sen

RNA-Helix-Destabilizing Proteins

John O. Thomas and Wlodzimierz Szer

Nucleotide Cyclases

Laurence S. Bradham and Wai Yiu Cheung

Cyclic Nucleotide Control of Protein Kinases

R. K. Sharma

List of Contributors

Numbers in parentheses indicate the pages on which the authors' contributions begin.

LAURENCE S. BRADHAM (189), *Department of Biochemistry, University of Tennessee Center for Health Sciences, Memphis, Tennessee 38163*

FRANÇOIS CHAPEVILLE (85), *Institut de Recherche en Biologie Moléculaire du Centre National de la Recherche Scientifique, Université Paris VII, 75221 Paris Cedex-05, France*

WAI YIU CHEUNG (189), *Saint Jude Children's Research Hospital, Memphis, Tennessee 38101*

ANNE-LISE HAENNI (85), *Institut de Recherche en Biologie Moléculaire du Centre National de la Recherche Scientifique, Université Paris VII, 75221 Paris Cedex-05, France*

SADHNA JOSHI (85), *Institut de Recherche en Biologie Moléculaire du Centre National de la Recherche Scientifique, Université Paris VII, 75221 Paris Cedex-05, France*

URIEL Z. LITTAUER (53), *Department of Neurobiology, The Weizmann Institute of Science, Rehovot, Israel 76100*

PAUL MANDEL (1), *Centre de Neurochimie du CNRS, 67084 Strasbourg Cedex, France*

CLAUDE NIEDERGANG (1), *Centre de Neurochimie du CNRS, 67084 Strasbourg Cedex, France*

HIDEO OKAZAKI (1), *Centre de Neurochimie du CNRS, 67084 Strasbourg Cedex, France*

GANES C. SEN (105), *Memorial Sloan-Kettering Cancer Center, New York, New York 10021*

R. K. SHARMA (233), *Department of Biochemistry, University of Tennessee Center for the Health Sciences, Memphis, Tennessee 38163*

HERMONA SOREQ (53), *Department of Neurobiology, The Weizmann Institute of Science, Rehovot, Israel 76100*

WLODZIMIERZ SZER (157), *Department of Biochemistry, New York University School of Medicine, New York, New York 10016*

JOHN O. THOMAS (157), *Department of Biochemistry, New York University School of Medicine, New York, New York 10016*

Abbreviations and Symbols

All contributors to this Series are asked to use the terminology (abbreviations and symbols) recommended by the IUPAC-IUB Commission on Biochemical Nomenclature (CBN) and approved by IUPAC and IUB, and the Editor endeavors to assure conformity. These Recommendations have been published in many journals (1, 2) and compendia (3) in four languages and are available in reprint form from the Office of Biochemical Nomenclature (OBN), as stated in each publication, and are therefore considered to be generally known. Those used in nucleic acid work, originally set out in section 5 of the first Recommendations (1) and subsequently revised and expanded (2, 3), are given in condensed form (I–V) below for the convenience of the reader. Authors may use them without definition, when necessary.

I. Bases, Nucleosides, Mononucleotides

1. *Bases* (in tables, figures, equations, or chromatograms) are symbolized by Ade, Gua, Hyp, Xan, Cyt, Thy, Oro, Ura; Pur = any purine, Pyr = any pyrimidine, Base = any base. The prefixes S–, H_2, F–, Br, Me, etc., may be used for modifications of these.

2. *Ribonucleosides* (in tables, figures, equations, or chromatograms) are symbolized, in the same order, by Ado, Guo, Ino, Xao, Cyd, Thd, Ord, Urd (Ψrd), Puo, Pyd, Nuc. Modifications may be expressed as indicated in (1) above. Sugar residues may be specified by the prefixes r (optional), d (=deoxyribo), a, x, l, etc., to these, or by two three-letter symbols, as in Ara-Cyt (for aCyd) or dRib-Ade (for dAdo).

3. *Mono-, di-, and triphosphates of nucleosides* (5') are designated by NMP, NDP, NTP. The N (for "nucleoside") may be replaced by any one of the nucleoside symbols given in II-1 below. 2'-, 3'-, and 5'- are used as prefixes when necessary. The prefix d signifies "deoxy." [Alternatively, nucleotides may be expressed by attaching P to the symbols in (2) above. Thus: P-Ado = AMP; Ado-P = 3'-AMP] cNMP = cyclic 3':5'-NMP; Bt₂cAMP = dibutyryl cAMP, etc.

II. Oligonucleotides and Polynucleotides

1. Ribonucleoside Residues

(a) Common: A, G, I, X, C, T, O, U, Ψ, R, Y, N (in the order of I-2 above).

(b) Base-modified: sI or M for thioinosine = 6-mercaptopurine ribonucleoside; sU or S for thiouridine; brU or B for 5-bromouridine; hU or D for 5,6-dihydrouridine; i for isopentenyl; f for formyl. Other modifications are similarly indicated by appropriate *lower-case* prefixes (in contrast to I-1 above) (2, 3).

(c) Sugar-modified: prefixes are d, a, x, or l as in I-2 above; alternatively, by *italics* or boldface type (with definition) unless the entire chain is specified by an appropriate prefix. The 2'-O-methyl group is indicated by *suffix* m (e.g., -Am- for 2'-O-methyladenosine, but -mA- for 6-methyladenosine).

(d) Locants and multipliers, when necessary, are indicated by superscripts and subscripts, respectively, e.g., -m₂⁶A- = 6-dimethyladenosine; -s⁴U- or -⁴S- = 4-thiouridine; -ac⁴Cm- = 2'-O-methyl-4-acetylcytidine.

(e) When space is limited, as in two-dimensional arrays or in aligning homologous sequences, the prefixes may be placed *over the capital letter*, the suffixes *over the phosphodiester symbol.*

2. Phosphoric Residues [left side = 5', right side = 3' (or 2')]

(a) Terminal: p; e.g., pppN . . . is a polynucleotide with a 5'-triphosphate at one end; Ap is adenosine 3'-phosphate; C > p is cytidine 2':3'-cyclic phosphate (1, 2, 3); p < A is adenosine 3':5'-cyclic phosphate.

(b) Internal: hyphen (for known sequence), comma (for unknown sequence); unknown sequences are enclosed in parentheses. E.g., pA-G-A-C(C$_2$,A,U)A-U-G-C > p is a sequence with a (5′) phosphate at one end, a 2′:3′-cyclic phosphate at the other, and a tetranucleotide of unknown sequence in the middle. (**Only codon triplets should be written without some punctuation separating the residues.**)

3. Polarity, or Direction of Chain

The symbol for the phosphodiester group (whether hyphen or comma or parentheses, as in 2b) represents a 3′-5′ link (i.e., a 5′ . . . 3′ chain) unless otherwise indicated by appropriate numbers. "Reverse polarity" (a chain proceeding from a 3′ terminus at left to a 5′ terminus at right) may be shown by numerals or by right-to-left arrows. Polarity in any direction, as in a two-dimensional array, may be shown by appropriate rotation of the (capital) letters so that 5′ is at left, 3′ at right when the letter is viewed right-side-up.

4. Synthetic Polymers

The complete name or the appropriate group of symbols (see II-1 above) of the repeating unit, **enclosed in parentheses if complex or a symbol,** is either (a) preceded by "poly," or (b) followed by a subscript "n" or appropriate number. **No space follows "poly"** (2, 5).

The conventions of II-2b are used to specify known or unknown (random) sequence, e.g., polyadenylate = poly(A) or A$_n$, a simple homopolymer;

poly(3 adenylate, 2 cytidylate) = poly(A$_3$C$_2$) or (A$_3$,C$_2$)$_n$, an *irregular* copolymer of A and C in 3 : 2 proportions;

poly(deoxyadenylate-deoxythymidylate) = poly[d(A-T)] or poly(dA-dT) or (dA-dT)$_n$ or d(A-T)$_n$, an *alternating* copolymer of dA and dT;

poly(adenylate,guanylate,cytidylate,uridylate) = poly(A,G,C,U) or (A,G,C,U)$_n$, a random assortment of A, G, C, and U residues, proportions unspecified.

The prefix copoly or oligo may replace poly, if desired. The subscript "n" may be replaced by numerals indicating actual size, e.g., A$_n$·dT$_{12-18}$.

III. Association of Polynucleotide Chains

1. *Associated* (e.g., H-bonded) chains, or bases within chains, are indicated by a *center dot* (not a hyphen or a plus sign) separating the *complete* names or symbols, e.g.:

$$\text{poly(A)} \cdot \text{poly(U)} \qquad \text{or} \qquad \text{A}_n \cdot \text{U}_m$$
$$\text{poly(A)} \cdot 2 \text{ poly(U)} \qquad \text{or} \qquad \text{A}_n \cdot 2\text{U}_m$$
$$\text{poly(dA-dC)} \cdot \text{poly(dG-dT)} \qquad \text{or} \qquad (\text{dA-dC})_n \cdot (\text{dG-dT})_m.$$

2. *Nonassociated* chains are separated by the plus sign, e.g.:

$$2[\text{poly(A)} \cdot \text{poly(U)}] \rightarrow \text{poly(A)} \cdot 2 \text{ poly(U)} + \text{poly(A)}$$
$$\text{or} \qquad 2[\text{A}_n \cdot \text{U}_m] \rightarrow \text{A}_n \cdot 2\text{U}_m + \text{A}_n.$$

3. Unspecified or unknown association is expressed by a comma (again meaning "unknown") between the completely specified chains.

Note: In all cases, each chain is completely specified in one or the other of the two systems described in II-4 above.

IV. Natural Nucleic Acids

RNA	ribonucleic acid or ribonucleate
DNA	deoxyribonucleic acid or deoxyribonucleate
mRNA; rRNA; nRNA	messenger RNA; ribosomal RNA; nuclear RNA
hnRNA	heterogeneous nuclear RNA
D-RNA; cRNA	"DNA-like" RNA; complementary RNA

mtDNA	mitochondrial DNA
tRNA	transfer (or acceptor or amino-acid-accepting) RNA; replaces sRNA, which is not to be used for any purpose
aminoacyl-tRNA	"charged" tRNA (i.e., tRNA's carrying aminoacyl residues); may be abbreviated to AA-tRNA
alanine tRNA or tRNA^{Ala}, etc.	tRNA normally capable of accepting alanine, to form alanyl-tRNA, etc.
alanyl-tRNA or alanyl-tRNA^{Ala}	The same, with alanyl residue covalently attached.

[*Note*: fMet = formylmethionyl; hence tRNA^{fMet}, identical with tRNA$_f^{Met}$]

Isoacceptors are indicated by appropriate subscripts, i.e., tRNA$_1^{Ala}$, tRNA$_2^{Ala}$, etc.

V. Miscellaneous Abbreviations

P_i, PP_i	inorganic orthophosphate, pyrophosphate
RNase, DNase	ribonuclease, deoxyribonuclease
t_m (not T_m)	melting temperature (°C)

Others listed in Table II of Reference 1 may also be used without definition. No others, with or without definition, are used unless, in the opinion of the editor, they increase the ease of reading.

Enzymes

In naming enzymes, the 1978 recommendations of the IUB Commission on Biochemical Nomenclature (4) are followed as far as possible. At first mention, each enzyme is described *either* by its systematic name *or* by the equation for the reaction catalyzed *or* by the recommended trivial name, followed by its EC number in parentheses. Thereafter, a trivial name may be used. Enzyme names are not to be abbreviated except when the substrate has an approved abbreviation (e.g., ATPase, but not LDH, is acceptable).

References*

1. *JBC* **241**, 527 (1966); *Bchem* **5**, 1445 (1966); *BJ* **101**, 1 (1966); *ABB* **115**, 1 (1966), **129**, 1 (1969); and elsewhere.†
2. *EJB* **15**, 203 (1970); *JBC* **245**, 5171 (1970); *JMB* **55**, 299 (1971); and elsewhere.†
3. "Handbook of Biochemistry" (G. Fasman, ed.), 3rd ed. Chemical Rubber Co., Cleveland, Ohio, 1970, 1975, Nucleic Acids, Vols. I and II, pp. 3–59.
4. "Enzyme Nomenclature" [Recommendations (1978) of the Nomenclature Committee of the IUB]. Academic Press, New York, 1979.
5. "Nomenclature of Synthetic Polypeptides," *JBC* **247**, 323 (1972); *Biopolymers* **11**, 321 (1972); and elsewhere.†

Abbreviations of Journal Titles

Journals	Abbreviations used
Annu. Rev. Biochem.	ARB
Arch. Biochem. Biophys.	ABB
Biochem. Biophys. Res. Commun.	BBRC

*Contractions for names of journals follow.

†Reprints of all CBN Recommendations are available from the Office of Biochemical Nomenclature (W. E. Cohn, Director), Biology Division, Oak Ridge National Laboratory, Box Y, Oak Ridge, Tennessee 37830, USA.

Biochemistry	Bchem
Biochem. J.	BJ
Biochim. Biophys. Acta	BBA
Cold Spring Harbor Symp. Quant. Biol.	CSHSQB
Eur. J. Biochem.	EJB
Fed. Proc.	FP
Hoppe-Seyler's Z. physiol. Chem.	ZpChem
J. Amer. Chem. Soc.	JACS
J. Bacteriol.	J. Bact.
J. Biol. Chem.	JBC
J. Chem. Soc.	JCS
J. Mol. Biol.	JMB
Nature, New Biology	Nature NB
Nucleic Acid Research	NARes
Proc. Nat. Acad. Sci. U.S.	PNAS
Proc. Soc. Exp. Biol. Med.	PSEBM
Progr. Nucl. Acid Res. Mol. Biol.	This Series

Some Articles Planned for Future Volumes

The Accuracy of Translation
  A. K. ABRAHAM

Hypermodified Nucleosides of tRNA
  A. ADAMIAK

Ribosomal RNA: Structure and Interactions with Proteins
  R. BRIMACOMBE

Participation of Aminoacyl-tRNA Synthetases and tRNAs in Regulatory Processes
  G. NASS

Queuine
  S. NISHIMURA

Template-Directed Synthesis of Oligonucleotides
  L. ORGEL

Nuclear RNA · Protein Interactions
  T. PEDERSON

Viral Inhibition of Host Protein Synthesis
  A. SHATKIN

Ribosomal Proteins: Structure and Function
  A. R. SUBRAMANIAN

Poly(adenosine diphosphate ribose)

PAUL MANDEL,
HIDEO OKAZAKI, AND
CLAUDE NIEDERGANG

Centre de Neurochimie du CNRS
Strasbourg, France

I. Introduction

The first description of poly(adenosine diphosphate ribose) [poly-(ADPR)] polymerase activity was that of Chambon, Weill, and Mandel in 1963 (*1*). They observed that ATP incorporation into an acid-insoluble fraction was enhanced by nicotinamide mononucleotide at least 1000-fold in chicken liver nuclei. Poly(ADPR) was identified as the enzyme product. NAD was shown to be the direct substrate of the poly(ADPR) polymerase (*2–4*). The structure of poly(ADPR) was re-

Progress in Nucleic Acid Research
and Molecular Biology, Vol. 27

ISBN 0-12-540027-6

ported by Chambon *et al.* (2) and by Doly and Petek (5) and was confirmed by the groups of Hayaishi (6) and of Sugimura (7). Poly-(ADPR) polymerase catalyzes the polymerization of the ADPR moiety of NAD. One of the main direct functions of poly(ADPR) polymerase seemed to be covalent ADP-ribosylation of proteins, since poly(ADPR) is generally found to be bound covalently to various proteins, especially nuclear proteins (8). The natural occurrence of poly(ADPR) was first demonstrated *in vivo* in chicken liver nuclei by Doly and Mandel (9).

An enzyme that hydrolyzes poly(ADPR) occurs in calf thymus (10) and in rat liver nuclei (11). The reaction products are ADPR and oligo(ADPR). This poly(ADPR) glycohydrolase does not split the linkage by which the polymer is bound to protein, but an enzyme that splits the bond between ADPR and histone was subsequently found (12). Snake venom phosphodiesterase (EC 3.1.4.1) is often used for chain-length analysis of the polymer. It splits the pyrophosphate bonds, yielding 5'-AMP and 2'-(5''-phosphoribosyl)-5'-AMP (also called PR-AMP, ΨADPR, or isoADPR). Figure 1 illustrates the structure of poly(ADPR) and the catalytic sites of the enzymes involved in ADP-ribosylation and degradation.

Several hypotheses have been formulated concerning the roles of poly(ADPR) and poly(ADPR) polymerase (or ADPR-transferase), and involvement of poly(ADPR) in DNA duplication and in cell prolifera-

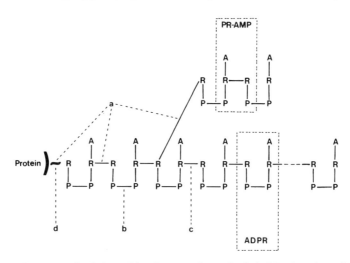

FIG. 1. Structure of poly(ADPR) and enzymology of poly(ADP-ribosylation). Synthesizing enzyme: poly(ADPR) polymerase (a). Degrading enzymes: venom phosphodiesterase (b); poly(ADPR) glycohydrolase (c); ADPR-protein hydrolase (d).

tion has been strongly suggested. Similarly, it was suggested that poly(ADPR) polymerase is involved in DNA repair. Participation in chromatin structure was suggested through ADP-ribosylation of histones, and ADP-ribosylation of other proteins was suggested to be involved in several other mechanisms.

Several comprehensive reviews that cover the details of work on the subject up to 1977 have appeared (13–16). The proceedings of the four last international meetings (17–20) have been published and are discussed in these reviews. Two brief reviews concerning chromatin structure and ADP-ribosylation of nuclear proteins have been published by Smulson (21) and by Hilz et al. (22), respectively.

This review includes published data from 1977 up to December 1980 and the proceedings of a seminar (23) held in October 1979 as well as unpublished results and personal communications kindly provided by many colleagues dealing with the following: higher-order structure of poly(ADPR); poly(ADPR) polymerase purification and its properties; molecular mechanisms of histone- and elongation factor (EF-2)-ADP-ribosylation; DNA-repair as one of the biological functions of poly(ADPR) polymerase; and new techniques for poly(ADPR) studies, including immunological analysis.

II. Poly(adenosine diphosphate ribose)

A. Structure of Poly(ADPR)

Poly(ADPR) is a unique homopolymer synthesized enzymically from NAD by poly(ADPR) polymerase, a ubiquitous enzyme found in the nuclei of all eukaryotic cells tested as well as in some prokaryotic cells (for reviews see 13–16). The ADPR moieties of NAD are polymerized through ribose–ribose (1″-2′) glycosidic bonds with concomitant release of nicotinamide moieties (Fig. 1). The structure of the ribose–ribose moiety of poly(ADPR) was determined to be that of a 2-O-α-D-ribofuranosyl-D-ribofuranose, from the ^{13}C chemical shifts of methyl-α- and methyl-β-D-ribofuranosides, and of the downfield displacement of ^{13}C NMR signals by glycosidic bond formation (24).

Poly(ADPR) is generally found covalently bound to various nuclear proteins. After digestion with Pronase and deproteinization with phenol, poly(ADPR) can be separated from the DNA or RNA fraction by hydroxyapatite column chromatography (25). The peak fractions from the hydroxyapatite column may each be separated by polyacrylamide gel electrophoresis into two distinct subfractions differing in chain length and terminal structure (26). Type-1 oligo(ADPR) has a complete structure and type-2 oligo(ADPR) has a terminal degraded structure, suggesting the existence of a new phosphodiesterase hydrolyzing poly(ADPR) endonucleolytically, like snake venom phosphodiesterase, or exonucleolytically from both termini. Individual polymers up to at least 33 units can be completely separated according to their chain length by electrophoresis in sodium dodecyl sulfate on polyacrylamide gels (27). Nuclei of Ehrlich ascites tumor cells produce a poly(ADPR) pattern distinctly different from that of rat liver nuclei with respect to the chain-length distribution (27).

Electrophoretic analysis on polyacrylamide gel has led to the discovery of a branched structure of poly(ADPR) (28). From the discrepancy between the size (more than 4.5×10^5) estimated by electrophoresis and the chain length determined by the ratio of total radioactivity to that derived from the terminus, it appears that the polymer has a branched structure (28). The trisaccharide 2'-[5-phospho-2(or 3)-(5-phosphoribosyl)ribosyl]adenosine 5'-phosphate, or 5-phosphoribosyl-(1 → 2 or 3)-5-phosphoribosyl-(1 → 2)-5-phosphoribosyl-(1 → 9)-adenine, was obtained by phosphodiesterase hydrolysis of poly(ADPR) (29). The existence of such a compound is evidence for a branched structure of poly(ADPR), previously thought to be a linear molecule (Fig. 1). The frequency of branching appeared to be about 1 per 20–30 ADPR residues of high-molecular-weight poly(ADPR). The finding of a branched structure suggests that poly(ADPR) may play an important role in chromatin architecture as well as in covalent modification of nuclear proteins. The natural occurrence as well as the enzymic mechanisms underlying the synthesis of this branched poly(ADPR) is yet unknown. If this branched polymer is also synthesized by poly(ADPR) polymerase, the enzyme catalyzes three different reactions: (*a*) ADPR transfer to acceptor protein (initiation); (*b*) addition of ADPR units on preexisting mono- or oligo(ADPR) (chain elongation); and (*c*) addition of ADPR units onto poly(ADPR) chains (branching).

B. Natural Occurrence of Poly(ADPR)

Poly(ADPR) was first discovered as an *in vitro* reaction product (1–4). There are several reports suggesting the natural occurrence of poly(ADPR) (see for review 13–16).

A specific antibody against purified poly(ADPR) synthesized *in vitro* affords a sensitive, reproducible radioimmunoassay system (30) that has produced evidence for the natural occurrence of poly(ADPR) in calf thymus, liver, kidney, brain, pancreas, and spleen (31). Naturally occurring poly(ADPR) in calf thymus is composed of molecules of various chain lengths like that synthesized by an *in vitro* system. Calf thymus was estimated to contain about 0.02 μg of poly(ADPR) per milligram of DNA (31).

Naturally occurring antibodies to poly(ADPR) suggest that poly-(ADPR) occurs naturally in human beings, although the evidence is indirect and is a result of complex biological events. The binding activities of the sera of patients with systemic lupus erythematosus (SLE) to [14C]poly(ADPR) were higher than those of the sera of normal individuals, and binding activities of the sera of SLE patients to [14C]poly(ADPR) were attributable to immunoglobulins, mainly to IgG, but not to nonspecific interactions between [14C]poly(ADPR) and IgG (32). The specificity of the binding was verified by inhibition tests using unlabeled poly(ADPR) and 14 related compounds. During this study, a population of antibodies cross-reacting with poly(A) · poly(U) was found among the antibodies to poly(ADPR), and this population could be completely removed by absorption of the SLE sera with poly(A) · poly(U). Moreover, rabbit antibodies to poly(ADPR) do not cross-react at all with synthetic homopolynucleotides. The mechanism of induction was studied with rabbits immunized with poly(ADPR) or poly(A) · poly(U) (33). A rabbit immunized with poly(A) · poly(U) induced antibodies specific to poly(ADPR) as well as antibodies specific to poly(A) · poly(U). In contrast, a rabbit immunized with a complex of poly(ADPR) with MBSA (methylated bovine serum albumin) in Freund's complete adjuvant showed no antibody activity to poly(A) · poly(U), although a sevenfold higher specific activity of antibody to poly(ADPR) was detected compared to that of rabbit immunized with poly(A) · poly(U).

The significance of antibodies to poly(ADPR) in systemic lupus erythematosus has been further studied (34). Of 82 human sera tested, antibodies to poly(ADPR) were found only in the SLE and in SLE-like rheumatic diseases (42 sera). Anti-DNA antibodies, on the other hand, were found not only in the SLE and SLE-like diseases, but also in rheumatoid arthritis and chronic active hepatitis. Therefore, estimation of poly(ADPR) binding was more specific for, and more discriminatory of SLE from other diseases than the estimation of double-stranded DNA binding. The results indicate that the estimation of poly(ADPR) binding in serum may be more useful in the diagnosis of SLE than the presently employed estimation of DNA binding using the Amersham kit. DNA · (anti-DNA) immune complexes were detected in some of the SLE sera after DNase I digestion, confirming earlier reports of the existence of circulating DNA · (anti-DNA) complexes in SLE patients. Snake venom phosphodiesterase treatment of some of the SLE sera also resulted in increased poly(ADPR) binding activity, suggesting the existence of poly(ADPR) · [anti-poly(ADPR)] immune complexes in the circulation of SLE patients. This observation raises the possibility that poly(ADPR) immune complexes may play some part in the pathogenesis of some cases of SLE.

C. Some Direct Biological Functions of Poly(ADPR)

Inhibition of rat liver Ca^{2+}, Mg^{2+}-dependent endonuclease activity by its poly(ADP-ribosylation) is a well known example of a biological function of poly(ADPR) (35, 36). Direct inhibition of deoxyribonuclease activity in an extract of rat liver nuclei by poly(ADPR) has been observed (37). Only one of the two DNase activities separated by DEAE-cellulose column chromatography was inhibited by poly-(ADPR) and poly(A).

The myeloid leukemia cells of mice differentiate into cells with phagocytic activity, Fc receptors, and lysozyme activity on treatment with poly(ADPR) (38). Cells with morphological characteristics of mature macrophages and granulocytes also appear on incubation with poly(ADPR). Dextran sulfate and polyvinylsulfate are also effective for the induction of phagocytic cells, but poly(A), poly(U), poly(C), poly(I) · poly(C), and poly(A) · poly(U) were not (38).

When a chromatin-bound neutral protease inhibitor isolated from rat peritoneal macrophages was incubated with poly(ADPR) glycohydrolase from calf thymus, the inhibitory potency was markedly decreased (39). An authentic poly(ADPR), with a mean chain length of approximately 30 ADPR units, produced significant inhibition of the neutral protease isolated from macrophage chromatin. No such inhibition was produced by DNA, RNA, poly(A), poly(C), or monomeric ADPR. It was concluded that the inhibitor isolated is identical with poly(ADPR) with an average chain length from 4 to 7 ADPR units (39*a*).

III. Poly(ADPR) Polymerase

A. Purification of Poly(ADPR) Polymerase

Poly(ADPR) polymerase is a chromatin-bound nuclear enzyme. The localization of this enzyme in cell nuclei suggests that the enzyme may play an important role in nuclear events. The enzyme activity was measured by the incorporation of labeled ADPR from radioactive NAD into the acid-insoluble fraction. To elucidate the biological function of this enzyme, the analysis of the enzyme reaction is indispensable. The purification of poly(ADPR) polymerase was one important step for this, as well as the analysis of the enzymic reaction products, poly(ADPR) or ADP-ribosylated proteins. Extensive enzyme purifications have been achieved by several groups, including ours. Much information is now available, and this is the first review describing the properties of purified poly(ADPR) polymerases obtained from various tissues or cell cultures.

Poly(ADPR) polymerase has been purified from calf thymus (40–45), pig thymus (46, 47), rat liver nuclei (48), Ehrlich ascites tumor cells (49, 50), and HeLa cells (51) (Table I). Like other nuclear enzymes, poly(ADPR) polymerase is highly unstable and insoluble under physiological conditions. Solubilization of the enzyme was achieved by high salt concentrations (40–42, 48, 51) or by DNase digestion (42). Enzyme activity was separated from the bulk of DNA by ultracentrifugation (41, 42), hydroxyapatite column chromatography (48), or protamine treatment (45). Affinity column chromatography with nicotinamide-Sepharose (40) or DNA-agarose (49) has been successfully utilized for enzyme purification. Enzyme activity was stabilized by utilization of protease inhibitors such as sodium bisulfite or phenylmethylsulfonyl fluoride (α-tosyl fluoride, αTosF) as well as SH-reagents, glycerol, and high salt concentration. Subzero temperature chromatography with an aqueous organic solvent, ethylene glycol, was also successfully used as an enzyme stabilizer during the enzyme purification (46, 47).

TABLE I
POLY(ADPR) POLYMERASES EXTENSIVELY PURIFIED

Enzyme (tissue)	Purification (fold)	Yield (%)	Purity[a]	References
Calf thymus	3100	6	1 band (M_r 130,000)	41, 42
Bovine thymus	1300	17	1 band (M_r 130,000)	44
Calf thymus	1250	14	1 band (M_r 120,000)	45
Pig thymus	9200	46	1 band (M_r 63,500)	47
Rat liver	5300	15	1 major band (M_r 50,000)	48
Ehrlich ascites tumor cells	700	21	1 major band (M_r 130,000)	49
HeLa cells	450	24	1 major band (M_r 112,000)	51

[a] Tested by electrophoresis on polyacrylamide gels containing sodium dodecyl sulfate. M_r = molecular weight.

B. Properties of Purified Poly(ADPR) Polymerase

Molecular weights of 120,000 ($\pm$10,000), 63,000 ($\pm$3000), and 50,000 were found for calf thymus (*42, 44, 45*), Ehrlich ascites (*49*) and Hela enzymes (*51*), pig thymus enzyme (*47*) and rat liver enzyme (*48*), respectively. The amino-acid compositions of enzymes purified from calf thymus and Ehrlich ascites are shown in Table II. The most remarkable feature of this composition is the high number of residues that are either acidic or basic. DNA dependency, cation requirement, SH-reagent requirement for activity are general common properties of purified poly(ADPR) polymerases. Nicotinamide, thymidine, and ADPR inhibit the activity of these purified enzymes.

1. ADP-RIBOSYLATING PROPERTIES

The precise mechanism of poly(ADPR) polymerase reaction has been intensively investigated with purified enzymes and many in-

TABLE II

AMINO-ACID COMPOSITION OF PURIFIED POLY(ADPR) POLYMERASES[a]

Amino acid	Calf thymus enzyme[b]	Calf thymus DNA-independent enzyme[c]	Ehrlich ascites tumor cells enzyme[d]
Alanine	63	75	94
Glycine	73	150	98
Valine	64	49	69
Threonine	47	44	45
Serine	73	107	109
Leucine	87	85	112
Isoleucine	52	49	37
Proline	40	46	59
Methionine	23	3	26
Phenylalanine	33	39	34
Aspartic acid	100	116	113
Lysine	117	104	151
Tyrosine	29	58	34
Glutamic acid	135	178	148
Arginine	33	42	43
Histidine	20	21	23
Cysteine	21	18	17
Tryptophan	21	—[e]	14

[a] The data are expressed as number of amino-acid residues per mole of enzyme.
[b] Data from Ito *et al.* (*45*).
[c] H. Okazaki, C. Niedergang, and P. Mandel, unpublished results.
[d] From Holtlund *et al.* (*50*).
[e] Not determined.

teresting features have been observed. The early reaction product synthesized by purified calf thymus poly(ADPR) polymerase without exogenous acceptor protein is oligo(ADPR) with a mean chain length of 2.6 and tightly bound to the enzyme protein. When ADP-ribosylated material synthesized in the absence or the presence of various histones (with 5000-fold purified rat-liver polymerase) was analyzed by sodium dodecyl sulfate/polyacrylamide gel electrophoresis, the major product in all cases migrated between histones H1 and H3-H2B with the same R_f value of 0.58 relative to the dye (48). No ADPR moved with any of the histones. It was suggested that, in the purified poly(ADPR) polymerase system, histones are not ADP-ribosylated but act as allosteric activators (48).

Histones were the first example among many proteins observed to be modified by poly(ADPR), and the subgroups H1 and H2B have been established as the major acceptors in nuclei (for review, see 14–16, 18). The apparent discrepancy between crude and purified enzyme systems concerning histone utilization suggested various possibilities, such as the existence of two kinds of enzyme, one for initiation and the other for subsequent elongation, or a certain factor(s) or structure necessary for initiation but lost during the purification of the enzyme. In order to examine these possibilities and to obtain a closer insight into the mechanism of poly(ADP-ribosylation), studies were carried out with purified rat liver poly(ADPR) polymerase on the enzymic elongation of chemically synthesized ADPR-histone adducts (52). The fact that chemically bound ADPR is the site of poly(ADP-ribosylation), that is, that the ADPR chain is elongated, is shown by the production of labeled PR-ADPR upon digestion with snake venom phosphodiesterase of an adenine-labeled ADPR-H1 adduct previously incubated with the synthetase and unlabeled NAD. In the presence of the ADPR-(histone-H1) adduct, most (50–90%) of the new chains originated from the preattached ADPR and the remainder from similar structures on an endogenous acceptor contained in the synthetase preparation. These results, taken together, suggested the poly(ADPR) synthetase is primarily engaged in chain elongation, but not in direct ADP-ribosylation of histones (chain initiation); it was also suggested that the latter reaction is probably catalyzed by an as yet unidentified enzyme, or that it requires other factor(s) or conditions.

The conditions of the enzyme reaction were confirmed as extremely important factors in the ADP-ribosylation of histones *in vitro* [with purified poly(ADPR) polymerases] (53–57). A preliminary report with a partially purified enzyme in which ADP-ribosylation of histone H1 was described had already appeared (58), but clear conclusions could not be obtained because of a proteic contamination in the enzyme preparation.

The mechanisms of poly(ADPR) synthesis and the transfer of poly(ADPR) to histone H1 by electrophoretically homogeneous calf thymus poly(ADPR) polymerase containing DNA was examined by analysis of an acid-insoluble radioactive complex obtained after incubation of purified calf thymus DNA-independent poly(ADPR) polymerase with [³H]NAD (53; see also Section III, B, 2) (Fig. 2). This revealed that the enzyme product is a poly(ADP-ribosylated) enzyme and that the mean chain-length of the poly(ADPR) covalently bound to the enzyme was between 20 and 30, while that of the poly(ADP-ribosylated) enzyme described earlier (43) was 2.6. When histone H1 was added to the above reaction mixture, a second acid-insoluble complex in addition to the ADP-ribosylated enzyme was observed, namely, poly(ADP-ribosylated) histone H1. This compound was identified by acid extraction, electrophoresis in the presence of dodecyl sulfate (Fig. 2), and CM-cellulose column chromatography. The mean chain-length of the poly(ADPR) bound covalently to H1 was between 5 and 20.

These results indicate that purified calf thymus poly(ADPR) polymerase can catalyze two different reactions—the transfer of ADPR to acceptor protein (initiation) and the elongation of ADPR chains. Other histone subgroups could also be ADP-ribosylated with this enzyme preparation under the same conditions (54) (Fig. 2). In all cases, poly(ADP-ribosylated) enzyme was detected simultaneously with ADP-ribosylated histones. Each histone subgroup was equally susceptible to ADP-ribosylation. However, under the conditions used, most of the poly(ADPR) chains synthesized were incorporated into the enzyme fraction. We do not as yet know whether or not these results have physiological significance, but we can suggest that poly(ADP-ribosylation) of the enzyme itself may play an important role like histone ADP-ribosylation.

DNA-dependent poly(ADPR) polymerase can also be obtained by removing DNA from the enzyme by hydroxyapatite column chromatography in the presence of 3 M KCl (see 60). This enzyme, as well as histone H1, but not the other histone subfractions, could be ADP-ribosylated, suggesting the importance of endogenous DNA copurified with the enzyme (54).

With the enzyme purified from bovine thymus, two types of enzyme reaction, one Mg^{2+}-dependent and the other one histone-dependent, that separately produce very different reaction products have been observed (55). The product of the Mg^{2+}-dependent reaction was a trypsin-resistant, alkali-stable polymer with an average chain length of 12 ADPR units. When Mg^{2+} was omitted, the reaction be-

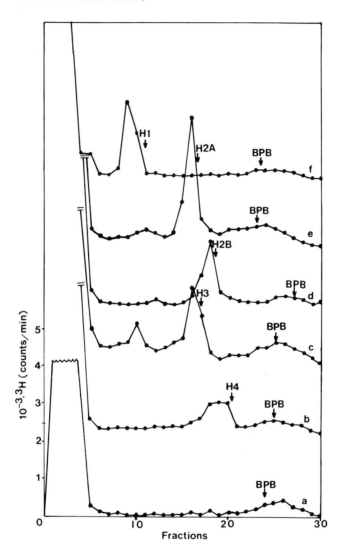

FIG. 2. Urea/dodecyl sulfate/polyacrylamide gel electrophoresis of ADP-ribosylated enzyme (a) and histones (b–f) obtained with purified calf thymus DNA-independent poly(ADPR) polymerase. BPB = bromophenol blue. From Okazaki *et al.* (54).

came nearly completely dependent on both histone and DNA, and the product was short-chain oligo(ADPR) bound to histone H1. The reaction mechanism depends on addition of exogenous DNA, which was separated during the purification steps, and which reacts with Mg^{2+}, histone, and the enzyme in an as yet unknown manner.

Similar results were obtained with rat liver nuclear enzyme (56, 57). Also, this purified rat liver enzyme can catalyze branching of the linear polymer (57).

We can now answer several important questions proposed by earlier investigators from the evidence obtained with highly purified enzymes. A single enzyme can catalyze the three distinct reactions of poly(ADPR) synthesis: (*a*) transfer of ADPR to acceptor proteins (initiation) (53–56); (*b*) addition of ADPR units to preexisting mono- or oligo(ADPR) (chain elongation) (52–56); (*c*) branching of the linear poly(ADPR) chain (57). Electrophoretically homogeneous DNA-independent poly(ADPR) polymerase can catalyze the ADP-ribosylation of all histone subgroups as well as the enzyme itself (auto-ADP-ribosylation) (54). Specific inhibitors or reaction conditions for separating these different reactions have not yet been found (53). An intermolecular reaction mechanism rather than an intramolecular one has been proposed (57).

2. DNA-SPECIFIC ACTIVATION

We here discuss the activation properties of DNA fragments obtained in various studies (59, 60). During the purification of bovine thymus poly(ADPR) polymerase, there was obtained a fraction 20 times more effective than the bulk of calf thymus DNA in activating the enzyme (59). Chemical analysis, UV spectrophotometry, and ultracentrifugation of the active fraction indicated that the active substance is double-stranded DNA. It was suggested that the high enzyme-activating ability of the DNA ("active DNA") is due to a DNA sequence(s), concentrated on the DNA, with a high enzyme-binding affinity. The DNA we isolated (60) from highly purified DNA-independent calf thymus poly(ADPR) polymerase is 5 times more effective than this "active DNA" (59); thus, it is 100 times more effective than commercial high-molecular-weight calf-thymus DNA. This DNA fraction we called sDNA. In fact, it is a heterogeneous population of DNA molecules with an average size, estimated on polyacrylamide agarose gels, of about 100–200 base-pairs. The apparent K_m for NAD of the DNA-dependent poly(ADPR) polymerase varies with the DNA concentration, being minimal when the amount of sDNA was 10% of that of the enzyme. The same percentage was found in the DNA-independent enzyme (60). The ratio of the apparent K_m for sDNA to the enzyme concentration was constant at any enzyme concentration. The estimated minimum number of base-pairs of sDNA required for maximal activation of one enzyme molecule was 16. For calf thymus DNA, the estimate was 640.

In a more recent study, the activity of the poly(ADPR) polymerase purified from bovine thymus was dependent on double-stranded DNA and was correlated with single or double-stranded breaks on the DNA (60a). A filter binding assay showed that the enzyme-activating efficiency of DNA was correlated with its enzyme-binding efficiency.

These results suggest that the activation of the enzyme requires the formation of some complex between the protein and a specific part of the DNA. Immunological studies also show the specific binding of sDNA to the enzyme molecule (61). The precise function of this small fragment of DNA is still unknown. The evidence suggests that the DNA neutralizes the charge effect between enzyme, a basic protein (45), and acceptor basic proteins like histones, and thus facilitates the enzyme reaction.

C. Natural Distribution of Poly(ADPR) Polymerase and Some Properties

Poly(ADPR) polymerase occurs in chicken liver nuclei (2), rat liver nuclei (3, 4), calf (40) or pig thymus (46), and in cell cultures derived from mouse (49) or human tissues (51). This strongly suggests that the poly(ADPR) polymerase is a ubiquitous nuclear enzyme, although a systematic search for it in a variety of prokaryote or eukaryote organisms has not been carried out. Here we describe further examples of enzyme distribution in living cells that confirm the biological importance of poly(ADPR) and the enzyme system for its synthesis. Subcellular distribution is also discussed, but subnuclear distribution is discussed later in Section V.

Poly(ADPR) polymerase occurs in bull spermatozoa (62). Bull seminal plasma inhibits the enzymes from a number of tissues, but not that from bull spermatozoa, whereas human seminal plasma inhibits only the enzyme from pig thymus nuclei. In rat pancreatic nuclei, only one basic nuclear protein, histone H1, is modified by the polymerase action as a result of the apparent covalent binding of the polymer with this protein fraction (63). In isolated trout testis nuclei, three proteins—very lysine rich histone (H1), a specific trout chromosomal protein (H6), and the sperm-specific protamines—incorporate ADPR residues (64). No significant labeling of the nucleosomal "core" histones (H2A, H2B, H3, and H4) was observed. The chain lengths of the poly(ADPR) vary as follows: 3.0 to 8.8 for H1, 3.2 to 4.5 for H6, and 2 to 35 for protamine. However, particularly in the case of protamine, in some experiments only small amounts of AMP relative to large amounts of PR-AMP were released, indicating either that the ADPR chains were very long, or that the terminal AMP was not available for release in free form.

Determination of the total chain-lengths of poly(ADPR) molecules in isolated nuclei of *Xenopus laevis* embryos by hydroxyapatite column chromatography generally gave higher values than when the radioactive portions of these molecules, synthesized *in vitro*, were measured by poly(ethyleneimine)-cellulose thin-layer chromatography after snake venom phosphodiesterase digestion (65), which showed that most of the poly(ADPR) synthesized *in vitro* was a covalent elongation of molecules previously initiated *in vivo*.

Poly(ADPR) polymerase also occurs in the slime mold *Physarum polycephalum* (66) and in *Tetrahymena pyriformis* (67). The specific activities of poly(ADPR) polymerase in nuclei and nucleoli of *T. pyriformis* are 1.4 and 1.2 units per milligram of DNA or 0.32 and 0.2 units per milligram of protein, respectively (one unit is defined as 1 nmol of NAD incorporated into acid-insoluble material in 1 min at 18°C (67). In the same nuclei and nucleoli, poly(ADPR) glycohydrolase specific activities are 0.46 and 0.44 unit per milligram of protein or 2 and 3.2 units per milligram of DNA, respectively (one unit is defined as 1 pmol of poly(ADPR) degraded in 5 min at 37°C). Enzymes metabolizing poly(ADPR) are apparently evenly distributed between transcriptionally active euchromatin and bulk chromatin. From this, the authors (67) concluded that there is no evidence for a direct involvement of these enzymes in transcription.

Poly(ADPR) has not been studied extensively in plants. This may arise from the greater difficulties in the isolation of highly purified and physiologically active nuclei from plant tissue. However, important insights into the enzymology and biological role of poly(ADPR) might be obtained if it were found in plant systems as well as in the much studied nonplant eukaryotes. Poly(ADPR) enzymes do occur in mature wheat seed chromatin and root-tip nuclei (68). The amount of poly(ADPR) polymerase in mature wheat seed chromatin was double than that found in wheat root-tip nuclei with respect to DNA or protein content. Poly(ADPR) glycohydrolase activity was detected in the seed chromatin, but at a lower level than in the root-tip nuclei. The covalent modification of chromosomal proteins by poly(ADPR) in plant nuclei obtained from transformed tissue cultures of *Nicotiana tabacum* has been described (69). This system shows a marked similarity to the animal systems previously described concerning the action of inhibitors, the average chain length, the fact that more than 80% of the poly(ADPR) is covalently bound to protein acceptors, the nature of this covalent linkage, and even the main acceptors among the histone species, i.e., H1, H2A, and H2B.

At least in certain cells, poly(ADPR) polymerase activity is detectable in mitochondria (70) and in cytoplasm (71). The activity in oocytes of *Xenopus laevis* is stimulated by treatment with progesterone (70). To demonstrate that the enzyme is functional under *in vivo* conditions, radioactive NAD was microinjected into oocytes. About 10% of the total radioactivity was converted to oligo(ADPR) with an average chain length of 1.8. Fractionation of the oocytes showed that the purified mitochondrial fraction possesses an active poly(ADPR) polymerase that is dependent on mitochondrial DNA and is inhibited by nicotinamide and thymidine. These results suggest that ADP-ribosylation of an unknown mitochondrial protein(s) may play a role in oocyte maturation (70).

A poly(ADPR) polymerase activity obtained from the cytoplasm of HeLa cells is stimulated more than 30-fold by the addition of both DNA and histones (71). A covalent attachment between histone H1 and poly(ADPR) was established using this cytoplasmic enzyme. The enzyme was associated primarily with ribosomes, both free ribosomes and those found in polysomes. The possibility that the cytoplasmic enzyme was a newly synthesized nuclear enzyme cannot be excluded.

IV. ADP-ribosylation

A. ADP-ribosylation of Histones and Nonhistone Proteins

Poly(ADPR) is attached covalently mainly to various nuclear proteins. ADP-ribosylated proteins are usually obtained from nuclei that have been incubated with NAD. To our knowledge, poly(ADPR) polymerase is a unique enzyme that can catalyze the initiation of ADP-ribosylation on these nuclear proteins, histones and nonhistones, and the polymerization of ADPR chains as described in the preceding section.

Five types of postsynthetic modifications of proteins are known: acetylation, phosphorylation, methylation, poly(ADP-ribosylation), and the formation of the basic chromosomal protein A24, consisting of histone H2A and ubiquitin attached by an isopeptide linkage (72; for review, see 73). It appears reasonable to think that ADP-ribosylation might modify dramatically the properties of histones and nonhistone proteins and thus the state of the chromatin. To elucidate the biological role of poly(ADPR) polymerase, analyses of ADP-ribosylated pro-

teins were carried out by many investigators (for review, see *13–16,
18*). We will report here some typical recent experiments *in vitro*
and *in vivo* and discuss the biological meaning of histone ADP-
ribosylation.

The distribution of poly(ADPR) in histones of HeLa cell nuclei was
investigated by incubating the nuclei with [³H]NAD (*74*). Analysis of
the product hydrolyzed with snake venom phosphodiesterase revealed
that it is a homopolymer consisting of 4–5 ADPR units. When
chromatographed on a sulfopropyl-Sephadex C-50 column, more than
90% of the [³H]poly(ADPR) was eluted with histones, not with nonhistone contaminants. On dodecyl-sulfate/polyacrylamide-gel electrophoresis, a major radioactive peak at a position very close to the
histone H1 band did not appear if there was treatment with alkali prior
to electrophoresis. A selective extraction of histone H1 with 5% per-
chloric acid showed that the histone H1 contained about 85% of the
radioactivity incorporated into whole histones.

The properties of the compound of histone H1 and poly(ADPR)
synthesized in HeLa cell nuclei have been further analyzed (*75*). The
incorporated radioactivity migrates as a sharply defined peak on
polyacrylamide-gel electrophoresis in association with a protein band
that moves more slowly than H1, the major protein component. The
observations indicated that this "complex" is composed of two molecules of H1 and a single chain of poly(ADPR) ("H1 dimer"), with one
detectable covalent linkage of polymer to protein. Although only one
such linkage between protein and polymer has been detected, the
"complex" was not dissociated when electrophoresed on dodecyl sulfate gels, nor could its noncovalently linked H1 histone be exchanged
readily with free H1. Further investigations of the control of this "H1
dimer" formation by poly(ADPR) glycohydrolase (*76*) suggest that the
dimeric form of the H1 protein is synthesized when poly(ADPR)
glycohydrolase activity is low, while ADP-ribosylated H1 monomers
are formed when the degrading enzyme activity is high (see also Section VI,A).

ADP-ribosylated histone H1 was isolated from intact HeLa cells
grown for 24 hours with [³H]adenosine and compared with ADP-
ribosylated histone H1 synthesized from [³H]NAD by isolated HeLa
nuclei (*77*). Most ADP-ribosylated H1 formed *in vivo* carried single
ADPR units that were not released by neutral NH₂OH to a significant
extent; alkali treatment (pH 10.5) liberated most but not all of the
ADPR residues, which may indicate the existence of a new type of
linkage so far found only in conjugates isolated from intact tissues; no

"H1 dimer" was detected in intact cells. By contrast, isolated HeLa nuclei formed ADP-ribosylated H1, which contained predominently polymeric ADPR residues linked by NH_2OH-sensitive and by NH_2OH-resistant, alkali (pH 10.5)–labile bonds; most of the conjugates appeared in the form of "H1 dimer." A comparison with the ADP-ribosylated nonhistone proteins indicated that histone H1 formed *in vivo* carried less than 2.5% of the total protein-bound ADPR residues and less than 1% of the protein-bound ADPR synthesized *in vitro*. Similar results have been reported in rat liver *in vivo* (78, 79).

Histones and some nonhistone proteins were extracted from rat-liver nuclei, and the ADP-ribosylated material was isolated by affinity chromatography on dihydroxyboryl gel columns and further purified by carboxymethyl-cellulose column chromatography (80). As judged by electrophoretic mobilities in various gel systems and by amino acid compositions, approximately 50% of the ADPR recovered in the carboxymethyl-cellulose fractions was associated with several nonhistone proteins with molecular weights of 2 to 6×10^4, while 35% and 15% were associated with histones H2B and H1, respectively. Since the average chain length of the polymer bound to any of these proteins was less than two ADPR units, the percentage distribution reflects the number of ADP-ribosylated sites rather than the chain length.

A unique protein, called A24, is ADP-ribosylated in isolated rat liver nuclei (81). This protein occurs in nucleoli (82), and it has been suggested that it plays a role in the regulation of nucleolar gene activity (83, 84). The phosphorylation and acetylation of protein A24 has been observed (85). Apparently, even though it is conjugated with ubiquitin, the histone H2A portion of protein A24 shows the same modification as free histone H2A.

In studies of the isolation and partial characterization of the ADP-ribosylated nuclear proteins from Ehrlich ascites tumor cells, 40% of the acceptor proteins were identified as nucleosomal core histones (86). Most of these histones, however, appeared in the nonhistone fraction because of extensive modification by poly(ADPR).

The effects of heparin or polyamines on histone H1-poly(ADPR) compound formation have been studied by several investigators. Treatment with heparin or preferential removal of H1 stimulates endogenous DNA polymerase and template activities in swine aortic nuclei (87). In contrast, the poly(ADPR) polymerase activity of the extracted nuclei was reversibly inhibited by extraction of H1. This might be due to the removal of the enzyme along with histone H1. Heparin, on the other hand, did not inhibit the poly(ADPR) polymerase. It appeared that the removal of histone H1 as well as poly(ADPR) polymerase exposed initiation sites for DNA polymerase. When the polyamines, spermine, spermidine, or putrescine at 1 or 2 mM were added to HeLa cell nuclei, there was a one- to threefold differential stimulation of [³H]NAD incorporation into an histone H1-poly(ADPR) complex with little effect on total poly(ADPR) synthesis (88). These results are apparently related to the chromatin-condensing action of these agents, as enhanced formation of the H1-poly(ADPR) compound and chromatin aggregation were closely correlated. Spermine-treated rat liver nuclei showed a twofold increase in ADPR incorporation into histone H1 and nonhistone nuclear proteins (89, 90). Conversely, there was a large reduction in ADP-ribosylation in core histones (H2A, H2B, H3) from the same nuclei. It was concluded (89, 90) that polyamines, which are in a higher concentration in rapidly dividing cells, may elicit a regulatory function by causing the preferential ADP-ribosylation of H1 histones, as well as of the more acidic of the nuclear proteins. In contrast, in isolated wheat nuclei, polyamines, in the presence or the absence of magnesium, stimulate the total synthesis of poly(ADPR) two to fourfold (90a). Moreover, this increase was due to the synthesis of new chains of polymer; the distribution of poly(ADPR) between histone H1 and the other core histones remained the same in control and treated nuclei.

The ADP-ribosylation of histone and nonhistone chromosomal proteins with NAD and "2'-deoxy-NAD" (2'd-NAD) has been studied (91). Nuclei isolated from HeLa cells and rat liver preferentially transferred the ADPR moiety from NAD to the H1 histones, namely, to the minor H1 histone, H1°, of nuclei from normal rat liver. In contrast, the 2'd-ADPR moiety of 2'd-NAD was transferred preferentially to the nonhistone proteins. This provides additional evidence to explain the earlier observations (92) that the replacement of the 2'-hydroxyl group of NAD with a hydrogen atom causes a 10-fold increase in the inhibition of DNA synthesis in nuclei isolated from normal rat liver and restores the ability to inhibit DNA synthesis in nuclei isolated from neoplastic tissue and fetal rat liver. This inhibition of DNA synthesis in neoplastic tissue and fetal rat liver was ineffective with NAD, but was restored by 2'd-NAD.

In mouse nuclei incubated with NAD, a large proportion of the poly(ADPR) is not attached to protein (93). The free poly(ADPR) does not appear to arise from degradation and its chain length is significantly longer than the poly(ADPR) attached to proteins. Free poly(ADPR) has not attracted much attention.

B. Mono(ADP-ribosylation) by Toxins and by Coliphage T4

Some major bacterial toxins appear to possess an ADP-ribosyl transferase activity. Both diphtheria toxin and *Pseudomonas aeruginosa* exotoxin A catalyze transfer of the ADPR moiety of NAD into a covalent linkage with elongation factor 2 (EF-2) (*94, 95*). EF-2 is thereby inactivated, which explains the toxin's inhibitory effect on protein synthesis.

Cholera toxin activates adenylate cyclase in a wide variety of eukaryotic cells, a process shown to depend upon exogenous NAD in purified rat liver plasma membranes (*96*), lysed avian erythrocytes (*97*), mouse neuroblastoma cells (*98*), and sarcoma 180 membranes (*99*). This NAD requirement suggests that cholera toxin may be involved in the ADP-ribosylation of a target protein regulating adenylate cyclase activity. The evidence indicates that this toxin catalyzes the transfer of the ADPR moiety of NAD to the guanidino moiety of arginine (*100*) as well as to several membrane components of lysed pigeon erythrocytes, one of which contains the guanine nucleotide regulatory site of adenylate cyclase (*101*). The kinetics of cholera toxin stimulation of ADP-ribosylation of macromolecules and adenylate cyclase activity in cloned, differentiated, diploid hepatocytes and in a crude membrane preparation derived from these cells lead to the conclusion that there may be a cause-and-effect relationship between both cholera toxin effects (*102*).

Cholera toxin's fragment A1 catalyzes the transfer of ADPR from NAD to a set of soluble and membrane-bound proteins present in pigeon erythrocytes (*103*). In erythrocyte lysates, transfer to the most readily modified membrane protein (M_r 42,000), thought to be the guanine nucleotide binding protein that associates with adenylate cyclase, apparently results in an inhibition of guanosine triphosphatase and a consequent activation of the cyclase. The NAD glycohydrolase and ADP-ribosyltransferase activities appear actually to be intrinsic to the A1 peptide of choleragen (*103a*).

In addition, the *Escherichia coli* heat-labile enterotoxin, the action of which is similar to that of cholera toxin, has the same enzymic activity. ADP-ribosylation of the guanine nucleotide regulator of adenylate cyclase is catalyzed (in the presence of NAD, GTP, and a small cytosolic protein) by a peptide of *E. coli* heat-labile enterotoxin, similar in size to the A1 fragment of cholera toxin (*104, 105*).

The supernatant fraction from turkey erythrocytes catalyzes the NAD-dependent ADP-ribosylation of arginine, and an ADP-

ribosyltransferase that activates rat brain adenylate cyclase in an
NAD-dependent reaction has been extensively purified from this
source (106). The purified transferase also catalyzes the incorporation
of label from adenine [14C]NAD into lysozyme, histones, and polyar-
ginine. An investigation of the substrate specificity of an NAD- and
guanidine-dependent ADP-ribosyltransferase from avian erythrocytes
indicates that, in addition to arginine, other guanidino derivatives may
serve as ADPR acceptors in the order: agmatine = arginine methyl
ester > arginine > guanidine > guanidinobutyrate > guanidino-
propionate (107). The stereospecificity of the transferase-catalyzed
reaction between NAD and arginine was established by NMR spectroscopy. The presence in the avian erythrocytes of a protein that, like
choleragen and E. coli heat-labile enterotoxin, apparently activates
adenylate cyclase and possesses ADP-ribosyltransferase activity is
consistent with the view that the mechanism through which bacterial
toxins produce pathological effects are not entirely foreign to vertebrate cells, at least some of which may possess and employ an analogous mechanism for activation of adenylate cyclase.

Infection of E. coli with bacteriophage T4 leads to a series of structural modifications of the DNA-dependent RNA polymerase: a very
fast ADP-ribosylation of one of the two α-subunits of the enzyme has
been termed alteration; a second change resulting from phage gene
expression occurs later after infection and has been termed modification (108). The purified NAD : ADP-ribosyltransferase (109) responsible for the phage-T4-induced modification of the α-subunits of the
DNA-dependent RNA polymerase of E. coli has a molecular weight
around 26,000, does not require magnesium ions, is protected by sulfhydryl reagents, and has an optimum temperature around 20°C. The
reaction is inhibited at increased ionic strength and by the reaction
products nicotinamide and T4-modified RNA polymerase. The only
reaction products formed to a significant extent in a crude extract were
T4 modified α-subunits and one smaller ADP-ribosylated peptide. As
in vivo, the reaction is complete and irreversible. Both α-subunits in
the RNA polymerase monomer were ADP-ribosylated in one and the
same position.

C. Characteristics of Mono- and Poly(ADPR) Protein Linkage

The nature of the covalent linkage of ADPR to an acceptor protein
has been studied both enzymically and chemically.

The compound ADPR-protein is solubilized by protease, by trypsin, and by alkali or hydroxylamine. It should be noted that protease or

trypsin treatment results in poly(ADPR) bound to a peptide fragment, whereas alkali or hydroxylamine treatment results in free mono or poly(ADPR). A novel enzyme from rat liver cytosol may cleave ADP-ribosyl histone linkages (12). This enzyme, partially purified, has a pH optimum of about 6.0 and is inhibited 80–90% by 5 mM ADPR. Analysis of the reaction product by chromatography indicated that the split product contains the ADPR moiety but is not exactly identical with ADPR. Essentially no amino acid was detected in this product by the dansyl method.

The existence of two kinds of ADPR-protein linkages—hydroxylamine sensitive or resistant—has been proposed (77, 110, 111). The mechanism of the hydrolytic action of hydroxylamine is not well understood. Using hydroxylamine sensitivity and anti-AMP antibodies (see also Section VI,B), the ADP-ribosylation pattern in HeLa (77), rat liver, and Ehrlich ascites tumor cells (111, 112) has been investigated. The bulk of the ADP-ribosylated proteins in eukaryotic cells was modified by single ADPR units rather than by poly(ADPR) chains, and histone H1 *in vivo* apparently carries only a very small fraction of the total protein-bound mono(ADPR) residues. Quantitation during the cell cycle of slime mold *Physarum polycephalum* revealed independent synthesis of the two species, the NH_2OH-resistant fraction being formed during the S phase, while the NH_2OH-sensitive conjugate increased sharply at the S/G2 boundary (66).

It had earlier been proposed that the linkage of poly(ADPR) to histones H1, H2A, H2B, and H3 is through the serine phosphate moiety of these histones (79, 113). It has since been reported that there are precise ADP-ribosylation sites in the molecule of histones H1 (114) and H2B (115).

When crude ADP-ribosylated H1 was purified from rat-liver nuclei, incubated with NAD, it was found that histone H1 was modified by oligo(ADPR) with an average chain length corresponding to trimers. Bisection of ADP-ribosylated H1 with chymotrypsin demonstrated that both halves of H1 were modified. The site of ADP-ribosylation of the COOH-terminal half was in the tryptic peptide, which contains the only glutamic acid residue in this fragment of H1. Pronase digestion of the NH_2-terminal half generated a series of ADP-ribosylated peptides. Among these peptides, one contained only serine and glutamic acid. The instability of the linkage between ADPR and H1 in dilute alkali and neutral hydroxylamine, characteristic of an ester bond, led to the suggestion that the two sites of ADP-ribosylation of H1 are the glutamic acid residues in positions 2 and probably 116 of the polypeptide chain. Two more possible sites of ADP-ribosylation of H1 are the

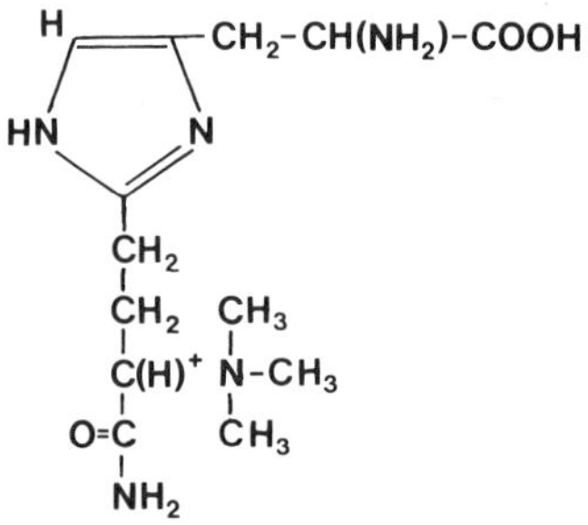

$$H\text{---}CH_2\text{-}CH(NH_2)\text{-}COOH$$

(structure)

HN — N

$\overset{|}{CH_2}$

$\overset{|}{CH_2}$ CH_3

$\overset{|}{C(H)^+}$ $\overset{|}{N}$-CH_3

$O{=}\overset{|}{C}$ $\overset{|}{C}H_3$

$\overset{|}{NH_2}$

FIG. 3. Structure of diphthamide, or 2-[3-(carbamoyl)-3-(trimethylammonio)propyl] histidine, the new amino acid involved in elongation factor EF-2 ADP-ribosylation. From Bodley, Van Ness, and Howard (*120a, 121*).

glutamic acid in position 14 and the COOH-terminal lysine residue (*116, 117*).

Hydrolysis of ADP-ribosylated histone H2B with trypsin generates a single peptide linked to mono(ADPR), which corresponds to the sequence Pro-Glu-Pro-Ala-Lys (*115*). The NH_2-terminal proline could be dansylated. These findings lead to the suggestion that the ADPR residue is linked to the γ-COOH group of the glutamic acid in position 2 of H2B. The same results were obtained by others (*116, 117a*).

The site of ADP-ribosylation in elongation factor EF-2 from rat liver (*118*), yeast (*119*), beef liver, and wheat (*120*) is a new amino acid, "amino acid X," which presumably results from a posttranscriptional modification of a standard amino acid. The NMR spectra (^{1}H and ^{13}C) of amino acid X from a trypsin-derived ADP-ribosyl-peptide of EF-2, and its ribosyl derivatives suggested that amino acid X in EF-2 has the structure shown in Fig. 3 (*120a, 121*). The data also support best the view that ADPR is attached by diphtheria toxin via a glycosidic linkage to the amide nitrogen of amino acid X ["diphthamide" (*120a*)], but do not exclude linkage to the imidazole ring. Acid hydrolysis of ribosyl-diphthamide cleaves the amide and yields the free acid, 2-[3-carboxy-3-(trimethylammonio)propyl]histidine. Diphthamide apparently arises by a rather elaborate posttranscriptional modification of a single histidine residue within a highly conserved sequence present in all eukaryotic elongation factors 2 (*119*).

V. Biological Function of Poly(ADPR) in the Nucleus

The absolute requirement of DNA fragments for poly(ADPR) polymerase activity (auto-ADP-ribosylation and histone ADP-ribosylation) are described in the preceding section. This, and the presence of enzyme in nucleosomal chromatin structure, suggest that poly(ADPR) polymerase might play an important role in DNA synthesis and/or repair. In this section, we present some results on the subnuclear distribution of poly(ADPR) polymerase and some evidence on the relationship between poly(ADPR) polymerase and chromatin structure and DNA metabolism, including cell division and cell differentiation.

A. Chromatin Structure and Poly(ADPR)

Although the mechanisms of gene expression in eukaryotes are very complex because of the higher order organization of chromatin structure, considerable progress to elucidate them has been made by hybridization techniques *in vitro* or *in vivo* with the *E. coli* genetic system (*122–124*). In differentiated cells, a relatively small portion of the genome is transcribed into RNA. Insight into the regulation of differential gene expression and into the possible involvement of ADP-ribosylation in the transcription process could be provided by the study of the structural and functional features of chromatin and the distinction between transcriptionally active and inactive chromatin (*125*).

A current model of chromatin structure, derived primarily from histone cross-linking (*126*), nuclease digestion studies (*127, 128*), and electron microscopy (*129–132*), consists of a linear array of repeating protein complexes, linked and circumscribed by a continuous thread of supercoiled duplex DNA. Each protein complex is composed of two each of histones H2A, H2B, H3, and H4, and chromosomes associated with 160 to 240 base pairs of DNA (*133–136*) to form a subunit of chromatin that has been called a "Nu (ν) body" or nucleosome. The octameric complex of the four histones (except histone H1) encircled by 140 base-pairs of DNA is termed the protein core of a nucleosome. Studies on the precise location of histone H1 within the strands of nucleosomes have suggested an association of this histone with the DNA that links nucleosomal cores (linker regions) (*137, 138*).

In HeLa cell nuclei, poly(ADPR) polymerase activity is associated primarily with the template active regions (euchromatin), whereas the transcriptionally inert chromatin fractions contain relatively low levels of ADP-ribosylating activity (*139*). In contrast, a nonpreferential localization of poly(ADPR) polymerase activity in transcriptionally active rat-liver chromatin has been observed (*140*). In extended forms of chromatin in HeLa cell nuclei contiguous to the DNA replicating fork, poly(ADPR) polymerase is maximally active, and in more condensed chromatin, distal to the replicating fork, poly(ADPR) polymerase activity is depressed two- to threefold (*141*).

There is a differential poly(ADP-ribosylation) of chromosomal proteins in nuclei compared to isolated nucleosomes, and an increase in the specific activity of the enzyme with increasing nucleosome repeat number (*142*). Considerable activity is also found in subnucleosomes. Definite evidence that poly(ADPR) polymerase is localized within internucleosomal "linker" regions of HeLa cell chromatin is shown by the fact that only monomers and dimers with linker regions contain poly(ADPR) polymerase activity (*143*). Moreover, when dimers are digested with micrococcal nuclease, the enzyme activity moves from the dimer to the monomer with linker.

Poly(ADP-ribosylation) has also proved to be a useful probe for ascertaining structural and perhaps functional aspects of higher ordered structures of chromatin. This enzymic activity increases progressively with increasing nucleosome repeat number, reaching a maximum at approximately 8–10 nucleosomes (*144*). On the other hand, micrococcal nuclease specifically cleaves HeLa chromatin at sites exhibiting an 8 and 16 nucleosome periodicity (*145*). These results are consistent with considerable evidence from a number of laboratories that, in the solenoidal form of polynucleosomes, approximately 7–9 nucleosomes comprise one complete turn of a helix. It is thus possible that this nuclear protein-modifying enzyme is situated at selected folded regions in higher ordered structures of chromatin.

In parallel with the studies on poly(ADPR) polymerase localization in chromatin, the pattern of histone modification in HeLa cell nuclei was also shown to be dependent on chromatin being in its "native" conformation within the nucleus (*142*) and on the functional form of chromatin (*141*). In intact nuclei, H1 and H2B are major acceptors, whereas in isolated nucleosomes, very little histone modification occurs while the ADP-ribosylation of the HMG (high mobility group) proteins, M1 and M4, is greatly enhanced (*142*). In extended forms of chromatin, histones H3, H1, H2B, and H2A are ADP-ribosylated, whereas in condensed structures of chromatin, nucleosomal and H1 histones are not significantly ADP-ribosylated (*141*).

In studies of chromatin structure through the cell cycle in nuclei of regenerating rat liver, no differences in the nucleosome-associated DNA lengths were observed, but there were differences with regard to histone phosphorylation and ADP-ribosylation and their relative association with nuclear material (*146*). Histones released from nuclei incubated in hypoosmolar medium, unlike those remaining bound to the nuclei, were more modified.

B. DNA Replication and Poly(ADPR)

As described in the preceding section, poly(ADPR) polymerase is associated with chromatin. Changes in the structural organization of chromatin are necessary for the progression of the cell cycle. These changes are thought to be regulated mainly by the modification of chromosomal proteins by reactions such as phosphorylation (*147, 148*), acetylation (*149–152*), methylation (*153, 154*) and also by ADP-ribosylation. It has already been suggested that ADP-ribosylation of histones and nonhistone proteins plays a role in the control of DNA replication (for review, see *14, 16*). To define better the biological significance of this reaction, the activity of poly(ADPR) polymerase in various cell nuclei during various phases of the cell cycle or in different physiological states of the same cell has been further investigated by many workers.

Maximal enzyme activity was observed in the G_1 phase using HeLa cell nuclei (*155–157*), in the S phase using L cells (*158*) and HeLa cell cytoplasm (*71*), and in the G_2 phase using transformed hamster lung cells (*159*) and HeLa S3 cells (*160*). Poly(ADPR) polymerase activity reaches its highest level during the G_1 phase in permeabilized Chinese hamster cells (*161*). These conflicting results suggest no direct correlation between cell cycle (DNA synthesis) and poly(ADPR) polymerase activity.

Poly(ADPR) polymerase activity has been found in mature wheat seed chromatin and root-tip nuclei (*68*). Unexpectedly, the amount of poly(ADPR) polymerase in mature wheat seed chromatin that may be considered to be metabolically completely inactive was double than that found in wheat root-tip nuclei with respect to DNA or protein content. With cultured chick embryo heart cells, poly(ADPR) polymerase activity increases in cells growing more slowly, indicating an inverse relation between poly(ADPR) polymerase activity and DNA synthesis (*162*). Poly(ADPR) polymerase activity has also been found in the nuclei of regenerating intestinal epithelial cells (*163*). Nondividing but differentiating and maturing cells of the same tissue contained no more than 10% of this activity.

ADP-ribosyltransferase activity associated with chromatin in simian virus 40 (SV40) transformed cells and untransformed cells is 2- to 10-fold higher in transformed cells than in untransformed cells (*164*). When confluent transformed cells were subcultured, the specific enzyme activity first decreased 2- to 4-fold and then rapidly increased during the logarithmic phase of growth. This increase slowed or ceased when the cells entered the stationary phase. In contrast, the activity in the untransformed cells remained low throughout the growth cycle. Immediately after infection of baby hamster kidney cells with herpes simplex virus (HSV), cellular DNA synthesis was blocked, while extensive HSV DNA synthesis began (*165*). These dramatic alterations of the control mechanisms for these two DNA synthesizing systems were not accompanied by a change in the poly(ADPR) polymerase activity.

Phytohemagglutinin (phytag) stimulation produced an increase of DNA synthesis in normal lymphocytes, whereas delayed and lower levels of DNA synthesis were observed in chronic lymphocytic leukemia (CLL) cells; poly(ADPR) synthesis increased in both the normal and the CLL cells (*166*). It was concluded that poly(ADPR) synthesis is dissociated from DNA synthesis in CLL cells, but varies directly with DNA synthesis in normal lymphocytes. In phytag-stimulated human lymphocytes, there is a characteristic increase in DNA and RNA synthesis paralleled by a strong increase of the measured poly(ADPR) polymerase activity (*167*). A high concentration of nicotinamide in the culture median reduces the poly(ADPR) polymerase activity as well as cell proliferation and DNA synthesis of phytag-stimulated cells. Thus it seems likely that inhibition of poly(ADPR) polymerase by a high concentration of nicotinamide is involved in the blockage of the response of lymphocytes to phytohemagglutinin, and that DNA synthesis is associated with poly(ADPR) synthesis.

ADP-ribosylation of nuclear proteins stimulates DNA synthesis in chick embryo-liver nuclei (*168*). In contrast, there is a significant decrease in template activity in hen liver nuclei treated with NAD, suggesting that poly(ADPR) polymerase plays a role as a regulator of DNA synthesis. It has also been suggested that the stimulation of DNA synthesis by poly(ADPR) formation is due to an increase in accessibility of nuclease to DNA as a result of the template activation (*169*). Glucocorticoid hormone administration reduces poly(ADPR) polymerase activity in parallel with a decrease in DNA synthesis in nuclei from chick embryo liver (*170, 170a*).

In view of the above results, no definitive conclusion can be drawn as to a relation between DNA synthesis and poly(ADPR) polymerase activity. However, DNA synthesis in growing tissues containing polyamines at high levels, such as is the case with tumors and the fetus, is stimulated by polyamine-mediated ADP-ribosylation of nuclear proteins (*170b*). In addition, from extensive studies in different cell types and by comparing dividing to resting cells, it has been concluded that mono and poly(ADPR) protein conjugates exhibit independent variations (22). Nevertheless, it should be kept in mind that measurements of poly(ADPR) polymerase activity indicate the poly(ADPR) synthesis potentially available under *in vitro* conditions, not the actual activity *in vivo*. One may expect that, depending on cell type and physiological state, there may be an increase or decrease of the poly(ADPR) polymerase activity *in vivo*. It should also be noted that there are two kinds of DNA synthesis, DNA duplication and DNA repair. New insights on the biological role of poly(ADPR) could be obtained by the study of DNA repair mechanisms (see Section V,C), and by the determination of the amounts of mono- and poly(ADPR) synthesized in various physiological conditions (see Section VI).

C. DNA Repair and Poly(ADPR)

Since earlier reports (*171, 172*) that suggested a relationship between poly(ADPR) metabolism and DNA repair, several investigations have been devoted to this aspect of the possible physiological function of the polymer. In this section we summarize, first, those using the permeabilized cell systems; second, those dealing with DNA-damaging agents; and third, those dealing with poly(ADPR) polymerase inhibitors.

1. STUDIES WITH PERMEABILIZED CELLS

Nuclear poly(ADPR) metabolism is difficult to study in intact cells because there is no specific membrane-permeable precursor. Therefore, most studies have been performed by incubating labeled NAD with isolated nuclei or soluble extracts containing the necessary enzymes. Damage to chromatin and other structures that subcellular fractionation entails may significantly alter nuclear metabolism. This obstacle has been partially overcome by the development of techniques that render cells permeable to macromolecules. Such systems permit "*in vivo*-like" metabolic studies on DNA and poly(ADPR) synthesis in cell cultures.

In mouse lymphoma L5178Y cells rendered permeable to nucleotides by treatment with hypotonic buffer, the activity of poly(ADPR) polymerase is very low (*173*), indicating that the previously reported high activity in isolated nuclei was an artifact of the nuclear isolation procedure (*173*). The high enzyme activity appears to be associated with fragmentation of the DNA, and it was argued that an evaluation of the *in vivo* poly(ADPR) polymerase activity requires at least the demonstration that the DNA is not decreased in size. This was the case in these permeabilized cells.

In studies of DNA synthesis in eukaryotic cells, mouse L cells were rendered permeable to deoxynucleoside triphosphates by a cold shock in a nearly isotonic buffer followed by the addition of 0.05% Triton X-100 (*174, 175*). In this permeable cell system, the replicative DNA polymerase was able to use the endogenous DNA template (*174*), DNA synthesis was inhibited by histones (*175*), and high-molecular-weight DNA intermediates were synthesized (*176*). By comparison, DNA synthesis was slower and the DNA synthesized was smaller in isolated L cell nuclei (*176*). Moreover, DNA synthesis in a permeable cell system (mouse P-815 cells) was reported to be a semiconservative continuation of the *in vivo* synthesis (*177*). In contrast to the activity measured in intact permeabilized Chinese hamster synchronized cells, at its highest level during G_1 phase, activity of poly(ADPR) synthesis appears to be relatively constant through the cell cycle in DNase-treated cells (*161*). However, there was a small peak at the end of the S phase, after which the activity decreased during the subsequent G_2-M period.

Berger *et al.* characterized and measured also the synthesis of DNA and of poly(ADPR) in permeable L cells subjected to different perturbations of cell growth (*178, 179*). The two enzymic systems were distinguished by a comparison of the effects of inhibitors of poly(ADPR) synthesis and DNA synthesis. In nucleotide-permeable cells, nicotinamide, 5-methylnicotinamide, thymidine, 5-bromodeoxyuridine, ADPR, caffeine, and formycin all inhibit poly(ADPR) synthesis but not DNA synthesis; in contrast, arabinosylcytosine triphosphate (araCTP), cytembena, and phosphonoacetic acid all inhibit DNA synthesis but not poly(ADPR) synthesis (*178*). Addition of DNase to the permeable cells caused a marked stimulation of poly(ADPR) synthesis. Suppression of DNA synthesis in these L cells by glucose deficiency, by infection with vaccinia virus, or by treatment with arabinosylcytosine (araC), was always associated with an increase in intrinsic activity of poly(ADPR) synthesis (*179*). Moreover, in contrast to the variations in intrinsic poly(ADPR) synthesis, which was low in the logarithmic growth phase but which increased in the plateau density phase, the total poly(ADPR) synthesis, measured in the presence of added DNase, remained relatively constant during the changes in cell growth status (*178*). This indicates that the physiologic activity of the enzyme varies while the total amount of enzyme remains constant.

Association of poly(ADPR) synthesis with cessation of DNA synthesis and DNA fragmentation was also investigated with CHO cells and cs4-D3 cells, which are cold-sensitive DNA synthesis arrest mutants of

CHO cells (*180*). These mutant cells can be used to examine the consequences of suppressing DNA synthesis without the use of chemical inhibitors or other toxic metabolites; upon incubation at 33°C, DNA synthesis in the cs4-D3 cells stops and the cells enter a prolonged G_1 or G_0 phase. Similar events occurred when wild-type CHO cells grew to high density. In both cases, DNA synthesis and cell growth stopped. The NAD concentration per cell was 20–25% lower and poly(ADPR) synthesis was three- to fourfold higher in growth-arrested cells than in logarithmically growing cells. The growth-inhibited cells developed DNA strand breaks.

2. Effects of DNA-Damaging Agents on Poly(ADPR) Synthesis

The possibility that poly(ADPR) polymerase may have a role in DNA repair was suggested earlier by several investigators. DNA fragmentation and NAD metabolism appear related through poly(ADPR) synthesis (*181, 182*). An interesting four-step mechanism was proposed (*171*) as follows: (*a*) DNA fragmentation initiates the synthesis of poly(ADPR); (*b*) the synthesis of this negatively charged polymer loosens the protein network around the break in the DNA; (*c*) repair enzymes mend the DNA; (*d*) the poly(ADPR) is degraded and the protein-DNA matrix is re-formed. The first step of this mechanism was further studied with bleomycin,[1] an antibiotic reported to fragment DNA, that increases the activity of poly(ADPR) polymerase in HeLa nuclei by 350–550% and in HeLa cells by 200–500% (*183*). In each case, alkaline sucrose density gradients showed that the drug was fragmenting the HeLa DNA. This damage could be repaired *in situ*, whereupon the poly(ADPR) polymerase activity returned to control levels. The results suggest again that the DNA fragmentation may be an initiation signal for the synthesis of poly(ADPR) and that poly(ADPR) polymerase may have a role in DNA repair. Recently, investigations using bleomycin-treated nuclei from regenerating rat liver and from Morris hepatoma 7777 showed that the latter incorporated less than half the amount of dTMP incorporated by the former, and this incorporation was not inhibited by poly(ADPR) as was the case in the normal nuclei (*184*).

Bleomycin as well as several other DNA-damaging agents, including ultraviolet irradiation,[2] *N*-methyl-*N*'-nitro-*N*-nitrosoguanidine (MNNG) or *N*-acetoxyacetamidofluorene (AAF)[3] cause an abrupt in-

[1] See article on bleomycin by Müller and Zahn in Vol. 20 of this series. [Ed.]
[2] See essay by Hall and Mount in Vol. 25 of this series. [Ed.].
[3] See essay by Grunberger and Weinstein in Vol. 23 of this series [Ed.].

crease in unscheduled DNA synthesis in permeabilized normal human lymphocytes, a result of the repair mode of DNA synthesis, and in poly(ADPR) synthesis (*185*). Cycloheximide does not inhibit the increase in DNA or poly(ADPR) synthesis.

There are several additional indirect observations suggesting the involvement of poly(ADPR) polymerase in DNA damage and repair systems, based on the use of DNA-damaging agents like nitrosoureas, γ- and UV-irradiations, and poly(ADPR) polymerase inhibitors (*186–190*).

Experiments with isolated nuclei showed a stimulation of poly(ADPR) polymerase activity after damage of HeLa cells by methylnitrosourea (MeNU) (*186, 187*). In contrast, a slight inhibitory effect on enzyme activity was observed after treatment of cells with various concentrations of chloroethylnitrosourea (ClEtNU) (*187*). MeNU interacted preferentially with internucleosome linker regions and histones, whereas ClEtNU alkylated the nucleosomal core DNA and affected mainly nonhistone proteins. A similar activation of the poly(ADPR) polymerase after treatment of HeLa cells with MeNU was observed at the nucleosomal level of chromatin (*187*). This stimulation of enzyme activity did not occur through an inhibition of the glycohydrolase or an increased enzyme protein biosynthesis, suggesting that MeNU increased the accessibility of nucleosome core histones for modification by poly(ADP-ribosylation). Studies on DNA and histones extracted from HeLa nuclei isolated from cells treated with MeNU suggested that the histone-histone interactions are affected, which may lead to altered DNA-histone interactions (*188*).

The ADPR metabolism of gently lysed HeLa and mouse L ghost cells containing relatively undamaged DNA is greatly altered by agents like DNase I or micrococcal nuclease or X-ray irradiation that introduce breaks in their DNA (*189*). The products formed by ghost cells without DNA breakage appeared to be metabolically stable mono or oligo(ADP-ribosylated) proteins. In contrast, the product in the DNA-damaged ghost cells was poly(ADPR) chains of up to at least 70 units in length, which turned over rapidly and had a half-life of less than 5 minutes.

The relation between poly(ADPR) synthesis and DNA repair was further investigated in cells obtained from patients with xeroderma pigmentosum (*190*). Since such cells are defective in their ability to repair UV-induced DNA damage and do repair some other types of DNA damage, such as that caused by N-methyl-N'-nitro-N-nitrosoguanidine (MNNG), it was reasoned that, if poly(ADPR) synthesis is a component of the DNA repair process, then cells from these patients might show a defective poly(ADPR) synthesis response to UV irradiation, but a normal response to treatment with MNNG. The failure of xeroderma pigmentosum cells to show an increase in poly(ADPR) synthesis in response to UV-irradiation, while an increase was observed in response to MNNG treatment, is consistent with a specific role for poly(ADPR) in the DNA repair process.

A quantitative relation between DNA repair and poly(ADPR) synthesis has been established (see Section VI,A and ref. *212*), by the demonstration that, in SV40-transformed 3T3 cells, treatment with MNNG produced, concomitantly with a decrease in NAD levels, a dramatic increase in the intracellular levels of poly(ADPR) (*190a*).

3. EFFECTS OF POLY(ADPR) POLYMERASE INHIBITORS AND NAD LEVEL

There is a synergistic potentiation of the cytotoxicity of DNA damaging agents such as methylnitrosourea and γ-radiation by poly(ADPR) polymerase inhibitors in mouse leukemia cells (*191*). Nontoxic concentrations of 5-methylnicotinamide, of methylxanthines like theobromine, theophylline, and caffeine, and of thymidine, in the presence of sufficient deoxycytidine to overcome the perturbation of deoxynucleotide metabolism, all potentiate the cytotoxicity of MeNU. Nicotinate, which does not inhibit poly(ADPR) polymerase, had no effect on this toxicity. It was suggested (*191*) that this potentiation of cytotoxicity is mediated by an inhibition of poly(ADPR) synthesis.

The biosynthesis of poly(ADPR) appears to be involved in the degradation of NAD caused by DNA damage (*192*). Both MeNU and γ-radiation lowered cellular NAD in mouse leukemia cells in a dose-dependent way. Several inhibitors of poly(ADPR) polymerase prevented this drop in cellular NAD, and the activity of the polymerase was in close temporal correlation with the NAD drop following both γ-radiation and MeNU. The enzyme activity was maximal when the NAD content was decreasing at the highest rate and returned to normal levels when it ceased falling. It was proposed that the decrease in cellular NAD level produced by MeNU and by γ-radiation was caused by an increased flux through poly(ADPR) mediated by an increased activity of poly(ADPR) polymerase. Further, DNA-damaging agents produce an activation of poly(ADPR) polymerase in permeabilized mouse leukemia cells (*193*). This activation was dose-dependent and in close correlation with the NAD drop. Comparison of the effects of a wide spectrum of agents lead to the conclusion that this activation is unlikely to be caused by a particular species of base damage but might be related to the production of single-strand breaks in DNA.

Studies with substances that specifically inhibit poly(ADPR) polymerase are required; nicotinamide and thymidine inhibit polymerase activity, but also cause many undesirable side effects. Methylated xanthines and cytokinins are potent inhibitors of poly(ADPR) polymerase (*194*), but both classes of compounds inhibit cAMP phosphodiesterase. In a search for more specific inhibitors of poly(ADPR) polymerase, various benzamides substituted in the 3-position were the most inhibitory compounds found (*195*). Two of the benzamides, 3-aminobenzamide and 3-methoxybenzamide, are competitive inhibitors, with K_i values of less than 2 μM. The interesting possibility that these two inhibitors work at the polymerization step, but not at the initiation step, has been suggested (*196*). These inhibitors will be useful for studies *in vitro* and, more important, since they are physiologically specific (*197, 198*), they could be valuable as probes for use as inhibitors of poly(ADPR) synthetase *in vivo*. They effect complete inhibition of poly(ADPR) synthesis in cultured cells (*197, 198*) without affecting the growth rate and normal growth parameters of the cells. As these cells contained no detectable poly(ADPR) and the mono(ADPR) levels remained nearly unchanged, it appears that poly(ADPR) function is required by the cells only at intermittent periods, the most likely function being DNA repair (*197*).

More direct evidence that poly(ADPR) is involved in DNA repair in permeabilized mouse leukemia cells exists (*198*). Alkylating reagents and radiations both lowered cellular NAD contents, and they both elevated poly(ADPR) polymerase activity. The drop in NAD content and the rejoining of strand breaks after treatment with dimethyl sulfate were inhibited by 3-aminobenzamide and other poly(ADPR) polymerase inhibitors, all of which potentiated the cytotoxicity of the alkylating agent. In addition, the rejoining of strand breaks was prevented by nutritionally depleting the cells of NAD. In a study of poly(ADPR) synthesis in human fibroblasts and lymphocytes, rendered semipermeable, in relation to DNA repair processes following UV irradiation, a stronger binding of poly(ADPR) (15 to 30 units in length) to the core region of the chromatin was found (*199*). The authors concluded that the exonuclease and ligase reaction within the DNA repair process can proceed in an uninhibited manner only after binding of poly(ADPR) to the core histone.

D. Differentiation and Poly(ADPR)

In 1975, Caplan and Rosenberg (*200*) presented evidence that NAD metabolism was involved in chick-lamb mesenchymal cell differentiation through newly synthesized poly(ADPR). Since then, several reports have been published on the relationship of poly(ADPR) polymerase activity to cell differentiation (201–207).

The activity of poly(ADPR) polymerase *in vitro* during the embryonic development of *Xenopus laevis* is low during the proliferative growth phase (stages 2 to 10); after this time activity rapidly increases together with the onset of the major differentiation events (201, 202). After stage 28, when the differentiation processes are well under way, the activity declines. It was concluded from these results that poly(ADPR) polymerase in these embryos is more involved in cell differentiation than in cell proliferation.

In erythroleukemic mouse cells, an increase in poly(ADPR) polymerase activity and the transition into G_1 phase occur concomitantly with induction of erythropoietic differentiation (203). In induced cells of the same system, poly(ADPR-ribosylation) of nonhistone proteins remains unaltered but increases twofold in the histone fraction (204).

The effect of hemoglobin synthesis inducers, such as dimethyl sulfoxide, hexamethylenebisacetamide, and butyrate on the rate of poly(ADPR) synthesis of Friend leukemia cells have been investigated (205). Poly(ADPR) synthesis in the nuclei of cells treated with the first two of these began to decrease (50 to 70%, compared to nontreated control) before many phenotypic changes, including hemoglobin production. In contrast, butyrate stimulated poly(ADPR) synthesis at an early stage of culture, but suppressed it at a later stage. Neither cell growth nor degradation of poly(ADPR) is correlated with the effect of inducers. These results suggested that the level of poly(ADPR) synthesis may be correlated with the differentiation of Friend leukemia cells. It was also suggested (205) that the apparent difference between these results and those that found an increase of poly(ADPR) synthesis upon treatment with inducers (203) may be due partly to (a) the difference in the properties of cell lines used in each study; and (b) the difference in the method of culture [refeeding the culture with fresh medium at daily intervals (203) vs. no medium change (205)]. The poly(ADPR) synthesis levels during cell growth in these two conditions are quite different (203).

Nicotinamide and related compounds, including benzamide, pyrazinamide, thymine, thymidine, and bromouracil, induce erythroid differentiation of murine erythroleukemia cells (MELC) (206, 206a). In contrast, 1-methylnicotinamide, nicotinic acid, and 3-acetylpyridine, which do not inhibit the enzyme, did not induce differentiation of MELC (206a). However, nicotinamide failed to in-

duce differentiation of mouse myeloid leukemia cells M1 (38), although M1 cells could be induced to differentiate by inclusion of
poly(ADPR) in the culture medium.

Using a new method for the estimation of poly(ADPR) amounts *in
vivo* (see Section VI,A and ref. 208), substantial changes in the levels

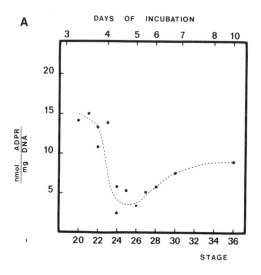

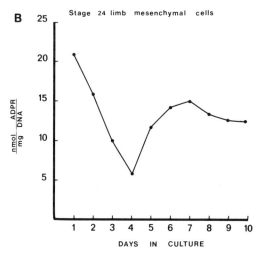

FIG. 4. Poly(ADPR) levels during chick-embryo mesenchymal cell differentiation
into cells with muscle or cartilage phenotypes. (A) Whole limb buds; (B) mesenchymal
cell culture. From Caplan *et al.* (207).

of poly(ADPR) during early phases of limb cell development can be observed (*207*). *In situ*, in embryonic stages 22 to 26, as well as in culture, days 1 to 4, the absolute amount of poly(ADPR) per unit DNA decreased to a third of its prior amount (Fig. 4). This minimum was followed by an increase of about twofold during the next embryonic stages or days of culture. In contrast, during the events involved in muscle formation (including myoblast proliferation, myoblast fusion, and multinuclear myotube maturation *in vivo*), the amount of poly(ADPR) was relatively unchanged. These observations were the first to indicate that the absolute levels of poly(ADPR) may be involved with early commitment events but do not play a major role in the later expressional events involved in chick limb mesenchymal cell development.

In summary, several reports suggest that the rate of poly(ADPR) synthesis—increased or decreased—is involved in cell differentiation. In addition, the distribution of poly(ADPR) synthesis in human blood cells suggests that the capacity for synthesizing poly(ADPR) may serve as a marker of differentiation (*207a*). Poly(ADPR) is synthesized in lymphocytes and monocytes whereas no synthesis is detected in granulocytes and erythrocytes. However, we do not know whether poly(ADPR) synthesis is involved in the indispensable process of the differentiation or occurs as a result of the differentiation process.

VI. New Methods in Studies of Poly(ADPR) and Poly(ADPR) Polymerase

The development of new methods or new systems may facilitate many studies on poly(ADPR) and poly(ADPR) polymerase. In this section we describe several new methods already successfully applied.

A. Chemical Methods

1. STUDIES ON THE POLYMER

A new technique for the isolation and fluorometric determination of poly(ADPR) was developed by us (*208*). The isolation involves acidic precipitation of homogenized nuclei, alkaline hydrolysis of RNA and proteins, separation of poly(ADPR) and DNA by cesium chloride equilibrium centrifugation, and chromatography on Sephadex G-10. The isolated poly(ADPR) is broken down into ADPR and then quantitatively determined by a fluorometric method modified for the determination of picomole quantities of ADPR residues. This method was very recently extended to the mono(ADPR) level (*209*). After the alkaline hydrolysis step of the isolation procedure for poly(ADPR), the acid-soluble nucleotides and ADPR residues liberated from the mono-ADPR-protein conjugates are passed through an acriflavine-Sephadex G-25 column, devised for the separation of nucleotides and related compounds by "charge-transfer chromatography" (*210, 211*). On this support, ADPR residues are well separated from AMP, enabling their estimation by the usual fluorometric method.

A novel purification method of ADP-ribosylated nuclear proteins by affinity chromatography on dihydroxyboryl polyacrylamide beads, which specifically interacts with *cis*-diols, has been reported (*80*). Advantages of this column over other purification procedures are that (*a*) a highly specific interaction between the borate residues and *cis*-diols enables them selectively to isolate ADP-ribosylated proteins from unmodified proteins; (*b*) differences in the chain length of the bound polymer have little or no effect on the chromatographic behavior of the attached protein on the column; and (*c*) the column works well even in the presence of a strong dissociating reagent, such as 6 M guanidinium chloride, which effectively reduces interactions among proteins. Applied to the isolation and partial characterization of the ADP-ribosylated nuclear proteins from Ehrlich ascites tumor cells (*86*), a 25-fold purification of the radioactive $(ADPR)_n$-containing material was achieved, as judged by the increase in specific labeling. Using dihydroxyboryl-Sepharose chromatography, a new method for the quantitative determination of the cellular amount of poly(ADPR), which achieved separation of poly(ADPR) from the bulk of RNA, DNA, and proteins was developed (*212*). The poly(ADPR) was then treated with snake venom phosphodiesterase and bacterial alkaline phosphatase to yield the unique nucleotide PR-AMP. Treatment with chloroacetaldehyde yielded a fluorescent derivative, which was separated from other fluorescent compounds by reverse-phase high-pressure liquid chromatography. Picomole amounts were quantified by fluorescence detection.

Hydroxyapatite column chromatography and/or polyacrylamide gel electrophoresis can be used to determine the distribution of oligo(ADPR) fractions of various chain lengths and terminal structures (*25, 26*). Individual polymers up to at least 33 units may be separated completely according to their chain length on electrophoresis in dodecyl sulfate gels (*27*). Polyacrylamide gel electrophoresis and staining poly(ADPR) by "Stains-all" (Eastman Kodak product) can detect about 0.8 μg of the polymer, and polymer mixtures can be resolved by size difference of 1 residue up to at least 65 residues (*28*).

2. ENZYMIC STUDIES

Snake venom phosphodiesterase is often used for poly(ADPR) chain-length determinations. Commercial preparations are available but are considerably contaminated by nonspecific alkaline phosphatase and 5'-nucleotidase, which interfere with precise quantitative analyses. A simple purification of this enzyme from a commercial preparation on Blue-Sepharose (Pharmacia) can give a 60-fold purification of the enzyme with a yield of 60% in a single step (213).

Poly(ADPR) glycohydrolase is an excellent tool for the identification of oligomers of ADPR. In addition, information about the properties of this enzyme would aid significantly in understanding the role of this hydrolytic activity in regulating poly(ADPR) synthesis in vivo. The presence and properties of this enzyme in calf thymus, slime mold, rat testis, and HeLa cells have been reported by several workers (214–217). Denatured DNA, poly(G), poly(I), and poly(A) are very potent inhibitors of glycohydrolase; in contrast, native DNA has little effect (216). The rate of the glycohydrolase-catalyzed hydrolysis of the polymer in the "H1 dimer" complex from HeLa cell nuclei is only one-ninth that of free poly(ADPR), indicating that the polymer is in a protected environment within the complex (75, 76, 217). In addition, the complex partially unfolds when it binds to native DNA, as evidenced by a twofold increase in the rate of glycolytic cleavage of poly(ADPR). These observations confirmed the utility of this enzyme for the structural analysis of "H1 dimer" complex.

Wheat embryos produce an effective inhibitor of poly(ADPR) glycohydrolase on imbibition of water; it becomes fully expressed over a period of 6 hours during which the poly(ADPR) glycohydrolase activity decreases by 95% (218). This was the first observation of an effective physiological inhibitor of the enzyme.

Inhibitors of poly(ADPR) synthetase include various benzamides and structurally related compounds, which have been synthesized and tested on poly(ADPR) synthetase activity in vitro (195–197). Two of the benzamides, 3-aminobenzamide and 3-methoxybenzamide, are the most inhibitory compounds found to date, with K_i values of less than 2 μM, and they appear to be more physiologically specific for poly(ADPR) polymerase than other inhibitors, such as nicotinamide, thymidine, methylated xanthines, and cytokinins. They have been successfully used to demonstrate the participation of poly(ADPR) in DNA excision repair (198), and in the purification of the polymerase, by covalent linking to Sepharose 4B (219), producing a very effective affinity medium.

A fluorescent analog of NAD, nicotinamide $1,N^6$-ethenoadenine dinucleotide (ϵNAD), can be used as a substrate in the reaction catalyzed by a preparation of bull or rat testis poly(ADPR) polymerase, substituting for NAD; a basic protein from bull or rat testis extracts was labeled (*220*).

We should also mention here the use of permeabilized cells (*173*, *174–176*). This technique has been used mainly for the study of the possible relationship of poly(ADPR) to DNA repair (see Section V,C), and the results obtained seem to be more meaningful than those obtained from isolated nuclei.

B. Immunological Methods

Four types of antibodies to study poly(ADPR) and poly(ADPR) polymerase have been prepared: anti-poly(ADPR) (*30*) and anti-PR-AMP (*221*) sera; antibodies highly specific against 5'-AMP (*222, 223*); and anti-poly(ADPR) polymerase serum (*60*). These antisera permit the quantitative estimation of poly(ADPR) and poly(ADPR) polymerase. The biological significance of the natural occurrence of anti-poly(ADPR) has been discussed elsewhere (see Section II,B). Here we describe briefly the method of preparation and the applications of these antibodies and discuss their specificities.

1. STUDIES ON THE POLYMER

Specific antibodies against poly(ADPR) have been produced in rabbits by the injection of poly(ADPR) mixed with methylated bovine serum albumin (*30*). Under standard conditions, 1 mg of purified anti-poly(ADPR) combined with 400 pmol (4 μg) of poly(ADPR) and was retained on a Millipore filter. The binding of poly(ADPR) was not inhibited by poly(A), ADPR, PR-AMP, yeast RNA, or calf-thymus DNA. However, cross-reaction of rabbit antibodies with double-stranded RNA, poly(A) · poly(U), or poly(I) · poly(C) was observed (*33*). Induction of specific antibodies to poly(ADPR) in rabbits could be achieved by injecting a complex of poly(A) · poly(U) and methylated bovine serum albumin in Freund's complete adjuvant; this was a specific effect, as neither poly(I) · poly(C) nor poly(A) induced antibodies to poly(ADPR) (*33*). The reactivity of these antibodies against poly(ADPR) was dependent on the chain length of the polymer (*224*). Antibodies produced in C3H/He mice were most reactive to poly(ADPR) with 20 repeating ADPR units.

Antibodies against poly(ADPR) have been prepared in other laboratories as well. They were first used in a radioimmunoassay in the study of changes in poly(ADPR) levels in synchronous cultures of

HeLa cells (225). Later, a radioimmunassay was developed in which poly(ADPR) was stabilized *in situ* by freeze-clamping of the whole organ at liquid nitrogen temperature, followed by freeze-drying, treatment in a colloid mill, and separation of the nuclear fraction in organic solvents by density centrifugation (226). Extraction of poly(ADPR) from nuclei separated by the nonaqueous technique was quantitative, and the radioimmunoassay was readily applicable to the nuclear extract. The size recognition of the anti-poly(ADPR) globulin fraction thus obtained, measured by displacing $(ADPR)_{15}$ in the binding assay, was almost the same for polymers composed of 4 to 40 ADPR units. However, oligo(ADPR) of an average chain-length of 2.5 was 6.5 times less effective than the polymer of an average size of 40 ADPR units. A 90,000-fold excess of ADPR did not inhibit the binding of poly(ADPR), whereas a 3600-fold excess of poly(A) or RNA inhibited the binding by 50%. This specificity is in contrast to the properties of the earlier antibody, where a 100,000-fold excess of ADPR over poly(ADPR) completely prevented the binding of poly(ADPR) whereas a 50,000-fold excess of poly(A) was not inhibiting (225). This difference in specificity between the two antibodies could be due to the larger size of poly(ADPR) used as antigen in the later work (226) or to differences in immune response between experimental animals.

Using an improved method of extraction of poly(ADPR) and a combination of the radioimmunoassay described here above, and molecular filtration, more than 99% of the naturally occurring poly(ADPR) larger than the tetramer was present in rat liver in covalent association with nonhistone proteins (227). The polydispersity of various histone-associated ADPR polymers present in small amounts indicates that the dimer of histone H1 (75–77, 217) is not a unique macromolecular species, although NAD-dependent polynucleosome condensation has been associated with H1 cross-linking (228).

Two kinds of antigens have been prepared by coupling adenine-N^6-carboxymethylated ADPR to serum albumin (Ag 1) or to methylated serum albumin (Ag 2) by the carbodiimide method (222). With antigen 1, 5'-AMP specific antisera were obtained that showed excellent discrimination between 5'-AMP and 3'-AMP, or AMP residues in nucleic acids. With antigen 2, ADPR-specific antibodies were obtained, but these sera contained similar titers of 5'-AMP antibodies. Using the 5'-AMP specific antibodies obtained with antigen 1 and on the basis of the selective conversion of ADPR to 5'-AMP by alkaline treatment (229), a specific and sensitive radioimmunoassay for ADPR was developed (223). The antibodies highly specific against 5'-AMP allowed quantification of ADPR converted to 5'-AMP in the range of 1 to 40 pmol and in the presence of large quantities of nucleic acids or

3'-AMP. Application of this technique permitted quantification of protein-bound ADPR residues in crude tissue extracts (66, 111, 112, 229a, 229b).

An extension of this technique for the rapid determination from the same acid extract of oxidized and reduced forms of NAD and NADP in picomole quantities involves the conversion of NAD to 5'-AMP via ADPR by alkaline treatment, while NADH is converted first to ADPR by incubation of the acid extract at 25°C followed by alkaline conversion to 5'-AMP (230). Then 5'-AMP is estimated with the aid of the highly specific immunoassay, allowing a quantification in the range of 0.1 to 10 pmol. The procedure was extended to NADP and NADPH by prior treatment of the extracts with alkaline phosphatase.

A specific antibody against PR-AMP, a monomer of poly(ADPR), was obtained by immunizing a rabbit with PR-AMP coupled to bovine serum albumin (221). The antibodies were purified 53-fold from serum by $(NH_4)_2SO_4$ precipitation, and various chromatographies. Inhibition experiments show that the adenine ring, 5'-phosphate residue, and ribose-ribose bond of PR-AMP are essential for the antigenic determinant of PR-AMP. Anti-PR-AMP antibody bound, not only with PR-AMP, but also with poly(ADPR) of various chain lengths, while poly(ADPR) antibody bound with poly(ADPR) but not with PR-AMP.

2. STUDIES ON THE POLY(ADPR) POLYMERASE

We have prepared a specific antibody against calf thymus poly(ADPR) polymerase (60). Purified enzyme coupled to N-acetylmuramyl-L-alanyl-D-isoglutamine was injected subcutaneously at several points on the back of two rabbits. After 2 weeks and after 1 month, the injections of the antigen were repeated under the same conditions.

The specific antibodies obtained were characterized, and a microcomplement-fixation method was devised for the quantitative estimation of poly(ADPR) polymerase at the nanogram level (61). The antisera tested by the Ouchterlony double-immunodiffusion technique produced a single precipitin line of identity against purified calf thymus DNA-independent and DNA-dependent poly(ADPR) polymerase, or against crude nuclear extracts from calf thymus, beef liver, and beef brain. Rat liver, rat brain, or rabbit brain nuclear extracts gave no precipitation line against this antibody. This species specificity observed has to be considered within the limits of this technique, since by the microcomplement-fixation method, and on the basis of DNA concentration, chick embryo cultured neurons showed about the same affinity as calf thymus nuclear extracts.

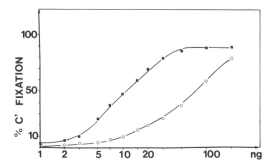

FIG. 5. Microcomplement-fixation reactions of native (O———O) and DNase treated (■———■) calf-thymus DNA-independent poly(ADPR) polymerase with rabbit antiserum.

Quantitative microcomplement-fixation analysis revealed a higher affinity of this antibody toward the DNA-dependent poly(ADPR) polymerase than toward the DNA-independent one, although this antibody was obtained with DNA-independent enzyme as antigen. Figure 5 shows that when the DNA-independent enzyme was treated by DNase, the affinity of the antibody toward the enzyme molecule was also increased. Addition of "sDNA" (see Section III,B,2) to the microcomplement reaction mixture with the DNA-independent enzyme had no effect, whereas with the DNA-dependent enzyme a slight inhibition of complement fixation was observed. These results taken together suggested strongly that the "sDNA" fragment, copurified with the DNA-independent enzyme, occupies a specific antigenic site on the enzyme molecule, supporting further the view that it is not a simple contaminant of the purified enzyme. In contrast, poly(ADP-ribosylation) of the enzyme or addition of histones had no effect on the micro complement-fixation reaction.

A specific antibody against poly(ADPR) synthetase of calf thymus quantitatively precipitated the enzyme activity and was cross-reactive, to much lesser extents, with the enzymes of rat, mouse and chicken livers and of HeLa cells (231). Like the antibody obtained by our group (61), this antibody was also reactive with auto-poly(ADP-ribosylated) calf thymus enzyme (231).

VII. Conclusion

Despite the increasing number of reports published on the subject, the biological functions of poly(ADPR), and of mono and poly(ADP-ribosylation) of acceptor proteins, are not fully understood. However, some specific effects of the ADP-ribosyl transferase of prokaryotes (certain toxins and coliphages), known to catalyze the mono(ADP-ribosylation) of specific proteins thus modifying the host-cell metabolism, have become clearer (see Section IV,B). In contrast, no specific role has been found for mono- and poly(ADP-ribosylation) of the nuclear proteins in eukaryotes.

After the initial discovery of poly(ADPR) as an *in vitro* reaction product, the natural occurrence of this polymer was demonstrated. Moreover, naturally occurring antibodies to poly(ADPR) were found in the sera of patients with systemic lupus erythematosus, and it was suggested that the estimation of poly(ADPR) binding in serum may be more useful in the diagnosis of this disease than the presently employed estimation of DNA binding.

Poly(ADPR) polymerase was confirmed as a ubiquitous nuclear enzyme that exists in a variety of eukaryotic cells, including some microorganisms and plants (see Section III,C). The reaction product, initially thought to be a linear polymer of ADPR-moieties of NAD, has been reported to have a branched structure.

Great progress was achieved in our knowledge of the enzymology of the mono- and poly(ADPR) synthesis. Poly(ADPR) polymerase has been extensively purified from various tissues, and its kinetic and acceptor characteristics, mainly concerning the requirement of specific DNA sequences, have been studied. Purified poly(ADPR) polymerase can both initiate and elongate poly(ADPR) chains on itself and, in contrast to earlier findings, on exogenously added histones. The sites of ADP-ribosylation on histones H1 and H2B have been determined, and at the same time the site of mono(ADP-ribosylation) of elongation factor EF-2 was discovered to be a new amino acid called diphthamide.

From studies on the possible involvement of this postsynthetic modification of proteins in cellular functions emerge three main points: (*a*) DNA synthesis, mainly DNA repair; (*b*) modification of chromatin structure; and (*c*) DNA expression or differentiation (see Section V). The lack of conclusive evidence may be mainly due to the great heterogeneity of this type of modification in terms of chain length, natural distribution, acceptor proteins, and ADP-ribosyl linkages (see Section IV).

The relation of poly(ADPR) synthesis to DNA synthesis or to cell growth is not clear. No clear-cut conclusion emerges as to the exact phase of the cell cycle in which the poly(ADPR) polymerase plays a regulatory role, or if poly(ADPR) synthesis is associated with increased

DNA synthesis during cell proliferation (see Section V,B). In contrast, experiments dealing with DNA damage have shown that DNA strand breakage is always associated with an increased poly(ADPR) polymerase activity and a decreased cellular NAD pool. It appears that the sites on the DNA capable of supporting this synthesis of poly(ADPR) are created by DNA strand breakage and are rapidly eliminated or repaired during subsequent incubation with NAD (232). Also, the DNA strand breaks more effective in their ability to support poly(ADPR) synthesis appear to be those assumed to be implicated in the DNA repair process *in vivo* (233). Additional evidence suggesting the involvement of poly(ADPR) polymerase in DNA damage and repair system comes from the effects of inhibitors of poly(ADPR) synthesis, which prevent the rejoining of DNA strand breaks caused by dimethyl sulfate (198). Thus, the synthesis of poly(ADPR) seems to be required for the repair of DNA strand breaks, although the mechanism and the exact intervention level of poly(ADPR) within the DNA repair process remain to be elucidated.

From *in vitro* studies it is clearly suggested that ADP-ribosylation of nuclear proteins is involved in chromatin architecture (21). Poly(ADPR) polymerase is primarily localized in the nucleosomal linker region, and its activity is higher at selected folded regions in higher-ordered structures of chromatin and is associated with transcriptionally active chromatin. Since the pattern of ADP-ribosylated nuclear proteins is also dependent on the state of the chromatin, it seems possible that one function of this modification may be to facilitate condensation and relaxation of regions in higher ordered structures of chromatin (21).

Differentiation of several cell types has also been related to poly(ADPR) through variations in poly(ADPR) polymerase activity and, more recently, to poly(ADPR) levels. Moreover, it has been proposed (234) that increased polymerase activity during differentiation of chick myoblasts *in vitro* is associated with the appearance of DNA strand breaks, and that poly(ADPR) polymerase is actively involved in the continuation of the differentiation process.

Until now, many of the results presented in this review and earlier came from *in vitro* studies that, as underlined by many authors, could be greatly dependent on experimental conditions. More recently, several new analytical techniques for *in vivo* studies on poly(ADPR) have been described. The use of permeabilized cells offers a better approach to particular cellular functions and has already been widely used in DNA repair system. On the other hand, studies on poly(ADPR) polymerase activity will be more relevant using 3-amino- and

3-methoxybenzamide, which are physiologically specific inhibitors of the enzyme. In addition, the specific antibody obtained against calf thymus poly(ADPR) polymerase should provide a useful tool for immunohistochemical studies on the enzyme.

Another approach to defining the function of ADP-ribosylation may be to study the mono- and poly(ADP-ribosylation) of specific protein fractions throughout a cellular activity. For this purpose new analytical methods for the quantitative estimation of mono- or poly(ADPR) levels have been devised and already applied to determinations *in vivo*.

In summary, the precise biological function of the poly(ADP-ribosylation) reaction has not yet been unequivocally established. However, the results are consistent with the occurrence of rapid transient modifications of proteins in localized regions of chromatin. These alterations in chromatin conformation appear to be induced by DNA strand breakage leading to the DNA repair process or to the differentiation process. Thus, after analytical studies *in vitro*, such as enzyme purification and properties determination and enzyme activity measurements in isolated nuclei, the use *in vivo* of new sensitive analytical techniques should allow a better understanding of the biological functions of mono- and poly(ADPR).

Addendum

Subsequent to the completion of this manuscript, three reviews dealing with ADP-ribosylation of nuclear proteins were published by Ueda *et al.* (235), Purnell, Stone, and Whish (236), and Sugimura *et al.* (237).

ACKNOWLEDGMENTS

We are grateful to many colleagues who kindly provided us with manuscripts in advance of publication. We thank Drs. M. E. Ittel and J. Bilen for helpful suggestions and Mrs. S. Ott and H. Urban for their help in typing the manuscript. Research that originated in our laboratory was supported by the Centre National de la Recherche Scientifique and by the Institut National de la Santé et de la Recherche Médicale.

REFERENCES

1. P. Chambon, J. D. Weill, and P. Mandel, *BBRC* **11**, 39 (1963).
2. P. Chambon, J. D. Weill, J. Doly, M. T. Strosser, and P. Mandel, *BBRC* **25**, 638 (1966).
3. Y. Nishizuka, K. Ueda, K. Nekazawa, and O. Hayaishi, *JBC* **242**, 3164 (1967).
4. S. Fujimura, S. Hasegawa, Y. Shimizu, and T. Sugimura, *BBA* **145**, 247 (1967).
5. J. Doly and F. Petek, *C. R. Hebd. Seances Acad. Sci. Ser. D* **263**, 1341 (1966).
6. R. Reeder, K. Ueda, T. Honjo, Y. Nishizuka, and O. Hayaishi, *JBC* **242**, 3172 (1967).

7. S. Hasegawa, S. Fujimura, Y. Shimizu, and T. Sugimura, *BBA* **149**, 369 (1967).
8. Y. Nishizuka, K. Ueda, T. Honjo, and O. Hayaishi, *JBC* **243**, 3765 (1968).
9. J. Doly and P. Mandel, *C. R. Hebd. Seances Acad. Sci. Ser. D* **264**, 2687 (1967).
10. M. Miwa and T. Sugimura, *JBC* **246**, 6362 (1971).
11. K. Ueda, J. Oka, S. Narumiya, N. Miyakawa, and O. Hayaishi, *BBRC* **46**, 516 (1972).
12. H. Okayama, M. Honda, and O. Hayaishi, *PNAS* **75**, 2254 (1978).
13. T. Sugimura, *This Series*, **13**, 127 (1973).
14. T. Sugimura, M. Miwa, Y. Kanai, K. Oda, K. Segawa, M. Tanaka, and H. Sakura, *Prog. Cancer Res. Ther.* **1**, 231 (1976).
15. H. Hilz and P. Stone, *Rev. Physiol. Biochem. Pharmacol.* **76**, 1 (1976).
16. O. Hayaishi and K. Ueda, *ARB* **46**, 95 (1977).
17. Proceedings of EMBO Workshop on Structure and Function of Poly(ADP-Ribose), *ZpChem* **353**, 843 (1972).
18. *Poly(ADP-Ribose), Int. Symp. 1973* (Fogarty International Center Proceedings n26), 1974.
19. Proceedings of the Seminar on Poly(ADP-Ribose) and ADP-Ribosylation of Proteins, *J. Biochem. (Tokyo)* **77**, 1p (1975).
20. "Proceedings of the 4th International Symposium on Poly(ADP-Ribose) and ADP-Ribosylation of Proteins" (H. Hilz, ed.). de Gruyter, Berlin, 1976.
21. M. Smulson, *TIBS* **4**, 225 (1979).
22. H. Hilz, P. Adamietz, R. Bredehorst, and K. Wielckens, *Adv. Enzyme Regul.* **17**, 195 (1979).
23. Proceedings of the 5th International Conference on Novel ADP-Ribosylations of Regulatory Enzymes and Proteins, *in* "Developments in Cell Biology" (M. Smulson and T. Sugimura, eds.), Vol. 6. Elsevier–North Holland, Amsterdam, 1980.
24. M. Miwa, H. Saitô, H. Sakura, N. Saikawa, F. Watanabe, T. Matsushima, and T. Sugimura, *NARes* **4**, 3997 (1977).
25. T. Sugimura, N. Yoshimura, M. Miwa, H. Nagai, and M. Nagao, *ABB* **147**, 660 (1971).
26. M. Tanaka, M. Miwa, K. Hayashi, K. Kubota, T. Matsushima, and T. Sugimura, *Bchem* **16**, 1485 (1977).
27. P. Adamietz, R. Bredehorst, and H. Hilz, *BBRC* **81**, 1377 (1978).
28. M. Tanaka, K. Hayashi, H. Sakura, M. Miwa, T. Matsushima, and T. Sugimura, *NARes* **5**, 3183 (1978).
29. M. Miwa, N. Saikawa, Z. Yamaizumi, S. Nishimura, and T. Sugimura, *PNAS* **76**, 595 (1979).
30. Y. Kanai, M. Miwa, T. Matsushima, and T. Sugimura, *BBRC* **59**, 300 (1974).
31. H. Sakura, M. Miwa, M. Tanaka, Y. Kanai, T. Shimada, T. Matsushima, and T. Sugimura, *NARes* **4**, 2903 (1977).
32. Y. Kanai, Y. Kawaminami, M. Miwa, T. Matsushima, T. Sugimura, Y. Moroi, and R. Yokohari, *Nature* **265**, 175 (1977).
33. Y. Kanai, T. Sugimura, and T. Matsushima, *Nature* **274**, 809 (1978).
34. E. E. Okolie and S. Shall, *Clin. Exp. Immunol.* **36**, 151 (1979).
35. L. Burzio and S. Koide, *BBRC* **53**, 572 (1973).
36. K. Yoshihara, Y. Tanigawa, and S. Koide, *BBRC* **59**, 658 (1974).
37. M. Yamada, M. Nagao, M. Miwa, and T. Sugimura, *BBRC* **56**, 1093 (1974).
38. M. Yamada, T. Shimada, M. Nakayasu, H. Okada, and T. Sugimura, *BBRC* **83**, 1325 (1978).
39. Y. Suzuki and T. Murachi, *J. Biochem.* **84**, 977 (1978).

39a. T. Inagaki, K. Miura, and T. Murachi, *JBC* **255**, 7746 (1980).

40. H. Okazaki, C. Niedergang, and P. Mandel, *FEBS Lett.* **62**, 255 (1976).

41. H. Okazaki, C. Niedergang, and P. Mandel, *C. R. Hebd. Seances Acad. Sci. Ser. D* **285**, 1545 (1977).

42. P. Mandel, H. Okazaki, and C. Niedergang, *FEBS Lett.* **84**, 331 (1977).

43. K. Yoshihara, T. Hashida, H. Yoshihara, Y. Tanaka, and H. Ohgushi, *BBRC* **78**, 1281 (1977).

44. K. Yoshihara, T. Hashida, Y. Tanaka, H. Ohgushi, H. Yoshihara, and T. Kamiya, *JBC* **253**, 6459 (1978).

45. S. Ito, Y. Shizuta, and O. Hayaishi, *JBC* **254**, 3647 (1979).

46. C. Tsopanakis, E. McLaren, A. Tsopanakis, and S. Shall, *Biochem. Soc. Trans.* **5**, 932 (1977).

47. C. Tsopanakis, E. Leeson, A. Tsopanakis, and S. Shall, *EJB* **90**, 337 (1978).

48. H. Okayama, C. M. Edson, M. Fukushima, K. Ueda, and O. Hayaishi, *JBC* **252**, 7000 (1977).

49. T. Kristensen and J. Holtlund, *EJB* **88**, 495 (1978).

50. J. Holtlund, T. Kristensen, and K. Sletten, *BJ* **185**, 779 (1980).

51. D. Jump and M. Smulson, *Bchem* **19**, 1024 (1980).

52. K. Ueda, M. Kawaichi, H. Okayama, and O. Hayaishi, *JBC* **254**, 679 (1979).

53. H. Okazaki, C. Niedergang, and P. Mandel, *Biochimie* **62**, 147 (1980).

54. H. Okazaki, C. Niedergang, M. Couppez, A. Martinage, P. Sautière, and P. Mandel, *FEBS Lett.* **110**, 227 (1980).

55. Y. Tanaka, T. Hashida, H. Yoshihara, and K. Yoshihara, *JBC* **254**, 12433 (1979).

56. M. Kawaichi, K. Ueda, and O. Hayaishi, *JBC* **255**, 816 (1980).

57. K. Ueda, M. Kawaichi, J. Oka, and O. Hayaishi, *Dev. Cell Biol.* (*Amsterdam*) **6**, 47 (1980).

58. A. Caplan, C. Niedergang, H. Okazaki, and P. Mandel, *ABB* **197**, 60 (1979).

59. T. Hashida, H. Ohgushi, and K. Yoshihara, *BBRC* **88**, 305 (1979).

60. C. Niedergang, H. Okazaki, and P. Mandel, *EJB* **102**, 43 (1979).

60a. H. Ohgushi, K. Yoshihara, and T. Kamiya, *JBC* **255**, 6205 (1980).

61. H. Okazaki, J. P. Delaunoy, F. Hog, J. Bilen, C. Niedergang, E. Creppy, M. E. Ittel, and P. Mandel, *BBRC* **97**, 1512 (1980).

62. B. Farina and M. R. Mennella, *Rend. Accad. Sci. Fis. Mat. Naples* (series 4) **44**, 17 (1977).

63. G. G. Poirier, P. Savard, D. Rajotte, J. Morisset, and A. Lord, *Can. J. Biochem.* **56**, 784 (1978).

64. N. Wong, G. G. Poirier, and G. Dixon, *EJB* **77**, 11 (1977).

65. F. Farzaneh and C. Pearson, *BBRC* **84**, 537 (1978).

66. K. Wielckens, W. Sachsenmaier, and H. Hilz, *ZpChem* **360**, 39 (1979).

67. C. Tsopanakis, J. C. Leer, O. F. Nielsen, E. Gocke, S. Shall, and O. Westergaard, *FEBS Lett.* **93**, 297 (1978).

68. A. Whitby and W. Whish, *Proc. FEBS Meet., 11th Abstr.* No. 163 (1977).

69. L. Willmitzer, *FEBS Lett.* **108**, 13 (1979).

70. L. Burzio, M. Luke, and S. Koide, *FP* **38**, 618 (1979).

71. J. Roberts, P. Stark, C. Giri, and M. Smulson, *ABB* **171**, 305 (1975).

72. I. Goldknopf and H. Busch, *PNAS* **74**, 864 (1977).

73. I. Isenberg, *ARB* **48**, 159 (1979).

74. S. Tanuma, T. Enomoto, and M. Yamada, *BBRC* **74**, 599 (1977).

75. P. Stone, W. Lorimer III, and W. Kidwell, *EJB* **81**, 9 (1977).

76. W. Lorimer III, P. Stone, and W. Kidwell, *Exp. Cell Res.* **106**, 261 (1977).

77. P. Adamietz, R. Bredehorst, and H. Hilz, *EJB* **91**, 317 (1978).
78. K. Ueda, A. Omachi, M. Kawaichi, and O. Hayaishi, *PNAS* **72**, 205 (1975).
79. M. Ord and L. Stocken, *BJ* **161**, 583 (1977).
80. H. Okayama, K. Ueda, and O. Hayaishi, *PNAS* **75**, 1111 (1978).
81. H. Okayama and O. Hayaishi, *BBRC* **84**, 755 (1978).
82. L. Orrick, M. Olson, and H. Busch, *PNAS* **70**, 1316 (1973).
83. N. Ballal, I. Goldknopf, D. Goldberg, and H. Busch, *Life Sci.* **14**, 1835 (1974).
84. N. Ballal, Y. J. Kang, M. Olson, and H. Busch, *JBC* **250**, 5921 (1975).
85. I. Goldknopf, F. Rosenbaum, R. Sterner, G. Vidali, V. Allfrey, and H. Busch, *BBRC* **90**, 269 (1979).
86. P. Adamietz, K. Klapproth, and H. Hilz, *BBRC* **91**, 1232 (1979).
87. K. Janakidevi, *Exp. Cell Res.* **112**, 345 (1978).
88. R. Byrne, P. Stone, and W. Kidwell, *Exp. Cell Res.* **115**, 277 (1978).
89. F. Perrella and M. Lea, *BBRC* **82**, 575 (1978).
90. F. Perrella and M. Lea, *Cancer Res.* **39**, 1382 (1979).
90a. A. Whitby, P. Stone, and W. Whish, *BBRC* **90**, 1295 (1979).
91. D. Lichtenwalner and R. Suhadolnik, *Bchem* **18**, 3749 (1979).
92. R. Suhadolnik, R. Baur, D. Lichtenwalner, T. Uematsu, J. Roberts, S. Sudhakar, and M. Smulson, *JBC* **252**, 4134 (1977).
93. D. Rickwood, A. MacGillivray, and W. Whish, *EJB* **79**, 589 (1977).
94. T. Honjo, Y. Nishizuka, I. Kato, and O. Hayaishi, *JBC* **246**, 4251 (1971).
95. B. Iglewski and D. Kabat, *PNAS* **72**, 2284 (1975).
96. B. R. Martin, M. D. Houslay, and E. L. Kennedy, *BJ* **161**, 639 (1977).
97. M. Gill, *PNAS* **72**, 2064 (1975).
98. S. L. Levinson and A. J. Blume, *JBC* **252**, 3766 (1977).
99. M. A. Wheeler, R. A. Solomon, C. Cooper, L. Herzberg, H. Mehta, N. Miki, and M. W. Bitensky, *J. Infect. Dis.* **133**, Suppl. S89 (1976).
100. J. Moss and M. Vaughan, *JBC* **252**, 2455 (1977).
101. D. Cassel and T. Pfeuffer, *PNAS* **75**, 2669 (1978).
102. S. Beckner and M. Blecher, *FEBS Lett.* **95**, 319 (1978).
103. M. Gill and R. Meren, *PNAS* **75**, 3050 (1978).
103a. J. Moss, S. Stanley, and M. Lin, *JBC* **254**, 11993 (1979).
104. M. Gill, *FP* **38**, 618 (1979).
105. J. Moss, S. Garrison, N. Oppenheimer, and S. Richardson, *JBC* **254**, 6270 (1979).
106. J. Moss and M. Vaughan, *PNAS* **75**, 3621 (1978).
107. J. Moss, S. Stanley, and N. Oppenheimer, *JBC* **254**, 8891 (1979).
108. W. Zillig, R. Mailhammer, R. Skorko, and H. Rohrer, *Curr. Top. Cell. Regul.* **12**, 263 (1977).
109. R. Skorko, W. Zillig, H. Rohrer, H. Fujiki, and R. Mailhammer, *EJB* **79**, 55 (1977).
110. P. Adamietz and H. Hilz, *ZpChem* **357**, 527 (1976).
111. R. Bredehorst, K. Wielckens, A. Gartemann, H. Lengyel, K. Klapproth, and H. Hilz, *EJB* **92**, 129 (1978).
112. R. Bredehorst, M. Goebel, F. Renzi, M. Kittler, K. Klapproth, and H. Hilz, *ZpChem* **360**, 1737 (1979).
113. J. Smith and L. Stocken, *BBRC* **54**, 297 (1973).
114. P. Riquelme, L. Burzio, and S. Koide, *JBC* **254**, 3018 (1979).
115. L. Burzio, P. Riquelme, and S. Koide, *JBC* **254**, 3029 (1979).
116. N. Ogata, K. Ueda, and O. Hayaishi, *Dev. Cell Biol.* (*Amsterdam*) **6**, 333 (1980).
117. N. Ogata, K. Ueda, H. Kagamiyama, and O. Hayaishi, *JBC* **255**, 7616 (1980).
117a. N. Ogata, K. Ueda, and O. Hayaishi, *JBC* **255**, 7610 (1980).

118. E. Robinson, O. Henriksen, and E. Maxwell, *JBC* **249**, 5088 (1974).

119. B. Van Ness, J. Howard, and J. Bodley, *JBC* **253**, 8687 (1978).

120. B. Brown and J. Bodley, *FEBS Lett.* **103**, 253 (1979).

120a. B. G. Van Ness, J. B. Howard, and J. W. Bodley, *JBC* **255**, 10710, 10717 (1980).

121. J. Bodley, B. Van Ness, and J. Howard, *Dev. Cell Biol. (Amsterdam)* **6**, 413 (1980).

122. C. Brack and S. Tonegawa, *PNAS* **74**, 5652 (1977).

123. G. Matthyssens and S. Tonegawa, *Nature* **273**, 763 (1978).

124. D. Goeddel, H. Heyneker, T. Hozumi, R. Arentzen, K. Itakura, D. Yansura, M. Ross, G. Miozzari, R. Crea, and P. Seeburg, *Nature* **281**, 544 (1979).

125. J. Saffitz and A. Caplan, *Bchem* **17**, 3487 (1978).

126. R. D. Kornberg and J. O. Thomas, *Science* **184**, 865 (1974).

127. D. R. Hewish and L. A. Burgoyne, *BBRC* **52**, 504 (1973).

128. M. Noll, *Nature* **251**, 249 (1974).

129. C. L. F. Woodcock, *J. Cell Biol.* **59**, 368a (1973).

130. A. L. Olins and D. E. Olins, *Science* **183**, 330 (1974).

131. K. E. Van Holde, C. G. Sahasrabuddhe, and B. R. Shaw, *NARes* **1**, 1579 (1974).

132. P. Oudet, M. Gross-Bellard, and P. Chambon, *Cell* **4**, 281 (1975).

133. R. D. Kornberg, *Science* **184**, 868 (1974).

134. J. L. Compton, M. Bellard, and P. Chambon, *PNAS* **73**, 4382 (1976).

135. J. O. Thomas and R. J. Thompson, *Cell* **10**, 633 (1977).

136. C. Spadafora, M. Bellard, J. L. Compton, and P. Chambon, *FEBS Lett.* **69**, 281 (1976).

137. B. O. Glotov, A. V. Itkes, L. G. Nikolaev, and E. S. Severin, *FEBS Lett.* **91**, 149 (1978).

138. C. Gorka and J. J. Lawrence, *NARes* **7**, 347 (1979).

139. D. Mullins Jr., C. Giri, and M. Smulson, *Bchem* **16**, 506 (1977).

140. M. Yukioka, Y. Okai, T. Hasuma, and A. Inoue, *FEBS Lett.* **86**, 85 (1978).

141. D. Jump, T. Butt, and M. Smulson, *Bchem* **18**, 983 (1979).

142. C. Giri, M. West, and M. Smulson, *Bchem* **17**, 3495 (1978).

143. C. Giri, M. West, M. Ramirez, and M. Smulson, *Bchem* **17**, 3501 (1978).

144. T. Butt, J. Brothers, C. Giri, and M. Smulson, *NARes* **5**, 2775 (1978).

145. T. Butt, D. Jump, and M. Smulson, *PNAS* **76**, 1628 (1979).

146. A. Caplan, M. Ord, and L. Stocken, *BJ* **174**, 475 (1978).

147. E. M. Bradbury, R. J. Inglis, H. R. Matthews, and T. A. Langan, *Nature* **249**, 553 (1974).

148. Y. Matsumoto, H. Yasuda, S. Mita, T. Marunouchi, and M. Yamada, *Nature* **284**, 181 (1980).

149. L. Sealy and R. Chalkley, *Cell* **14**, 115 (1978).

150. V. Jackson, A. Shires, R. Chalkley, and D. K. Granner, *JBC* **250**, 4850 (1975).

151. M. T. Sung and H. Dixon, *PNAS* **67**, 1616 (1970).

152. A. Ruiz-Carrillo, L. J. Wangh, and V. G. Allfrey, *Science* **190**, 117 (1975).

153. T. Tiddwell, V. G. Allfrey, and A. E. Mirsky, *JBC* **243**, 707 (1968).

154. H. W. Lee, W. K. Paik, and T. W. Borun, *JBC* **248**, 4194 (1973).

155. M. Smulson, O. Henriksen, and C. Rideau, *BBRC* **43**, 1266 (1971).

156. J. Roberts, P. Stark, and M. Smulson, *BBRC* **52**, 43 (1973).

157. M. Smulson, P. Stark, M. Gazzoli, and J. Roberts, *Exp. Cell Res.* **90**, 175 (1975).

158. R. A. Colyer, K. E. Burdette, and W. Kidwell, *BBRC* **53**, 960 (1973).

159. M. Miwa, T. Sugimura, N. Inui, and S. Takayama, *Cancer Res.* **33**, 1306 (1973).

160. S. Tanuma, T. Enomoto, and M. Yamada, *Exp. Cell Res.* **117**, 421 (1978).

161. N. A. Berger, A. Kaichi, P. Steward, R. Klevecz, G. Forrest, and S. Gross, *Exp. Cell Res.* **117**, 127 (1978).
162. Q. P. Ghani and M. Hollenberg, *BBRC* **81**, 886 (1978).
163. J. Porteous, H. Furneaux, C. Pearson, C. Lake, and A. Morrison, *BJ* **180**, 455 (1979).
164. M. Miwa, K. Oda, K. Segawa, M. Tanaka, S. Irie, N. Yamaguchi, T. Kuchino, K. Shiroki, H. Shimojo, H. Sakura, T. Matsushima, and T. Sugimura, *ABB* **181**, 313 (1977).
165. W. Müller, D. Falke, R. Zahn, and J. Arendes, *Intervirology* **11**, 182 (1979).
166. N. A. Berger, J. Adams, G. Sikorski, S. Petzold, and W. Shearer, *J. Clin. Invest.* **62**, 111 (1978).
167. C. Rochette-Egly, M. E. Ittel, J. Bilen, and P. Mandel, *FEBS Lett.* **120**, 7 (1980).
168. Y. Tanigawa, M. Kawamura, A. Kitamura, and M. Shimoyama, *BBRC* **81**, 1278 (1978).
169. Y. Tanigawa, A. Kitamura, M. Kawamura, and M. Shimoyama, *EJB* **92**, 261 (1978).
170. A. Kitamura, Y. Tanigawa, T. Yamamoto, M. Kawamura, S. Doi, and M. Shimoyama, *BBRC* **87**, 725 (1979).
170a. A. Kitamura, Y. Tanigawa, S. Doi, D. Kawakami, and M. Shimoyama, *ABB* **204**, 455 (1980).
170b. Y. Tanigawa, K. Kawakami, Y. Imai, and M. Shimoyama, *BBA* **608**, 82 (1980).
171. E. Miller, BBA **395**, 191 (1975).
172. E. Miller, *BBRC* **66**, 280 (1975).
173. H. Halldorsson, D. Gray, and S. Shall, *FEBS Lett.* **85**, 349 (1978).
174. N. A. Berger and E. Johnson, *BBA* **425**, 1 (1976).
175. N. A. Berger, W. Erickson, and G. Weber, *BBA* **447**, 65 (1976).
176. N. A. Berger, S. Petzold, and E. Johnson, *BBA* **478**, 44 (1977).
177. P. Reinhard, M. Burkhalter, and J. Gautschi, *BBA* **474**, 500 (1977).
178. N. A. Berger, G. Weber, and A. S. Kaichi, *BBA* **519**, 87 (1978).
179. N. A. Berger, G. Weber, A. S. Kaichi and S. Petzold, *BBA* **519**, 105 (1978).
180. N. A. Berger, S. Petzold, and S. Berger, *BBA* **564**, 90 (1979).
181. M. Yamada, M. Nagao, T. Hidaka, and T. Sugimura, *BBRC* **54**, 1567 (1973).
182. M. I. Davies, S. Shall, and C. Skidmore, *Biochem. Soc. Trans.* **5**, 949 (1977).
183. E. Miller, *FP* **36**, 906 (1977).
184. F. Perrella and M. Lea, *Dev. Cell Biol. (Amsterdam)* **6**, 99 (1980).
185. N. A. Berger, G. Sikorski, S. Petzold, and K. Kurohara, *J. Clin. Invest.* **63**, 1164 (1979).
186. S. Sudhakar, K. Tew, P. Schein, P. Wooley, and M. Smulson, *Cancer Res.* **39**, 1411 (1979).
187. S. Sudhakar, K. Tew, and M. Smulson, *Cancer Res.* **39**, 1405 (1979).
188. D. Jump, S. Sudhakar, K. Tew, and M. Smulson, *Chem.-Biol. Interact.* **30**, 35 (1980).
189. R. Benjamin and D. M. Gill, *Dev. Cell Biol. (Amsterdam)* **6**, 227 (1980).
190. N. A. Berger, G. Sikorski, S. Petzold, and K. Kurohara, *Bchem* **19**, 289 (1980).
190a. H. Juarez-Salinas, J. Sims, and M. Jacobson, *Nature* **282**, 740 (1979).
191. N. Nduka, C. Skidmore, and S. Shall, *EJB* **105**, 525 (1980).
192. C. Skidmore, M. Davies, P. Goodwin, H. Halldorsson, P. Lewis, S. Shall, and A. Zia'ee, *EJB* **101**, 135 (1979).
193. C. Skidmore, M. Davies, P. Goodwin, O. Omidiji, A. Zia'ee, and S. Shall, *Dev. Cell Biol. (Amsterdam)* **6**, 197 (1080).
194. V. Levi, E. Jacobson, and M. Jacobson, *FEBS Lett.* **88**, 144 (1978).

195. M. Purnell and W. Whish, BJ 185, 775 (1980).
196. C. Surowy and W. Whish, Biochem. Soc. Trans. 8, 174 (1980).
197. M. Purnell, P. Stone, C. Surowoy, and W. Whish, Dev. Cell Biol. 6, 285 (1980).
198. B. Durkacz, O. Omidiji, D. Gray, and S. Shall, Nature 283, 593 (1980).
199. H. Altmann, E. Dolejs, A. Topaloglou, and A. Sooki-Toth, Stud. Biophys. 76, 195 (1979).
200. A. Caplan and M. Rosenberg, PNAS 72, 1852 (1975).
201. F. Farzaneh and C. Pearson, Biochem. Soc. Trans. 5, 733 (1977).
202. F. Farzaneh and C. Pearson, Dev. Biol. 72, 254 (1979).
203. E. Rastl and P. Swetly, JBC 253, 4333 (1978).
204. J. S. Zlatanova and P. Svetly, BBRC 92, 1110 (1980).
205. K. Morioka, K. Tanaka, T. Nokuo, M. Ishizawa, and T. Ono, Gann 70, 37 (1979).
206. M. Terada, H. Fujiki, P. Marks, and T. Sugimura, PNAS 76, 6411 (1979).
206a. M. Terada, M. Yamada, H. Fujiki, M. Nakayasu, L. Umezawa, T. Matsushima, T. Utakoji, and T. Sugimura, Dev. Cell Biol. (Amsterdam) 6, 251 (1980).
207. A. Caplan, C. Niedergang, H. Okazaki, and P. Mandel, Dev. Biol. 72, 102 (1979).
207a. K. Ikai, K. Ueda, M. Fukushima, T. Nakamura, and O. Hayaishi, PNAS 77, 3682 (1980).
208. C. Niedergang, H. Okazaki, and P. Mandel, Anal. Biochem. 88, 20 (1978).
209. C. Niedergang, Ph.D. Thesis, University Louis Pasteur of Strasbourg, 1980.
210. J. M. Egly, FEBS Lett. 93, 369 (1978).
211. J. M. Egly and J. Porath, J. Chromatogr. 168, 35 (1979).
212. J. Sims, H. Juarez-Salinas, and M. Jacobson, Anal. Biochem. 106, 296 (1980).
213. J. Oka, K. Ueda, and O. Hayaishi, BBRC 80, 841 (1978).
214. M. Miwa, M. Tanaka, T. Matsushima, and T. Sugimura, JBC 249, 3475 (1974).
215. M. Tanaka, M. Miwa, T. Matsushima, T. Sugimura, and S. Shall, ABB 172, 224 (1976).
216. L. Burzio, P. Riquelme, E. Ohtsuka, and S. Koide, ABB 173, 306 (1976).
217. P. Stone, W. Lorimer, III, J. Ranchalis, M. Danley, and W. Kidwell, NARes 5, 173 (1978).
218. A. Whitby and W. Whish, Biochem. Soc. Trans. 8, 192 (1980).
219. M. Purnell and W. Whish, FEBS Proc. Meet., 11th, Abstr. No. 164 (1977).
220. B. Farina, M. R. Mennella, and A. Mauro, Rend. Accad. Sci. Fis. Mat. Naples (series 4) 46, 1 (1979).
221. H. Sakura, M. Miwa, Y. Kanai, T. Matsushima, and T. Sugimura, NARes 5, 4025 (1978).
222. R. Bredehorst, A. Ferro, and H. Hilz, EJB 82, 105 (1978).
223. R. Bredehorst, A. Ferro, and H. Hilz, EJB 82, 115 (1978).
224. Y. Kanai, M. Miwa, T. Matsushima, and T. Sugimura, Immunology 34, 501 (1978).
225. W. Kidwell and M. Mage, Bchem 15, 1213 (1976).
226. A. Ferro, T. Minaga, W. Piper, and E. Kun, BBA 519, 291 (1978).
227. T. Minaga, A. Romaschin, E. Kirsten, and E. Kun, JBC 254, 9663 (1979).
228. M. Smulson, T. Butt, N. Nolan, D. Jump, and B. Decoste, Dev. Cell Biol. (Amsterdam) 6, 59 (1980).
229. M. Goebel, P. Stone, H. Lengyel, and H. Hilz, Zpchem. 358, 13 (1977).
229a. K. Wielckens, M. Garbrecht, M. Kittler, and H. Hilz, EJB 104, 279 (1980).
229b. R. Bredehorst, K. Klapproth, H. Hilz, C. Scheidegger, and G. Gerisch, Cell Differ. 9, 95 (1980).
230. R. Bredehorst, H. Lengyel, and H. Hilz, EJB 99, 401 (1979).
231. K. Ikai and K. Ueda, BBRC 97, 279 (1980).

232. R. Benjamin and D. M. Gill, *JBC* **255,** 10493 (1980).
233. R. Benjamin and D. M. Gill, *JBC* **255,** 10502 (1980).
234. F. Farzaneh, S. Shall, and R. Zalin *Dev. Cell Biol. (Amsterdam)* **6,** 217 (1980).
235. K. Ueda, O. Hayaishi, M. Kawaichi, N. Ogata, K. Ikai, J. Oka, and H. Okayama, *in* "Modulation of Protein Function" (D. E. Atkinson and C. F. Fox, eds.), p. 47. Academic Press, New York, 1979.
236. M. Purnell, P. Stone, and W. Whish, *Biochem. Soc. Trans.* **8,** 215 (1980).
237. T. Sugimura, M. Miwa, H. Saito, Y. Kanai, M. Ikejima, M. Terada, M. Yamada, and T. Utakoji, *Adv. Enzyme Regul.* **18,** 195 (1980).

The Regulatory Function of Poly(A) and Adjacent 3' Sequences in Translated RNA

URIEL Z. LITTAUER AND
HERMONA SOREQ

Department of Neurobiology
The Weizmann Institute of Science
Rehovot, Israel

I. Introduction

Messenger RNA chains from various biological sources contain, in addition to coding sequences, regions located at the 3'- and 5' termini that are not translated. The nontranslated region at the 3' terminus is followed by a poly(A) segment of varying length. The voluminous literature on this topic, accumulated during the 1970s, has been covered in several excellent reviews (1–8). The present review is confined to a description of the properties and the possible regulatory functions of the nontranslated sequences and the poly(A) region located at the 3' termini of the RNA molecules.

53

Progress in Nucleic Acid Research
and Molecular Biology, Vol. 27

Interest in the nontranslated 3' regions was aroused by the discovery that most eukaryotic mRNA species contain a relatively long (50–250 nucleotides) poly(A) sequence covalently linked to the 3' end. The 3' poly(A) tracts are not coded for by nuclear DNA, but result from enzymic posttranscriptional polyadenylation, which occurs in the nucleus during and after processing of newly synthesized hnRNA (5). After maturation and conversion into mRNA, the polyadenylated mRNA molecules are transported from the nucleus into the cytoplasm, where the poly(A) tails of the aging mRNA chains are gradually reduced in size. The paring results in a heterogeneous size distribution of steady-state poly(A) (9–16).

Poly(A)-containing mRNA chains are present in all types of yeast (17) and slime molds (18) as well as in such subcellular organelles as mitochondria (19, 20). The poly(A) segments may be found in mRNA of prokaryotic origin, although their average size is much smaller than that in eukaryotic mRNA, and the bulk of the prokaryotic mRNAs lacks these tracts. Poly(A) tails containing about 25 residues have been reported for some *Escherichia coli* and *Caulobacter crescentus* mRNA chains (21, 22) and 60 residues for *B. brevis* mRNA (22a). In addition, several eukaryotic viruses—such as vaccinia virus (23), adenovirus (24), SV40 (25), Rous sarcoma virus (26), and poliovirus (27)—carry or specify the synthesis of translated RNA molecules that have a poly(A) tail at the 3' end. The presence of a poly(A) is, however, not a general feature of all translated RNAs, and poly(A) tracts are absent from some classes of these molecules (28). Histone mRNAs (29, 30), mammalian viral RNAs such as reovirus (31), plant virus RNAs such as TMV RNA (32), and bacteriophage RNAs such as MS2 (33) are examples of translated RNA species devoid of poly(A) sequences.

The role of the polyadenylated 3' regions, as well as that of the adjacent untranslated RNA sequences, in controlling gene expression have been the subject of intense interest during the last few years, and yet remains to be firmly established. Involvement of the poly(A) region in the cleavage of heterogeneous nuclear RNA and in the transport of mRNA through the nuclear membrane has been suggested (30, 34–37). Other findings, such as curtailment of the poly(A) segment during aging of mRNA (9, 15), cytoplasmic polyadenylation (13, 38), and the presence of a poly(A) segment in a viral message synthesized in the cytoplasm (39), suggest additional, extranuclear roles for the poly(A) segment. More recent studies have shown, in fact, that the poly(A) region has an important function in the stabilization of several species of mammalian cytoplasmic mRNA and viral RNA (16, 40–43).

II. Detection and Analysis

A. Purification of Translated RNA

The development of methods for the isolation of translated RNAs requires efficient inhibition and removal of ribonucleases, dissociation of ribonucleoprotein complexes, and satisfactory separation of such chains from DNA, ribosomal RNA, tRNA, and other small RNA species. Poly(A)-containing RNA molecules have been isolated from whole tissue preparations and from cytoplasmic supernatant or subcellular fractions (nuclei, polysomes, microsomes, and mitochondria).

A variety of reagents have been used for the extraction of RNA, the most common of which is a mixture of phenol and appropriate buffer (*44, 45*). During phenol extraction at neutral pH, the poly(A)-containing RNA tends to adsorb to the denatured proteins and, after phase separation, concentrates in the interphase. This results in considerable loss of poly(A)-containing mRNA from the aqueous phase and also in cleavage of poly(A) sequences from the mRNA (*46, 47*). Such loss may be avoided if extraction is performed with a mixture of chloroform and phenol at pH 9.0 (*46, 48*). Efficacious deproteinization is achieved by the inclusion of 8-hydroxyquinoline (*44*) or chloroform and isoamyl alcohol (*47, 49, 50*) in the phenol extraction mixture. Alternatively, polysomes may be digested with proteinase K (EC 3.4.21.14) in the presence of 0.5% sodium dodecyl sulfate, followed by phenol extraction of the mRNA (*51*). Ribonuclease inhibitors, such as polyvinyl sulfonic acid (*52, 53*), heparin (*54*), or rat liver postmicrosomal supernatant (*55*), have often been included in the buffer, particularly if subcellular fractionation has preceded the phenol extraction. Other denaturing reagents, such as guanidinium chloride (*56, 57*), or thiocyanate (*58, 59*), have also been used. In the isolation of hnRNA, the phenol–chloroform extraction mixture has sometimes been maintained at 60°C (*50*).

The poly(A) sequences provide the basis for several methods for the isolation of mRNAs. Various agents and methods have been used to select for the poly(A)-containing RNA. These include adsorption onto polystyrene beads (*48*), Millipore filters (*46*), and cellulose (*60*); chromatography on columns of poly(U)-cellulose (*61*), benzoylated-cellulose (*62, 63*), poly(U) complexed to glass beads (*64*), poly(U)-Al^{3+}-mica (*65*), and poly(A)-binding protein linked to Sepharose (*66*); and hybridization of mRNA with poly(U) followed by chromatography on a hydroxyapatite column (*29*). Affinity chromatography on oligo(dT)-cellulose (67–70) or poly(U)-Sepharose (15, 16, 71, 72) are the more commonly used methods. Heating of the RNA preparations prior to affinity chromatography reduces rRNA contamination and removes small RNA chains bound to the mRNA (73, 74).

Eukaryotic mRNAs have been classified as poly(A)-containing and poly(A)-deficient on the basis of affinity chromatography on oligo(dT)-cellulose or poly(U)-Sepharose (28). At room temperature, the affinity of oligo(dT)-cellulose [with oligo(dT) chains of 12–18 residues] is significant only for RNA chains containing poly(A) sequences of about 30 or more residues (41). Poly(U)-Sepharose retains RNA chains containing shorter poly(A) sequences of about 20 nucleotides (75, 76), while at 4° oligo(dT)-cellulose binds poly(A) sequences as short as 15 residues (41). On the other hand, Millipore filters retain RNA chains with poly(A) sequences longer than 50 residues (77). Judicious use of these methods allows fractionation of mRNA on the basis of poly(A) size (76, 78–83). Other fractionations of the poly(A)-containing RNA have utilized stepwise elution from the affinity columns, using increasing formamide concentrations (16), increasing temperatures (84, 85), or decreasing salt concentrations (86, 87).

Efficient in vitro translation of mRNA has been carried out in various cell-free systems. Among the most commonly used are incubated wheat germ extract (88) and nuclease-treated rabbit reticulocyte lysate with (89) or without (90) the addition of dog-pancreas microsomes. Analysis of the translation products directed by mRNA preparations in vitro serves to establish the integrity of the mRNA chains. The translation products are identified by polyacrylamide gel electrophoresis, immunological methods, or analysis of the proteolytic cleavage peptides. A different approach is the microinjection of translatable RNA in nanogram quantities into Xenopus laevis oocytes. This method provides one of the most efficient translation systems for mRNA (91).

Further enrichment of poly(A)-containing RNA and poly(A)-deficient RNAs has been achieved by sucrose gradient centrifugation (92, 93) and by electrophoresis on polyacrylamide and agarose gels (94–96). Immunoprecipitation of polysomes has also been used for the enrichment of a specific mRNA fraction. This method has been successful whenever the mRNA species in question is in high abundance in the total RNA extract and the polypeptide product is of high antigenicity (97, 98). Recombinant plasmids containing a single specific complementary DNA (cDNA) sequence have been constructed for the isolation of highly purified and specific mRNA species. The cDNA is enzymically excised and isolated from a bacterial clone carrying the recombinant plasmid. After denaturation, the cDNA is immobilized on a suitable solid support such as nitrocellulose filters (59, 99), diazobenzyloxymethyl-cellulose (100) or diazobenzyloxymethyl-paper (101). Total RNA is then hybridized to the immobilized cDNA, and the complementary RNA sequences thus selected are subsequently eluted and isolated.

B. Location and Size of the Poly(A) Tail

In order to determine the location of the poly(A) region, it is released from the RNA by pancreatic ribonuclease digestion, isolated, and hydrolyzed with alkali, which generates adenosine from the 3' terminus of the poly(A) and adenylic acid from the internal positions (9). The presence of adenosine in the hydrolysis products establishes that the poly(A) sequence is located at the 3' end of the RNA chains, and the ratio of released adenylic acid to the released adenosine provides an estimate of the average length of the poly(A) tail. The location of the poly(A) sequences in the RNA may also be established by end-group labeling of the 3'-hydroxyl terminus: the ribose moiety of the terminal nucleoside is oxidized with periodate and then labeled by reduction with tritiated borohydride (102, 103). A different method utilizes polynucleotide phosphorylase or mammalian 3'-exoribonuclease, both of which degrade only polynucleotides bearing free hydroxyls at the 3' termini. Both enzymes hydrolyze the poly(A) tail in mRNA to completion, indicating that these regions are at the 3'-OH termini. Similar results are obtained when the poly(A) is removed from the mRNA by ribonuclease digestion and subjected to phosphorolysis or exonuclease digestion (104–109).

Several other methods have been used to determine the size of the covalently linked polyadenylated region in mRNA chains. In one, the poly(A) tail is excised from the RNA molecule by the combined endonucleolytic action of pancreatic ribonuclease and T1 ribonuclease under conditions allowing the poly(A) region to remain intact while the rest of the RNA molecule is digested to completion; the size of the poly(A) sequence is then determined by polyacrylamide gel electrophoresis (77, 110). In other studies, the enzymically excised poly(A) sequences were resolved by gel electrophoresis, the gel slices were eluted, and their poly(A) content was determined by hybridization with [^{3}H]poly(U). Yet another approach utilizes the annealing of mRNA preparations with radioactively labeled poly(U) (38, 111, 112) or poly(dT) (113) followed by digestion of unhybridized regions with specific single-strand endonuclease. The length of the hybridized labeled probe was then determined and used in calculating the length of the poly(A) tail.

The 3'-exonucleolytic activity of polynucleotide phosphorylase has also been used for the analysis of the size and composition of the 3'-terminal sequence of RNA molecules (41, 95, 106, 114–118). The method is based on the ability of the enzyme to phosphorolyze long polynucleotides by a processive mechanism. The inclusion of a molar excess of the enzyme establishes a synchronous mode of phosphorolysis, in which nucleoside diphosphate molecules are sequentially released from the 3' termini of the RNA chains. In order to follow the course of phosphorolysis, [^{32}P]orthophosphate is included in the reaction mixture; the released β-labeled nucleoside diphosphates are then separated by DEAE-cellulose paper chromatography (106, 119) or by ascending PEI-cellulose thin-layer chromatography (107). The sizes of the pruned RNA molecules are then determined by gel electrophoresis in composite gels of polyacrylamide/agarose (106, 120), or of polyacrylamide/formamide (i.e., under denaturing conditions) (95, 116). In some cases, ^{32}P-labeled or [^{3}H]uridine-labeled RNA was used in the phosphorolysis reaction; the released nucleoside diphosphates were then labeled in the α-position or uridine, respectively (95, 116).

We have observed that at 0° and in the presence of 0.3 M NaCl, the poly(A) tails of mRNA molecules are readily phosphorolyzed while the rest of the RNA chains remain intact (41, 106). By comparing the electrophoretic mobility of the deadenylated mRNA to that of the native mRNA, the length of the poly(A) tail can be estimated. An independent means of measuring poly(A) size is determination of the number of moles of adenosine diphosphate liberated per mole of input RNA (106).

Through use of these methods, it has been established that the average size of the poly(A) sequence in different preparations of rabbit globin mRNA is between 120 and 150 residues (106, 117). It should be noted that the deadenylated globin mRNA migrates in gel electrophoresis as a narrow band, whereas native mRNA migrates as a broad zone. This difference in migration pattern is probably due to the polydisperse nature of the poly(A) tails (106, 107). The variability in poly(A) length, as well as unknown effects of the poly(A) tail on the rate of migration of the mRNA, may complicate estimation of the apparent molecular weight by this method. The sizes of the poly(A) tracts obtained by use of polynucleotide phosphorylase tend to be somewhat higher than that obtained through release of this region by pancreatic and T1 RNase. Using the latter method, great variations in the length of this region have been reported, ranging from 10 to 120 nucleotides for rabbit globin mRNA (48, 112, 121) and mouse globin mRNA (77, 103). The reported differences in poly(A) size may be due to variations in the methods used in mRNA preparation, the stage of maturation of the reticulocytes serving as a source for the mRNA isolated, and ambiguity in the molecular size of the markers used to estimate the length of the poly(A) fragment (113, 122, 123).

It should be noted that the use of both pancreatic and T1 RNase has its limitations. Since large quantities of pancreatic RNase degrade poly(A) (124), even in the presence of high salt concentrations (125), underestimation of the size of the poly(A) region after nuclease digestion is possible. Moreover, if nucleotides other than adenylic acid are interdispersed in the poly(A) segment, digestion with these endonucleases may effect chain cleavage. It has also been observed that the size distribution of the poly(A) region is highly heterogeneous (77, 96, 103, 121, 126), and that two size classes are present in globin mRNA (77, 103) as well as in mRNA from Xenopus laevis (82). Newly synthesized cytoplasmic mRNA has poly(A) tracts of narrow size distribution. On the other hand, poly(A) tails of aging mRNA chains are gradually reduced in size. Thus, analysis of steady-state poly(A) shows this sequence to be highly heterogeneous and of smaller average size than the nuclear or newly synthesized segments (13–15, 84, 85, 110, 121).

C. Poly(A)-Deficient mRNA

In addition to polyadenylated mRNA, there are mRNAs that are associated with polysomes but fail to bind to poly(U) or oligo(dT); i.e., they are deficient in poly(A) sequences. Suppression of rRNA labeling by specific inhibitors permits quantitation of the proportion of the poly(A)-deficient mRNA fraction (28). Thus, about 30% of the pulse-labeled polyribosomal mRNA in HeLa cells appears to be poly(A)-deficient. Similar results have been obtained for L-cell mRNA (127). In addition, in early stages of the development of sea urchin embryos, a large fraction of the newly synthesized mRNA appears to be deficient in poly(A) sequences (128, 129).

It should be noted, as stated above, that molecules that fail to bind to oligo(dT)-cellulose or poly(U)-Sepharose need not be altogether lacking the poly(A)-segment and may still contain short poly(A) sequences of up to 20–30 nucleotides. The physiological lability of the poly(A) tracts in many cells and their preferential cleavage by nucleases during mRNA isolation add to the difficulties in estimating the proportion of the poly(A)-deficient mRNA within the cells. Electrophoretic analyses of the most abundant in vitro translation products induced by the poly(A)-deficient RNA fraction of HeLa cells reveal a great similarity to those induced by the poly(A)-containing fraction (83, 130). By contrast, hybridization analysis showed that some of the steady-state, low-frequency poly(A)-deficient mRNA species differ in their sequences from the polyadenylated mRNAs (130–132). However, it has not yet been demonstrated that these rare molecules are indeed translated RNAs.

Thus, it appears that mRNAs coding for some of the abundant proteins can appear in two forms: nonadenylated and polyadenylated (130). However, the distribution of individual mRNA species between the polyadenylated and poly(A)-deficient fraction varies widely. The most notable cases are histone mRNAs from HeLa cells (29, 30, 127), sea urchins (11, 133, 134), Xenopus oocytes (135), and neuroblastoma cells (83), all of which are predominantly deficient in poly(A)-sequences. In addition to not being retained on affinity columns, the nonadenylated histone mRNA molecules are unable to serve effectively as templates for the synthesis of cDNA directed by reverse transcriptase in the presence of oligo(dT) primer (135, 136). Addition of poly(A) to the 3'-OH ends of histone mRNAs converts them into efficient templates for reverse transcriptase (EC 2.7.7.6) (136). The absence of poly(A) sequences in sea urchin histone mRNA was proved by sequence analysis of these mRNA molecules (133). However, not all the histone mRNA molecules are deficient in poly(A) tracts, and poly(A)-containing histone mRNA chains have been detected in amphibian oocytes (81, 137), HeLa cells (138), and yeast cells (139). The significance of the existence of two classes of histone mRNA, adenylated and nonadenylated, is not yet clear. Upon fertilization, the poly(A)-containing histone mRNA of Xenopus oocytes is replaced by poly(A)-deficient RNA, leading to the suggestion that polyadenylation may play a role in the storage of histone mRNA during oogenesis (140).

Actin mRNA also contains a small but significant proportion of poly(A)-deficient chains unable to bind to oligo(dT)-cellulose (76, 78, 130, 141). Furthermore, a substantial portion of the β-actin mRNA, but very little of the α- or γ-actin mRNA, is deficient in poly(A). These findings would argue that the poly(A)-deficient β-actin mRNA is not the result of overall degradation of the poly(A) tracts occurring during mRNA extraction (76). This conclusion agrees with the finding that specific mRNA species from mouse sarcoma polysomes are selectively sensitive to enzymatic cleavage of their poly(A) (142). In differentiated L6E9 myotubes, newly synthesized myosin heavy chain (MHC) mRNA is predominantly polyadenylated while steady-state MHC mRNA is poly(A)-deficient (143). The results suggest a processing event in which the poly(A) tail of MHC mRNA is progressively shortened. Several other mRNA species also appear to be quite deficient in poly(A) sequences. These include polyoma-specific mRNA for capsid protein VP-2 (76), mRNA for R1 and R2 cAMP binding proteins from neuroblastoma cells (83), and several mitochondrial mRNA chains (144). Chloroplast mRNAs for the large subunit of ribulosebisphosphate carboxylase (EC 4.1.1.39) (79, 145, 146) and for the precursor of a 32,000-dalton chloroplast membrane protein (147) appear to be deficient in poly(A). However, a poly(A)-containing mRNA for the large subunit of ribulosebisphosphate carboxylase of chloroplasts has also been detected, which may indicate a rapid turnover of the poly(A) sequences in chloroplast mRNA rather than their absence (148).

Fractionation of the β-actin mRNA by preferential binding to oligo(dT)-cellulose and poly(U)-Sepharose suggests a continuous spectrum of poly(A) lengths rather than two discrete classes of β-actin mRNA, one of which lacks poly(A) (76). A similar conclusion has been reached through analysis of neuroblastoma mRNA that directs the synthesis of several abundant proteins (83). It remains to be determined whether the mature poly(A)-deficient mRNA molecules are originally synthesized with a short poly(A) segment, or whether the nascent molecules possess a long poly(A) tract that is more rapidly degraded in some mRNA species than in others.

III. The Nuclear Role of Untranslated 3'-Terminal Sequences

A. Conservation of Untranslated 3' Domains

Some genes coding for mammalian mRNAs have evolved into gene families, each of which includes several independent transcription units that yield identical or closely similar protein products. One might speculate that some untranslated domains have been conserved within such gene families and must be important for the coordinated expression of these genes. The extent of sequence conservation was studied, therefore, using cDNA. A certain degree of homology was retained in the untranslated regions of mRNA transcribed from two nonallelic mouse β-globin genes. The extent of conservation of the untranslated 3' sequences is much lower than that of the coding sequences, indicating that 3'-terminal regions may not be essential to the expression of these globin genes (149).

The involvement of sequences adjacent to the 3' end in nuclear poly(A)-containing RNA chains in posttranscriptional mechanisms has also been approached by studies of the hybridization kinetics of mRNA with cDNA. In these studies, determination of the sequence complexity and the frequency distribution of mRNA was used as a measure of the extent and the abundance of transcriptional and posttranscriptional processes (*132*). Experiments in cross hybridization between polysomal mRNA and cDNA complementary to the 3'-adjacent sequences of hnRNA have indicated that most (*132*) but not all of these sequences are conserved in polysomal mRNA (*150, 151*). However, the frequency of the conserved sequences is greatly altered. Furthermore, these and related experiments (*132, 152*) indicate that a larger fraction of the nucleotide sequences adjacent to the 3' end is conserved during posttranscriptional events in mRNA biogenesis as compared to the rest of the hnRNA molecules. Generally, the 3'-terminal parts of polysomal mRNA sequences are characterized by a much wider frequency distribution than that of the nuclear precursor sequences, indicating that posttranscriptional processes mostly determine the steady-state concentration of 3'-terminal sequences in cytoplasmic mRNAs.

B. Polyadenylation of Nuclear hnRNA

The presence of 3'-poly(A) sequences in primary transcripts of mammalian genes as well as in their processed products has been demonstrated in several instances (cf. *8, 152*). Primary transcripts of many eukaryotic genes also contain intervening sequences ("introns"). Poly(A) is added to nuclear RNA at 3'-termini created by endonucleolytic action on the primary transcript, and the introns are removed from the primary transcript in one or more steps by an RNA "splicing" process (*153*). As polyadenylation seems to precede splicing (*154–157*), the possibility remains that the poly(A) tail or a sequence near the 3' terminal of the primary transcript is involved in the splicing process. However, it appears that these putative signals are not obligatory for the processing of all primary transcripts. This is borne out by the fact that specific transcripts of adenovirus type 2 are terminated "downstream" from the polyadenylation site (*158*) and that there are several instances of unspliced cytoplasmic mRNAs, such as those for sea urchin histone (*159*), adenovirus polypeptide IX (*160*), and interferon (*160a*). However, there is at present, no case known of a spliced mRNA lacking poly(A). The inhibition of posttranscriptional polyadenylation by the adenosine analog cordycepin (3'-deoxyadenosine) substantially reduces the flow of mRNA from the nucleus to the cytoplasm (*8, 161, 162*). This observation gave rise to the suggestion that nuclear polyadenylation is an essential step in the biogenesis of mRNA or in its transfer to the cytoplasm (*8, 34–37*). Splicing of newly formed nuclear RNA transcripts in the absence of poly(A) addition during adenovirus mRNA formation in the presence of cordycepin in HeLa cells has very recently been demonstrated. The apparently correctly spliced mRNA lacking the poly(A) sequence did not, however, enter the cytoplasm. This further suggests a role for poly(A) in mRNA transport, but not in the splicing mechanism (*162a*). However, several alternative mechanisms could be suggested to account for the action of cordycepin (*37, 163, 163a*), which is not inhibitory in all cases (*164*).

IV. The Cytoplasmic Role of the Poly(A) Tail of mRNA

A. Translation of Deadenylated mRNA

Considerable effort has been made to elucidate the biological function(s) of the poly(A) tail of mRNA. Experiments carried out in this and other laboratories have shown that the poly(A) segment of mRNA is not essential for its translation in cell-free systems (*40, 106, 165–171*). One approach to this problem was to anneal the poly(A) region of total mRNA from HeLa cells to poly(U) to form mRNA · [poly(U)]$_2$ complexes and test their translation activity *in vitro* (*169*). Using a different method, the poly(A) tails of rabbit globin mRNA have been annealed to poly(dT) and the resulting hybrid regions cleaved with RNase H (*165, 172*). Selective removal of the poly(A) regions has also been achieved by phosphorolysis of rabbit or mouse globin mRNA with polynucleotide phosphorylase (*106, 166, 171*), or by limited digestion of L cell mRNA with 3'-OH-specific exoribonuclease from ascites cell nuclei (*168*). Selective hydrolysis of oviduct mRNA with endoribonuclease IV from chick oviducts has also been used (*170*). The exoribonuclease seemed to digest several adjacent nonpoly(A) residues (*168*), whereas the endoribonuclease tended to leave a residual oligo(A) of about five adenylate residues (*170*). In all these experiments, the deadenylated mRNA preparations appeared to direct active *in vitro* protein synthesis.

We have used a highly purified *E. coli* polynucleotide phosphorylase preparation (EC 2.7.7.8) (*109*) to phosphorolyze the poly(A) tracts of rabbit globin mRNA under conditions in which the rest of the molecule remains intact (*106, 118*). During the first 45-minute period of incubation in a Krebs-II ascites cell-free system, the deadenylated globin mRNA was translated as efficiently as native mRNA; upon longer incubation, the rate of protein synthesis decreased more rapidly with the deadenylated mRNA than with the native mRNA (*106*). In parallel experiments it was found that a prior incubation in cell-free extracts decreases the template activity of deadenylated globin mRNA more than that of the native mRNA (*165*).

These observations suggest that the poly(A) sequence may stabilize the *in vitro* functional activity of globin mRNA molecules. The decrease in the functional activity of poly(A)-free mRNA does not derive from a change in the rate of formation of the initiation complex, since the interaction between globin mRNA and the initiation factor that binds methionyl tRNA^{fMet} remained unchanged upon removal of the poly(A) tail or even the 90 nucleotides adjacent to it in the untranslated 3' sequence (117). Repeated reinitiation by deadenylated mouse globin mRNA has also been demonstrated in a rabbit reticulocyte lysate cell-free system (167). In contrast, deadenylation of ovalbumin mRNA appears to reduce the initiation process (171). However, it is not clear in these experiments whether other regions of the mRNA were not altered as well during the deadenylation reaction. The 3'-terminal poly(A) has also been shown to inhibit RNase activity in human spleen extracts (173), indicating possible involvement of the poly(A) in shielding mRNA from nucleolytic degradation.

B. Stabilization of Specific mRNA Species by Poly(A)

1. GLOBIN mRNA

Since the average half-life of a eukaryotic mRNA is about 10 hours (cf. 7), whereas the *in vitro* systems last no longer than one to 2 hours, cell-free protein-synthesizing systems are inadequate for detection of long-term effects of 3' sequences on mRNA stability. Therefore, we (in collaboration with G. Huez and G. Marbaix) began to use *Xenopus* oocytes in order to compare the translation of various mRNA species from which precisely determined sequences had been removed from the 3'-OH terminus by polynucleotide phosphorylase (41, 106, 109). In agreement with earlier findings (174), native globin mRNA appeared to be very stable and was efficiently translated for over 70 hours in the injected oocytes. On the other hand, the functional stability of the deadenylated globin mRNA was much lower, with a half-life of 5 to 10 hours (40). Similar results have been obtained using human globin mRNA (87). In that study, the mRNA was fractionated by oligo(dT)-cellulose column chromatography and then injected into oocytes. Translation of the poly(A)-rich RNA continued for longer periods than that of the poly(A)-poor fraction. Experiments involving microinjection of α_{2u}-globulin mRNA fractionated on oligo(dT)-cellulose failed to reveal differences in stability between molecules with an average of 175 terminal adenylate residues and those with 40 such residues (174a).

Molecular hybridization experiments using a labeled cDNA probe complementary to globin mRNA established that accelerated degradation of the deadenylated mRNA in microinjected *Xenopus* oocytes is responsible for its reduced translation (45). A critical test for the validity of the above conclusions is to attempt to restore the functional activity of the deadenylated globin mRNA. It was indeed possible to show that enzymic readdition of a poly(A) segment to deadenylated globin mRNA resulted in complete restoration of the latter's functional and physical stability in frog oocytes, indicating that enzymic phosphorolysis had not damaged the rest of the mRNA molecule (175).

The degradation of deadenylated α-globin mRNA appears to be linked to its translation (176). This finding may indicate that, in the absence of the poly(A) tail and/or proteins bound to it, the ability of the mRNA to be normally involved in protein synthesis may be affected, leading to its rapid destruction. The stability of deadenylated globin mRNA after injection into HeLa cells (43, 172) is also much lower than that of native polyadenylated mRNA. This shows that the very short translational half-life of globin mRNA lacking poly(A) in Xenopus oocytes is not a peculiarity of this system, but holds true in somatic cells as well.

In growing cell cultures, mRNA decays according to first-order kinetics (177, 178). This stochastic decay of mRNA implies that new and old mRNA chains have an equal probability of being destroyed. From this, it was deduced that the decay is independent of the continuous shortening of the poly(A) segment during the life of the mRNA molecules (178). It is also assumed that, although there are several stability classes of cellular mRNA populations, most of the mRNA species follow this mode of decay (72, 179). The lack of correlation between poly(A) length and mRNA decay can also be deduced from the observation that new mRNA [with a longer poly(A) segment] and old mRNA [with a shorter poly(A) segment] engage ribosomes with roughly equivalent efficiencies (168). However, since molecules containing poly(A) segments of less than 30–40 nucleotides are not retained by the affinity methods used, only mRNA molecules containing poly(A) sequences of at least 30–40 adenylate residues have been examined in these studies. Therefore, the possibility that mRNA chains with poly(A) tails shorter than 30–40 nucleotides have a shorter half-life in vivo is not excluded. In sea urchin embryos, mRNA species containing poly(A) tend, in fact, to load larger polysomes than those loaded with poly(A)-deficient nonhistone mRNAs (180). In addition, the relative rate of reduction of poly(A) tails is correlated to the relative turnover rate of two different adenovirus type-2 mRNA species (16). On the other hand, there is no correlation between poly(A) length and mRNA longevity in Dictyostelium discoideum (181).

In a study aimed at clarifying this issue, globin mRNA preparations containing poly(A) segments of decreasing lengths were prepared by partial phosphorolysis with polynucleotide phosphorylase. These preparations allowed direct examination of the effect of the size of the poly(A) tails on the stability of globin mRNA. The functional stability of globin mRNA species containing 30 or more adenylate residues injected into *Xenopus laevis* oocytes, equaled that of the native globin mRNA. On the other hand, the functional stability of mRNA containing 16 adenylate residues was as low as that of the deadenylated mRNA preparation (*41*). It was also observed that extension of the poly(A) tracts of native globin mRNA by an additional 45 adenylate residues did not alter the rate of poly(A) degradation in injected oocytes (*182*). Thus, there is no change in the half-life of the globin mRNA until the poly(A) tails are shortened below a critical length.

The data obtained by *in vitro* manipulation of mRNA populations, followed by functional analysis in *Xenopus* oocytes, agree well with statistical correlates. Species of mRNA of various origin were compared with respect to length of poly(A) sequence and *in vivo* half-life. According to this statistical analysis, there is an increase in mRNA *in vivo* half-life, at a length of about 30 adenosine residues per mRNA chain (*7*), that correlates with the increase observed previously for globin mRNA in oocytes (*41*). Stochastic endonucleolytic cleavage of poly(A)-containing mRNA may eventually result in the appearance of aged, unstable mRNA molecules with poly(A) sequences shorter than 30 residues per chain; the process of mRNA aging is bound to occur at a faster rate in organisms in which the average size of the poly(A) is short to begin with. One possibility is that a minimal size of poly(A) tail is essential for binding of the protein(s) normally found associated with this region of the molecule (*183, 184*). These protein(s) may in turn be involved in the recycling of mRNA on the ribosomes and may protect the mRNA from nucleolytic degradation (*41, 106, 142, 185, 186*).

2. HISTONE mRNAs

Globin mRNA molecules are not generally found in significant amounts in *Xenopus* oocytes, nor do they appear until late stages of embryonic development. It seemed important, therefore, to test the validity of the findings obtained in the oocyte system by manipulating additional mRNA species.

An mRNA class abundant in oocytes is that coding for histones. These molecules are short-lived (*187*) and naturally lack poly(A) tails (cf. *133–136*). Histone mRNAs of HeLa cells were enzymically polyadenylated and injected into *Xenopus laevis* oocytes, and their functional stability was examined by measuring the kinetics of histone synthesis. It was found that the enzymic polyadenylation of histone mRNAs increased their stability in the oocytes. This indicates that the stabilizing effect observed with globin mRNA is not unique to this one mRNA species, and that an added poly(A) region may, in some cases, even stabilize mRNAs naturally lacking this sequence (188). On the other hand, the Xenopus histone mRNAs are remarkably stable in ovo and accumulate for several weeks for future use in embryonic development (189), although about 25–50% of the stable histone mRNA of the oocyte is not polyadenylated (140).

Histone mRNA from sea urchin embryos was also injected into Xenopus oocytes (187). Most of the injected material appeared to decay stochastically, with a half-life of about 3 hours, as judged by measurement of translation products. However, a minor component (1–5%) remained stable in the oocytes for as long as 4 weeks. Therefore, it appears that compartmentalization of unused stored mRNA sequences may be an alternative means for stabilization of mRNA sequences.

C. mRNA Species Not Stabilized by Poly(A) Sequences

The physical and functional stability of interferon mRNA species, which direct the synthesis and secretion of interferon from microinjected oocytes, was unaffected by the removal of their poly(A) tails (95, 190). 5,6-Dichloro-1-β-D-ribofuranosylbenzimidazole, a selective and reversible inhibitor of hnRNA and mRNA biosynthesis, greatly increases the cumulative yield of interferon mRNA in "superinduced" human fibroblast cells (cf. 136). Since the poly(A) of interferon mRNA continues to be reduced in size in the presence of the benzimidazole, it is unlikely that the increased stability of interferon mRNA results from inhibition of poly(A) metabolism (191). In human fibroblasts, interferon is coded for by two different mRNA species (192, 193). These two mRNAs differ in length of poly(A) tail as well as in length and structure of 3'-noncoding sequences (95), but at the same time show a certain structural homology in coding regions (193). However, the enzymic removal of poly(A) from both species of interferon mRNA does not affect their turnover in Xenopus oocytes (95, 190). The same is true for mengovirus RNA and for mRNA 4 from alfalfa mosaic virus (118, 194; see the following section).

V. Structure and Function of 3'-Terminal Sequences in Viral RNA

There is a wide array of possible combinations in structure and function of the 3'-terminal sequences in various viral RNA species. In some viral families, the RNA may be polyadenylated, in others it is not, and some exist in both forms. In other cases, the nonadenylated 3'

sequences display a specific tertiary structure that resembles that of
tRNA and can be specifically aminoacylated. Several experiments
suggest the involvement of viral poly(A) tracts in translation efficiency,
physical stability, and/or infectivity of viral RNA species; nonadenylated 3' sequences seem also to be involved in viral function. Examples of some of these observations are discussed below.

A. The Role of the Poly(A) Tail in Viral RNA

Messenger RNA from vaccinia virus appears in polyadenylated and
nonadenylated forms. Both are efficiently translated *in vitro*, indicating that in this virus the poly(A) tail is not essential for translation
(*195*). The case is different in encephalomyocarditis virus RNA (EMC
RNA). Like mengovirus RNA (*118*), the RNA of this virus also appears
in vivo in polyadenylated (*196*) and in poly(A)-deficient forms. It has
been suggested that the presence of the poly(A) tail in EMC RNA
improves its infectivity (*197, 198*) and enhances its *in vitro* functional
translatability. It was further suggested that the *in vitro* effect is due to
a higher rate of reinitiation of polyadenylated EMC RNA (*199*). On the
other hand, both the poly(A)-deficient and the polyadenylated forms of
mengovirus RNA are translated equally efficiently in *Xenopus* oocytes
(*118*). The protective effect of the poly(A) region on viral RNA translatability is, therefore, not a general phenomenon. The rate of decay of
[³H]uridine-labeled mengovirus RNA in microinjected oocytes appears to be biphasic: there is an initial phase with a half-life in the
range of 4–6 hours accounting for most of the decay, and a late phase
with a half-life of approximately 20 hours. These findings correlate
well with previously published observations describing the survival in
Xenopus oocytes of a variety of microinjected RNAs (*95, 187, 200,
201*). The mode of decay of poly(A)-containing mengovirus RNA in
these oocytes is similar to that of nonadenylated mengovirus RNA,
indicating that the presence of the poly(A) tail does not affect the
survival of this RNA in oocytes.

In order to determine whether the poly(A) tail has an effect on the
translation mechanism or on the posttranslational processing of the
proteins directed by mengovirus RNA, we compared the polypeptides
synthesized in oocytes injected either with poly(A)-containing or with
poly(A)-deficient mengovirus RNA populations. Injected and control
oocytes were incubated with [³⁵S]methionine between 0 and 20 hours
or between 40 and 60 hours after injection, and the electrophoretic
profiles of the labeled proteins were compared. In extracts of oocytes
injected with either of the two RNA species, new proteins were ob-

served, with apparent electrophoretic mobilities similar to those of mengovirus polypeptides directed *in vivo*, and with molecular weights quite similar to those reported (*202*) for EMC RNA products in injected oocytes. In the 0 to 20 hour pulse, precursor polypeptides were detected; at 40 to 60 hours posttranslational processing took place, and proteins of low molecular weight became more prominent. The polypeptide patterns in extracts of oocytes injected with poly(A)-deficient and poly(A)-containing mengovirus RNA were indistinguishable, indicating that the poly(A) tail of mengovirus RNA does not affect its translation or the nature of posttranslational processing of its peptide products in *Xenopus* oocytes (*118*).

Poly(A) sequences enzymically added to Qβ RNA molecules with the aid of calf thymus terminal transferase (EC 2.7.7.31), retained full infectivity in a spheroplast assay system (*203*). Foot-and-mouth disease virion RNA (*204*), and RNA from tobacco etch virus (TEV) (*205*) are also infective both in their polyadenylated and nonadenylated forms. Therefore, poly(A) sequences are apparently not involved in the infectivity of these viral RNA species. On the other hand, the 3'-poly(A) tail of Sendai virus mRNA shields it from exonucleolytic attack by polynucleotide phosphorylase (*206*).

The involvement of poly(A) squences in viral RNA infectivity has been clearly demonstrated in the case of poliovirus RNA. The genome-like strand in double-stranded (replicative form) poliovirus RNA molecules contains 3'-poly(A) sequences, while the minus strand contains poly(U) tracts at its 3' terminus (*39*). During infection of HeLa cells, poly(A) stretches of heterogeneous size (75–200) appear in newly synthesized poliovirus RNA molecules (*207*). However, virion RNA contains poly(A) sequences of up to 75 adenosine residues, indicating that the amount of poly(A) that can be encapsidated is limited (*208*). When the poly(A) region is removed from poliovirus RNA with the aid of ribonuclease H (EC 3.1.26.4) (*209*) or with polynucleotide phosphorylase (EC 2.7.7.8) (*210*), the specific infectivity of the poliovirus RNA is markedly reduced, although this has no effect on its translatability (*211*). An enzyme capable of terminal polyadenylation of poliovirus RNA has been detected in both infected and uninfected HeLa cell extracts (*212*). In addition, poliovirus replicase was found to copurify with an enzymic activity that specifically polymerizes poly(U) and showed preference for poliovirus RNA templates (*213*). Only poly(A)-containing poliovirus RNA could serve as template for the replicating enzyme, further pointing out the indispensability of the poly(A) region for replication of poliovirus RNA (*210*).

B. Biological Role and Evolutionary Conservation of Untranslated 3′ Sequences in Viral RNA

As in eukaryotic cellular mRNAs (cf. *220*), the 3′-terminal sequences in viral RNAs contain regions of variable lengths that are not translated (*214–219*). Several roles have been suggested for these regions, such as involvement in replication (*214*) and translation of the viral RNA (*215*). Complete integrity of the 3′ terminus is absolutely essential for the infectivity of the RNA of tobacco mosaic virus, which becomes noninfectious upon the removal of one or several nucleotides from this terminus by polynucleotide phosphorylase (*118, 221*). The 3′ regions from enteroviruses, cardioviruses, and foot-and-mouth-disease viruses (all picornaviruses) have been sequenced and show extensive sequence homology within each genus, whereas there is little similarity between viruses of different genera (*222*). Sequence homology was also observed in the 3′ sequences of four mRNAs from alfalfa mosaic virus (*223, 224*). These four mRNAs contain a common tRNA-like structure at the 3′ terminus (*225*) that, in mRNA$_4$, strongly interacts with the viral coat protein (*226*) and is involved in recognition of the viral replicase (*227*). In alfalfa mosaic virus, the nontranslated 3′ region may, therefore, have a biological role in viral replication.

Three of the polyadenylated "late" mRNAs of adenovirus type 2 (*228*) appear to have coterminal 3′-terminal sequences. There are similar findings for murine leukemia virus mRNAs and polyoma virus mRNAs (*229, 230*; cf. *153*).

The 3′ region of avian sarcoma virus RNA has been conserved in several, but not all, subgroups of this genus, and appears in avian leukosis sarcoma viruses, even when large deletions affect an adjacent viral gene (src). No homology was found between this sequence and the 3′-terminal regions of Moloney strains of murine sarcoma virus and murine leukemia virus (*231, 232*). Conservation of the 3′ sequences is, therefore, not a general phenomenon.

The genomic RNA of Rous sarcoma virus is terminally redundant: a sequence of 20 nucleotide residues immediately adjacent to the 3′-terminal poly(A) also appears at the 5′ terminus of the viral RNA (*218*). The presence of this sequence in the 3′ region of the viral RNA may indicate the existence of a mechanism by which the nascent DNA is switched from one end of the viral RNA to the other (*233, 234*). Small RNA molecules, complementary to the 3′-terminal sequence of viral genomic RNA, appear in purified virions of vesicular stomatitis virus (VSV). These small RNAs represent the initiated lead-in RNA segments, removed during formation of VSV mRNAs (*235*). Defective interfering particles of VSV are divergent in their 3'-end region, yet they are sufficiently similar to the original virus to allow replicase initiation on both RNAs and to induce the formation of defective interfering particles in vesicular stomatitis virus (VSV)-infected cells (236). Using cDNA hybridization, sequences similar to the 3' region of RNA from mouse mammary tumor virus were found to be 20-fold more abundant in normal lactating tissue than the total viral sequences, whereas the ratio between 3' sequences to total viral genomic sequences decreased in virus producing C3H tumor cells (152). This differential 3'-terminal expression has been explained by the possible integration of fragmented 3' sequences of the viral RNA into the genome of normal, but not of neoplastic tissue.

C. Nonpolyadenylated 3' Sequences in Viral RNA Species

Many viral RNAs of phage, plant, and mammalian origin possess a common 3'-terminal sequence C-C-A(OH) that, in several cases, may be aminoacylated with specific amino acids. Within a given group, these heteropolymeric untranslated regions appear to be highly conserved; when blocked or removed, infectivity may be abolished in bacteriophage RNAs (237, 238) or in viral RNAs (221, 239, 240). In other cases, such as in carnation mottle virus RNA, the infectivity is gradually reduced following the processive removal of the 3' sequences. This is accompanied by selective decrease in the translatability of one of the three viral RNA protein products (120). It has been implied, therefore, that this viral RNA-directed polypeptide may be essential for infectivity and that the translation of the RNA from carnation mottle virus into this essential protein depends upon the integrity of the vulnerable 3' terminus (118).

The main representatives of viral RNAs that can be aminoacylated have been reviewed (241). Among plant RNA viruses these include RNAs from tobamoviruses, which can be aminoacylated with histidine (221, 242, 243), RNAs from tymoviruses, which may be charged with valine (244, 245), multicomponent RNAs from bromoviruses, each of which accepts tyrosine (246, 247), and others. Of the few animal viruses examined, mengovirus RNA can be aminoacylated with histidine (248) and encephalomyocarditis RNA with serine (249). Since mengovirus RNA appears in nature both in a polyadenylated and in a poly(A)-deficient form (118), it seems likely that the poly(A)-deficient form of this viral RNA is the one to be aminoacylated in vitro at the 3' terminus. The aminoacylation of TYMV RNA may also be carried out by a 100-nucleotide fragmented sequence derived from the 3' terminus (250). Within viral particles, TYMV is not aminoacylated. However, it is aminoacylated when injected into *Xenopus* oocytes, suggesting that this process may also take place in infected leaves (*251*). The aminoacylated TYMV RNA can also react with other enzymes that recognize tRNAs *in vivo*, such as tRNA nucleotidyl transferase (EC 2.7.7.25) (*252*), peptidyl-tRNA hydrolase (*253*), tRNA methyltransferase (EC 2.1.1.29-36) (*241*), and others. Moreover, it may serve as an amino-acid donor in protein synthesis (*254*).

The nucleotide sequences of the 3'-terminal regions of several aminoacylated viral RNAs show no similarities to those of the corresponding tRNAs (*216, 255*), whereas others appear to possess a tRNA-like 3' structure (*225*). The relationship between the 3'-terminal structure and aminoacylation is therefore not yet clear. Several viral RNAs contain nonadenylated 3' sequences that do not accept amino acids under conditions in which other viral RNAs are specifically aminoacylated. These include genome RNA from pea enation virus (*256*) and carnation mottle virus (Salomon and Littauer, unpublished results). These findings do not exclude the possibility that under certain conditions the examined viral RNAs may be transiently aminoacylated.

VI. The Role of Noncoding 3' Sequences in Translation and Functional Stability of mRNA

In all known mRNAs or viral RNAs, whether polyadenylated or not, the coding regions are followed by untranslated heteropolymeric 3' sequences of various lengths. In human and rabbit β-globin mRNAs, these sequences are 134 and 95 nucleotides long, respectively (*220*). In sea urchin histone H4 mRNA, an untranslated region of about 30 nucleotides terminates the mRNA at its nonadenylated 3' end (*257*). The nonadenylated RNA of MS2 bacteriophage is terminated at its 3' end by a CCA triplet preceded by 171 nontranslated nucleotides (*33*). Large untranslated 3' regions have also been detected in mRNA for hen ovalbumin (*258*) and ovomucoid (*259*). The mRNAs that code for mouse dihydrofolate reductase greatly differ in their untranslated 3'-terminal sequences, which include up to 850 nucleotides (*260*).

The function of the noncoding 3' region of mammalian mRNA is obscure. The complementary DNA region includes the conserved sequence AATAAA [or its variant ATTAAA (*261–263*)], implicated as a possible polyadenylation signal in several mammalian and viral transcription units (*264*), as well as the sequence ACTTCACAGC, often found just prior to the poly(A) addition site (*265*). Some observations, however, suggest that the AAUAAA sequence alone may be neither sufficient nor obligatory for the polyadenylation of RNA transcripts

(258, 266). It appears that the deletion of large segments of the noncoding 3' region, including the AAUAAA hexanucleotide, does not abolish translational efficiency (95, 117, 118, 267), nor does it alter the functional stability of some mammalian mRNA species (95).

We have used polynucleotide phosphorylase to prepare human fibroblast β_1 and β_2 interferon mRNA species lacking both poly(A) sequences and a substantial portion of the adjacent 3'-terminal noncoding region (100 and 200 residues for β_1 and β_2, respectively). A homogeneous population of human fibroblast mRNA chains all terminating at the junction between the noncoding 3' region and the poly(A) region was first obtained by phosphorolysis at 0°C of the native mRNA population, which contained poly(A) tails of heterogeneous size distribution. The deadenylated RNA was then synchronously phosphorolyzed at 37°C with a molar excess of the phosphorylase, and the extent of phosphorolysis was determined by methylmercury/polyacrylamide gel electrophoresis. Oocyte bioassay of the separated interferon mRNA species showed that the translational efficiency or stability of the two mRNA species is not affected by the removal of the poly(A) tails and large stretches of the adjacent sequences. Since the shortened regions of both the β_1 and β_2 interferon mRNA species include the AAUAAA hexanucleotide sequence (193), our results suggest that this hexanucleotide and the entire noncoding 3' region do not contribute to the regulation of interferon mRNA stability in *Xenopus* oocytes.

Limited synchronous phosphorolysis of unfractionated mRNA from human fibroblasts decreased the translatability of the mRNA *in vitro*. This reduction was clearly correlated with the lack of synthesis of several discrete proteins and was not merely a general decline in overall protein synthesis. The residual translational activity of mRNA digested with a molar excess of polynucleotide phosphorylase for up to 20 minutes at 37°C represented the synthesis not of truncated polypeptides, but mainly that of discrete proteins whose mRNA species appear to resist phosphorolysis under the experimental conditions used. It thus appears that 3' sequences in individual mRNA species differ in their susceptibility to exonucleolytic degradation (Soreq and Sehgal, unpublished observations).

VII. Conclusions

From the foregoing, the mRNA regions most vulnerable to nucleolytic cleavage appear to be the poly(A) tail and the adjacent nontranslated sequences (142, 186). Therefore, the stability of these regions seems to be a decisive element in determining the expression and turnover rate of these molecules. At steady state, mRNAs *in vivo* retain about 40–60 adenylate residues in their poly(A) tail (*10, 14, 15, 111, 181*). This length of the poly(A) generally suffices to ensure physical and functional stability of the polyadenylated RNAs. Poly(A) sequences longer than this minimal length of 40–60 nucleotides do not regulate or extend mRNA longevity, whereas molecules with shorter poly(A) tracts are considerably less stable in some but not all individual mRNA species. Thus, globin mRNA with a poly(A) sequence shorter than 30 residues is unstable after injection into oocytes and HeLa cells, and polyadenylation of HeLa cell histone mRNAs, normally poly(A)-deficient, markedly increases their stability. On the other hand, the presence of poly(A) sequences in mengovirus RNA and interferon mRNAs does not confer stability on these molecules. Hence, it would seem that individual mRNAs are stabilized to different extents by the poly(A) tail.

What are the factors that maintain the poly(A) tail at a steady-state length, which seems necessary to ensure the stability of some mRNA species? One possible explanation is dynamic equilibrium between nucleolytic degradation and cytoplasmic polyadenylation. However, such a theory would not explain the uneven distribution of poly(A) size in different mRNAs: (*83*). Moreover, there is no evidence that cytoplasmic polyadenylation plays a major role in the maintenance of this steady state. A more likely explanation correlates the individual steady-state length of the poly(A) sequence with the binding of specific protective proteins (*183, 184*). In *Physarum polycephalum*, the binding protein does not cover the entire length of the poly(A) region but appears to be located at or near its 5′ end and extends for about 45 adenylate residues toward the 3′ terminus (*268*). In mammalian mRNA, with longer poly(A) tracts, the entire length of the poly(A) tail appears to be protected against nucleolytic attack by the binding protein(s) (*8, 106*). The removal of the binding protein may result in the formation of molecules prone to degradation by nucleolytic attack (*106, 183, 186, 269*).

The poly(A) tails of various mRNAs are essentially similar in sequence and structure, and yet they seem to differ in their roles. Therefore, the difference between the stabilizing effects that these poly(A) tails confer on different mRNA species must be hidden elsewhere along the mRNA molecule. Also, the poly(A)-binding protein has a high affinity for binding sites in the nontranslated 3′ sequence adjacent to the poly(A) segment (*186, 270*).

It has been suggested that the nontranslated 3′ sequence can modulate the affinity of this protein for the poly(A) region, thus permitting control of poly(A) stability in individual mRNAs (186). We suggest that in order for this protein(s) to express its protective role it must interact with both the poly(A) tail and the nontranslated 3' region, and that the specificity of this interaction is influenced by the nucleotide sequence of the nontranslated 3' region. Furthermore, it is assumed that the role of the poly(A) tail is to mediate this interaction by inducing a conformational change in the protein that results in the unfolding of a masked binding site to the nontranslated 3' sequence. The model is depicted in Fig. 1; in order to allow for the two binding sites to interact with the two regions, we have assumed that these sequences are wrapped around the protein.

According to this hypothesis, translated RNA chains may belong to one of several possible categories, depending on the structure at their 3' terminus. In category (a), the nontranslated 3' sequence may favor binding of the poly(A) protein, and the RNA may be polyadenylated. In this case, the mRNA will be stable owing to the protective effect of the bound protein. The enzymic paring of the poly(A) region from such mRNA molecules to a length shorter than 30 adenylate residues will transfer these chains to category (b), in which the poly(A) binding site for the protein is absent. These mRNA molecules become labile and unstable as the protective protein is rapidly dissociated, as is the case

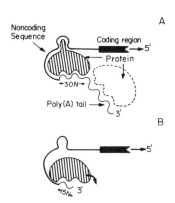

FIG. 1. Effect of reduction of poly(A) tail on mRNA-protein interaction. (A) A model for the interaction of poly(A) binding protein(s) with the nontranslated 3' sequences of mRNA belonging to category a (e.g., globin mRNA). The poly(A) tail of the mRNA mediates interaction of the protein(s) with the nontranslated 3' sequence by unfolding a masked binding site on the protein located close to the 3' noncoding sequence. (The same model applies whether one or more protein molecules bind to a single poly(A) tail.) (B) Molecules of mRNA with poly(A) sequence shorter than 30 adenylate residues are unable to induce a conformational change in the binding protein, which rapidly dissociates from the mRNA.

with deadenylated globin mRNA. A similar situation may exist *in vivo* for histone mRNA, which appears to lack poly(A) tracts and is unstable; upon enzymic polyadenylation, histone mRNA is transformed to category (*a*) and converted into a more stable molecule.

Interferon mRNA and mengovirus RNA may represent a third category (*c*). These mRNAs contain poly(A) tails at their 3′ termini, but the absence of these tails does not affect their stability (*95*, *118*). Therefore, it may be assumed that in these molecules the nontranslated 3′ sequences adjacent to the poly(A) tail do not favor attachment of the poly(A)-binding protein, and that the physical binding site provided by the poly(A) is a necessary, but not sufficient, requirement to ensure stability of mRNA chains from this category. Deadenylated interferon mRNA and mengovirus RNA would belong, according to this hypothesis, to category (*d*) and would display a half-life similar to that of the native molecules from which they originate. An *in vivo* example of translated RNA from category d would be RNA_4 of alfalfa mosaic virus. This RNA, which codes for the viral coat protein, is not polyadenylated *in vivo*, and enzymic polyadenylation does not increase its stability in *Xenopus* oocytes (*194*). One might predict the existence of a fifth category of mRNA species, in which other parts of the RNA sequence (and, possibly, protein(s) bound to these other parts) greatly contribute to the stability of the mRNA chains (*185*). Such mRNA chains would display a long half-life, independent of the length and nature of the 3′ sequences and/or poly(A) tails. It might also be expected that within each of these categories numerous factors would variably contribute to the stability of mRNA molecules, and the number of possible combinations envisioned would be very high.

We suggest that the role of the poly(A) tail is to stabilize translatable RNA chains by binding specific protein(s), provided that the properties of the adjacent 3′ sequence favor such binding. Our hypothesis may now be examined by the following experiment: Using DNA recombination techniques followed by transcription of the respective genes, let the nontranslated 3′ regions of globin and interferon mRNA be interchanged. The stability of the resulting poly(A)-containing RNA can then be compared in *Xenopus* oocytes. Such sequence rearrangement should affect the stability of these molecules: the poly(A)-containing globin mRNA with the interferon nontranslated 3′ sequence would become unstable, whereas polyadenylated interferon mRNA with the globin nontranslated 3′ sequence should become greatly stabilized, the increased half-life dependent on the presence of the poly(A) tail.

REFERENCES

1. J. E. Darnell, W. R. Jelinek, and G. R. Molloy, *Science* **181**, 1215 (1973).
2. G. Brawerman, ARB **43**, 621 (1974).
3. H. Nakazato and M. Edmonds, *Basic Life Sci.* **3**, 317 (1974).
4. G. Brawerman, *This Series* **17**, 117 (1976).
5. M. Edmonds and M. A. Winters, *This Series* **17**, 149 (1976).
6. M. Revel and Y. Groner, *ARB* **47**, 1079 (1978).
7. R. K. Carlin, *J. Theor. Biol.* **71**, 323 (1978).
8. G. Brawerman, *CRC Crit. Rev. Biochem.* **10**, 1 (1981).
9. J. Mendecki; S. Y. Lee, and G. Brawerman, *Bchem* **11**, 792 (1972).
10. J. R. Greenberg and R. P. Perry, *BBA* **287**, 361 (1972).
11. F. H. Wilt, *PNAS* **70**, 2345 (1973).
12. E. Derman and J. E. Darnell, *Cell* **3**, 255 (1974).
13. J. Diez and G. Brawerman, *PNAS* **71**, 4091 (1974).
14. G. Brawerman and J. Diez, *Cell* **5**, 271 (1975).
15. D. Sheiness and J. E. Darnell, *Nature NB* **241**, 265 (1973).
16. M. C. Wilson, S. G. Sawicki, P. A. White, and J. E. Darnell, Jr., *JMB* **126**, 23 (1978).
17. C. S. McLaughlin, J. R. Warner, M. Edmonds, H. Nakazoto, and M. H. Vaughan, *JBC* **248**, 1466 (1973).
18. R. A. Firtel, A. Jacobson, and H. F. Lodish, *Nature NB* **239**, 225 (1972).
19. S. Perlman, H. T. Abelson, and S. Penman, *PNAS* **70**, 350 (1973).
20. D. Ojala and G. Attardi, *JMB* **82**, 151 (1974).
21. H. Nakazato, S. Venkatesan, and M. Edmonds, *Nature* **256**, 144 (1975).
22. N. Ohta, M. Sanders, and A. Newton, *PNAS* **72**, 2343 (1975).
22a. N. Sarkar, D. Langley, and H. Paulus, *Bchem* **17**, 3468 (1978).
23. J. Kates and J. Beeson, *JMB* **50**, 19 (1970).
24. L. Philipson, R. Wall, G. Glickman, and J. E. Darnell, *PNAS* **68**, 2806 (1971).
25. R. A. Weinberg, Z. Ben-Ishai, and J. E. Newbold, *Nature NB* **238**, 111 (1972).
26. M. M. C. Lai and P. H. Duesberg, *Nature* **235**, 383 (1972).
27. J. A. Armstrong, M. Edmonds, H. Nakazato, B. A. Phillips, and M. H. Vaughan, *Science* **176**, 526 (1972).
28. C. Milcarek, R. Price, and S. Penman, *Cell* **3**, 1 (1974).
29. J. R. Greenberg and R. P. Perry, *JMB* **72**, 91 (1972).
30. M. Adesnik and J. E. Darnell, *JMB* **67**, 397 (1972).
31. C. M. Stoltzfus, A. J. Shatkin, and A. K. Banerjee, *JBC* **248**, 7993 (1973).
32. R. S. S. Fraser, *Virology* **56**, 379 (1973).
33. W. Fiers, R. Contreras, F. Duerinck, G. Haegeman, D. Iserentant, J. Merregaert, W. Min Jou, F. Molemans, A. Raeymaekers, A. Van den Berghe, G. Volckaert, and M. Ysebaert, *Nature* **260**, 500 (1976).
34. W. Jelinek, M. Adesnik, M. Salditt, D. Sheiness, R. Wall, G. Molloy, L. Philipson, and J. E. Darnell, *JMB* **75**, 515 (1973).
35. M. Adesnik, M. Salditt, W. Thomas, and J. E. Darnell, *JMB* **71**, 21 (1972).
36. P. K. Sarkar, B. Goldman, and A. A. Moscona, *BBRC* **50**, 308 (1973).
37. R. Levenson, J. Kernen, and D. Housman, *Cell* **18**, 1073 (1979).
38. I. Slater and D. W. Slater, *PNAS* **71**, 1103 (1974).
39. Y. Yogo and E. Wimmer, *Nature NB* **242**, 171 (1973).
40. C. Hucz, G. Marbaix, E. Hubert, M. Leclercq, U. Nudel, H. Soreq, R. Salomon, B. Lebleu, M. Revel, and U. Z. Littauer, *PNAS* **71**, 3143 (1974).

41. U. Nudel, H. Soreq, U. Z. Littauer, G. Marbaix, G. Huez, M. Leclercq, E. Hubert, and H. Chantrenne, *EJB* **64**, 115 (1976).
42. G. Marbaix, G. Huez, A. Burny, Y. Cleuter, E. Hubert, M. Leclercq, H. Chantrenne, H. Soreq, U. Nudel, and U. Z. Littauer, *PNAS* **72**, 3065 (1975).
43. G. Huez, C. Bruck, and Y. Cleuter, *Arch. Int. Physiol. Biochim.* **88**, B285 (1980).
44. K. S. Kirby, *Methods Enzymol.* **12B**, 87 (1968).
45. R. Laskov, E. Margoliash, U. Z. Littauer, and H. Eisenberg, *BBA* **33**, 247 (1959).
46. S. Y. Lee, J. Mendecki, and G. Brawerman, *PNAS* **68**, 1331 (1971).
47. R. P. Perry, J. La Torre, D. E. Kelley, and J. R. Greenberg, *BBA* **262**, 220 (1972).
48. L. Lim and E. S. Canellakis, *Nature* **227**, 710 (1970).
49. M. Edelman, I. M. Verma, and U. Z. Littauer, *JMB* **49**, 67 (1970).
50. S. Penman, *JMB* **17**, 117 (1966).
51. M. R. Morrison, F. Baskin, and R. N. Rosenberg, *BBA* **476**, 228 (1977).
52. U. Z. Littauer and M. Sela, *BBA* **61**, 609 (1962).
53. T. Cheng, S. K. Polmar, and H. H. Kazazian, Jr., *JBC* **249**, 1781 (1974).
54. R. E. Rhoads, G. S. McKnight, and R. T. Schimke, *JBC* **248**, 2031 (1973).
55. J. A. Grasso and G. P. Casale, *BJ* **183**, 105 (1979).
56. R. A. Cox, *Methods Enzymol.* **12B**, 120 (1968).
57. J. D. Harding and W. J. Rutter, *JBC* **253**, 8736 (1978).
58. A. Ullrich, J. Shine, J. Chirgwin, R. Pictet, E. Tischer, W. J. Rutter, and H. M. Goodman, *Science* **196**, 1313 (1977).
59. H. Soreq, M. Harpold, M. Wilson, and J. E. Darnell, Jr., *BBRC* **92**, 485 (1980).
60. N. Sullivan and W. K. Roberts, *Bchem* **12**, 2395 (1973).
61. J. Kates, *CSHSQB* **35**, 743 (1970).
62. W. K. Roberts, *Bchem* **13**, 3677 (1974).
63. J. Van Ness, I. H. Maxwell, and W. E. Hahn, *Cell* **18**, 1341 (1979).
64. R. Sheldon, C. Jurale, and J. Kates, *PNAS* **69**, 417 (1972).
65. P. Pulkrabek, K. Klier, and D. Grunberger, *Anal. Biochem.* **68**, 26 (1975).
66. B. Axelsson, R. Ohlsson, A. Deutsch, and B. Jergil, *Mol. Cell. Biochem.* **15**, 67 (1977).
67. P. T. Gilham, *JACS* **86**, 4982 (1964).
68. M. Edmonds and M. G. Caramela, *JBC* **244**, 1314 (1969).
69. H. Aviv and P. Leder, *PNAS* **69**, 1408 (1972).
70. G. Brawerman, *Methods Cell Biol.* **7**, 1 (1973).
71. U. Lindberg and T. Persson, *EJB* **31**, 246 (1972).
72. L. Puckett, S. Chambers, and J. E. Darnell, *PNAS* **72**, 389 (1975).
73. H. Nakazato and M. Edmonds, *Basic Life Sci.* **3**, 317 (1974).
74. W. Jelinek and L. Leinwand, *Cell* **15**, 205 (1978).
75. R. A. Firtel, K. Kindle, and M. P. Huxley, *FP* **35**, 13 (1976).
76. T. Hunter and J. I. Garrels, *Cell* **12**, 767 (1977).
77. J. Gorski, M. R. Morrison, C. G. Merkel, and J. B. Lingrel, *JMB* **86**, 363 (1974).
78. T. E. Geoghegan, G. E. Sonenshein, and G. Brawerman, *Bchem* **17**, 4200 (1978).
79. D. Sagher, H. Grosfeld, and M. Edelman, *PNAS* **73**, 722 (1976).
80. D. Rosen and M. Edelman, *EJB* **63**, 525 (1976).
81. R. G. Levenson and K. B. Marcu, *Cell* **9**, 311 (1976).
82. M. O. Cabada, C. Darnbrough, P. J. Ford, and P. C. Turner, *Dev. Biol.* **57**, 427 (1977).
83. M. R. Morrison, R. Brodeur, S. Pardue, F. Baskin, C. L. Hall, and R. N. Rosenberg, *JBC* **254**, 7675 (1979).
84. C. M. Palatnik, R. V. Storti, and A. Jacobson, *JMB* **128**, 371 (1979).

85. C. A. Saunders, K. A. Bostian, and H. O. Halvorson, *NARes* **8**, 3841 (1980).
86. I. Gozes, H. Schmitt, and U. Z. Littauer, *PNAS* **72**, 701 (1975).
87. G. M. Maniatis, F. Ramirez, A. Cann, P. A. Marks, and A. Bank, *J. Clin. Invest.* **58**, 1419 (1976).
88. B. E. Roberts and B. M. Paterson, *PNAS* **70**, 2330 (1973).
89. D. Shields and G. Blobel, *JBC* **253**, 3753 (1978).
90. H. R. B. Pelham and R. J. Jackson, *EJB* **67**, 247 (1976).
91. J. B. Gurdon, C. D. Lane, H. R. Woodland, and G. Marbaix, *Nature* **233**, 177 (1971).
92. M. M. Harpold, P. R. Dobner, R. M. Evans, and F. C. Bancroft, *NARes* **5**, 2039 (1978).
93. I. Gozes, A. de Baetselier, and U. Z. Littauer, *EJB* **103**, 13 (1980).
94. E. Jacob, G. Malacinski, and M. L. Birnstiel, *EJB* **69**, 45 (1976).
95. H. Soreq, D. A. Sagar, and P. B. Sehgal, *PNAS* **78**, 1841 (1981).
96. S. L. C. Woo, J. M. Rosen, C. D. Liarakos, Y. C. Choi, H. Busch, A. R. Means, B. W. O'Malley, and D. L. Robberson, *JBC* **250**, 7027 (1975).
97. I. Schechter, *PNAS* **70**, 2256 (1973).
98. D. J. Shapiro and R. T. Schimke, *JBC* **250**, 1759 (1975).
99. R. P. Ricciardi, J. S. Miller, and B. E. Roberts, *PNAS* **76**, 4927 (1979).
100. B. E. Noyes and G. R. Stark, *Cell* **5**, 301 (1975).
101. G. R. Stark and J. G. Williams, *NARes* **6**, 195 (1979).
102. H. Nakazato, D. W. Kopp, and M. Edmonds, *JBC* **248**, 1472 (1973).
103. J. N. Mansbridge, J. A. Crossley, W. G. Lanyon, and R. Williamson, *EJB* **44**, 261 (1974).
104. G. R. Molloy, M. B. Sporn, D. E. Kelley, and R. P. Perry, *Bchem* **11**, 3256 (1972).
105. R. Sheldon, J. Kates, D. E. Kelley, and R. P. Perry, *Bchem* **11**, 3829 (1972).
106. H. Soreq, U. Nudel, R. Salomon, M. Revel, and U. Z. Littauer, *JMB* **88**, 233 (1974).
107. J. N. Vournakis, R. E. Gelinas, and F. C. Kafatos, *Cell* **3**, 265 (1974).
108. C. N. Nair and D. L. Panicali, *J. Virol.* **20**, 170 (1976).
109. H. Soreq and U. Z. Littauer, *JBC* **252**, 6885 (1977).
110. D. Sheiness, L. Puckett, and J. E. Darnell, *PNAS* **72**, 1077 (1975).
111. W. R. Jeffery and G. Brawerman, *Bchem* **13**, 4633 (1974).
112. J. A. Hunt, *BJ* **131**, 327 (1973).
113. S. J. Kaufman and K. W. Gross, *BBA* **353**, 133 (1974).
114. U. Z. Littauer, R. Salomon, H. Soreq, G. Fleischer, and I. Sela, *Organ. Expression Viral Genome/Mol. Interact. Genet. Transl. Proc. FEBS Meet.* **39**, 133 (1975).
115. J. N. Vournakis, A. Efstratiadis, and F. C. Kafatos, *PNAS* **72**, 2959 (1975).
116. H. Grosfeld, H. Soreq, and U. Z. Littauer, *NARes* **4**, 2109 (1977).
117. R. Kaempfer, R. Hollender, H. Soreq, and U. Nudel, *EJB* **94**, 591 (1979).
118. U. Z. Littauer, H. Soreq, and P. Cornelis, *Enzyme Regul. Mech. Action, Proc. FEBS Meet.* **60**, p. 233 (1980).
119. G. Kaufmann, H. Grosfeld, and U. Z. Littauer, *FEBS Lett.* **31**, 47 (1973).
120. R. Salomon, M. Bar-Joseph, H. Soreq, I. Gozes, and U. Z. Littauer, *Virology* **90**, 288 (1978).
121. P. Nokin, A. Burny, G. Huez, and G. Marbaix, *EJB* **68**, 431 (1976).
122. M. R. Morrison, C. G. Merkel, and J. B. Lingrel, *Mol. Biol. Rep.* **1**, 55 (1973).
123. A. T. H. Burness, I. U. Pardoe, and N. O. Goldstein, *BBRC* **67**, 1408 (1975).
124. R. F. Beers, Jr., *JBC* **235**, 2393 (1960).
125. N. Imura, M. Irie, and T. Ukita, *J. Biochem. (Tokyo)* **58**, 264 (1965).
126. P. Nokin, G. Huez, G. Marbaix, A. Burny, and H. Chantrenne, *EJB* **62**, 509 (1976).
127. J. R. Greenberg, *Bchem* **15**, 3516 (1976).

80   URIEL Z. LITTAUER AND HERMONA SOREQ

128. M. Nemer, M. Graham, and L. M. Dubroff, *JMB* **89**, 435 (1974).
129. D. Fromson and A. Duchastel, *BBA* **378**, 394 (1975).
130. Y. Kaufmann, C. Milcarek, H. Berissi, and S. Penman, *PNAS* **74**, 4801 (1977).
131. L. J. Grady, A. B. North, and W. P. Campbell, *NARes* **5**, 697 (1978).
132. W. E. Hahn, J. Van Ness, and I. H. Maxwell, *PNAS* **75**, 5544 (1978).
133. M. Grunstein and P. Schedl, *JMB* **104**, 323 (1976).
134. H. R. Woodland and F. H. Wilt, *Dev. Biol.* **75**, 214 (1980).
135. J. V. Ruderman and M. L. Pardue, *JBC* **253**, 2018 (1978).
136. C. L. Thrall, W. D. Park, H. W. Rashba, J. L. Stein, R. J. Mans, and G. S. Stein, *BBRC* **61**, 1443 (1974).
137. J. V. Ruderman and M. L. Pardue, *Dev. Biol.* **60**, 48 (1977).
138. T. W. Borun, K. Ajiro, A. Zweidler, T. W. Dolby, and R. E. Stephens, *JBC* **252**, 173 (1977).
139. K. Fahrner, J. Yarger, and L. Hereford, *NARes* **8**, 5725 (1980).
140. J. V. Ruderman, H. R. Woodland, and E. A. Sturgess, *Dev. Biol.* **71**, 71 (1979).
141. H. F. Lodish, A. Jacobson, R. Firtel, T. Alton, and J. Tuchman, *PNAS* **71**, 5103 (1974).
142. I. E. Bergmann and G. Brawerman, *JMB* **139**, 439 (1980).
143. R. M. Medford, R. M. Wydro, H. T. Nguyen, and B. Nadal-Ginard, *PNAS* **77**, 5749 (1980).
144. F. Amalric, C. Merkel, R. Gelfand, and G. Attardi, *JMB* **118**, 1 (1978).
145. A. M. Wheeler and M. R. Hartley, *Nature* **257**, 66 (1975).
146. S. H. Howell, P. Heizmann, S. Gelvin, and L. L. Walker, *Plant Physiol.* **59**, 464 (1977).
147. A. Reisfeld, K. M. Jakob, and M. Edelman, *in* "Chloroplast Development" (G. Akoyunoglou, ed.), p. 669. Elsevier/North-Holland, Amsterdam, 1978.
148. H. Sano, E. Spaeth, and W. G. Burton, *EJB* **93**, 173 (1979).
149. A. Efstratiadis, J. W. Posakony, T. Maniatis, R. M. Lawn, C. O'Connell, R. A. Spritz, J. K. DeRiel, B. G. Forget, S. M. Weissman, J. L. Slighton, A. E. Blechl, O. Smithies, F. E. Baralle, C. C. Shoulders, and N. J. Proudfoot, *Cell* **21**, 653 (1980).
150. G. P. Siegal, T. J. Quinlan, H. L. Moses, and M. J. Getz, *J. Cell. Physiol.* **98**, 283 (1979).
151. R. C. Herman, J. G. Williams, and S. Penman, *Cell* **7**, 429 (1976).
152. J. P. Dudley, J. M. Rosen, and J. S. Butel, *PNAS* **75**, 5797 (1978).
153. Y. Aloni, This Series, **25**, 1 (1981).
154. C.-J. Lai, R. Dhar, and G. Khoury, *Cell* **14**, 971 (1978).
155. J. R. Nevins and J. E. Darnell, Jr., *Cell* **15**, 1477 (1978).
156. J. M. Blanchard, J. Weber, W. Jelinek, and J. E. Darnell, *PNAS* **75**, 5344 (1978).
157. J. Weber, J. M. Blanchard, H. Ginsberg, and J. E. Darnell, Jr., *J. Virol.* **33**, 286 (1980).
158. N. W. Fraser, J. R. Nevins, E. Ziff, and J. E. Darnell, Jr., *JMB* **129**, 643 (1979).
159. W. Schaffner, G. Kunz, H. Daetwyler, J. Telford, H. O. Smith, and M. L. Birnstiel, *Cell* **14**, 655 (1978).
160. P. Aleström, G. Akusjarvi, M. Perricaudet, M. B. Mathews, D. F. Klessig, and U. Pettersson, *Cell* **19**, 671 (1980).
160a. S. Nagata, N. Mantei, and C. Weissmann, *Nature* **287**, 401 (1980).
161. S. Penman, M. Rosbash, and M. Penman, *PNAS* **67**, 1878 (1970).
162. J. E. Darnell, L. Philipson, R. Wall, and M. Adesnik, *Science* **174**, 507 (1971).
162a. M. Zeevi, J. R. Nevins, and J. E. Darnell, Jr., *Cell* **26**, 39 (1981).
163. L. R. Beach and J. Ross, *JBC* **253**, 2628 (1978).

163a. R. F. Kleitzien, *BJ.* **192**, 753 (1980).
164. I. Tamm and P. B. Sehgal, *in* "Effects of Drugs on the Cell Nucleus" (H. Busch, S. T. Crooke, and Y. Daskal, eds.), p. 251. Academic Press, New York, 1979.
165. A. E. Sippel, J. G. Stavrianopoulos, G. Schutz, and P. Feigelson, *PNAS* **71**, 4635 (1974).
166. R. Williamson, J. Crossley, and S. Humphries, *Bchem* **13**, 703 (1974).
167. S. Humphries, M. Doel, and R. Williamson, *BBRC* **58**, 927 (1974).
168. E. Bard, D. Efron, A. Marcus, and R. P. Perry, *Cell* **1**, 101 (1974).
169. R. F. Munoz and J. E. Darnell, *Cell* **2**, 247 (1974).
170. W. E. G. Müller, G. Seibert, R. Steffen, and R. K. Zahn, *EJB* **70**, 249 (1976).
171. M. T. Doel and N. H. Carey, *Cell* **8**, 51 (1976).
172. G. Huez, C. Bruck, and Y. Cleuter, *PNAS* **78**, 908 (1981).
173. P. A. Hieter, S. M. LeGendre, and C. C. Levy, *JBC* **251**, 3287 (1976).
174. J. B. Gurdon, J. B. Lingrel, and G. Marbaix, *JMB* **80**, 539 (1973).
174a. A. K. Deshpande, B. Chatterjee, and A. K. Roy, *JBC* **254**, 8937 (1979).
175. G. Huez, G. Marbaix, E. Hubert, Y. Cleuter, M. Leclercq, H. Chantrenne, R. Devos, H. Soreq, U. Nudel, and U. Z. Littauer, *EJB* **59**, 589 (1975).
176. G. Huez, G. Marbaix, A. Burny, E. Hubert, M. Leclercq, Y. Cleuter, H. Chantrenne, H. Soreq, and U. Z. Littauer, *Nature* **266**, 473 (1977).
177. J. R. Greenberg, *Nature* **240**, 102 (1972).
178. R. P. Perry and D. E. Kelley, *JMB* **79**, 681 (1973).
179. R. H. Singer and S. Penman, *JMB* **78**, 321 (1973).
180. M. Nemer, L. M. Dubroff, and M. Graham, *Cell* **6**, 171 (1975).
181. C. M. Palatnik, R. V. Storti, A. K. Capone, and A. Jacobson, *JMB* **141**, 99 (1980).
182. G. Marbaix, G. Huez, H. Soreq, D. Gallwitz, E. Weinberg, R. Devos, E. Hubert, and Y. Cleuter, *Gene Funct. Proc. FEBS Meet.* **51**, 427 (1979).
183. S. W. Kwan and G. Brawerman, *PNAS* **69**, 3247 (1972).
184. G. Blobel, *PNAS* **70**, 924 (1973).
185. S. Goldenberg, A. Vincent, and K. Scherrer, *NARes* **8**, 5057 (1980).
186. I. E. Bergmann and G. Brawerman, *Bchem* **16**, 259 (1977).
187. H. R. Woodland and F. H. Wilt, *Dev. Biol.* **75**, 199 (1980).
188. G. Huez, G. Marbaix, D. Gallwitz, E. Weinberg, R. Devos, E. Hubert, and Y. Cleuter, *Nature* **271**, 572 (1978).
189. E. D. Adamson and H. R. Woodland, *Dev. Biol.* **57**, 136 (1977).
190. P. B. Sehgal, H. Soreq, and I. Tamm, *PNAS* **75**, 5030 (1978).
191. P. B. Sehgal, D. S. Lyles, and I. Tamm, *Virology* **89**, 186 (1978).
192. P. B. Sehgal and A. D. Sagar, *Nature* **288**, 95 (1980).
193. J. Weissenbach, Y. Chernajovsky, M. Zeevi, L. Shulman, H. Soreq, U. Nir, D. Wallach, M. Perricaudet, P. Tiollais, and M. Revel, *PNAS* **77**, 7152 (1980).
194. G. Marbaix and G. Huez, *in* "Transfer of Cell Constituents into Eukaryotic Cells" (J. E. Celis, A. Graessmann, and A. Loyter, eds.), p. 347. Plenum, New York, 1980.
195. J. R. Nevins and W. K. Joklik, *Virology* **63**, 1 (1975).
196. M. V. Marshall and R. B. Arlinghaus, *J. Virol.* **19**, 743 (1976).
197. N. O. Goldstein, I. U. Pardoe, and A. T. H. Burness, *J. Gen. Virol.* **31**, 271 (1976).
198. D. E. Hruby and W. K. Roberts, *J. Virol.* **19**, 325 (1976).
199. D. E. Hruby and W. K. Roberts, *J. Virol.* **23**, 338 (1977).
200. C. C. Allende, J. E. Allende, and R. A. Firtel, *Cell* **2**, 189 (1974).
201. Y. Furuichi, A. LaFiandra, and A. J. Shatkin, *Nature* **266**, 235 (1977).
202. R. A. Laskey, J. B. Gurdon, and L. V. Crawford, *PNAS* **69**, 3665 (1972).
203. C. Gilvarg, F. J. Bollum, and C. Weissmann, *PNAS* **72**, 428 (1975).

204. M. J. Grubman, B. Baxt, and H. L. Bachrach, *Virology* **97**, 22 (1979).
205. V. Hari, A. Siegel, C. Rozek, and W. E. Timberlake, *Virology* **92**, 568 (1979).
206. P. A. Marx, Jr., C. Pridgen, and D. W. Kingsbury, *J. Gen. Virol.* **27**, 247 (1975).
207. J. A. Armstrong, M. Edmonds, H. Nakazato, B. A. Phillips, and M. H. Vaughan, *Science* **176**, 526 (1972).
208. D. H. Spector and D. Baltimore, *J. Virol.* **15**, 1418 (1975).
209. D. H. Spector and D. Baltimore, *PNAS* **71**, 2983 (1974).
210. A. Dasgupta, P. Zabel, and D. Baltimore, *Cell* **19**, 423 (1980).
211. D. H. Spector, L. Villa-Komaroff, and D. Baltimore, *Cell* **6**, 41 (1975).
212. D. H. Spector and D. Baltimore, *J. Virol.* **15**, 1432 (1975).
213. A. Dasgupta, M. H. Baron, and D. Baltimore, *PNAS* **76**, 2679 (1979).
214. M. Kozak and A. J. Shatkin, *JMB* **112**, 75 (1977).
215. R. Dasgupta, D. S. Shih, C. Saris, and P. Kaesberg, *Nature* **256**, 624 (1975).
216. J. P. Briand, G. Jonard, H. Guilley, K. Richards, and L. Hirth, *EJB* **72**, 453 (1977).
217. R. F. Pettersson, J. B. Flanegan, J. K. Rose, and D. Baltimore, *Nature* **268**, 270 (1977).
218. W. A. Haseltine, A. M. Maxam, and W. Gilbert, *PNAS* **74**, 989 (1977).
219. A. G. Porter, J. Merregaert, J. Van Emmelo, and W. Fiers, *EJB* **87**, 551 (1978).
220. N. J. Proudfoot, *Cell* **10**, 559 (1977).
221. R. Salomon, I. Sela, H. Soreq, D. Giveon, and U. Z. Littauer, *Virology* **71**, 74 (1976).
222. A. G. Porter, P. Fellner, D. N. Black, D. J. Rowlands, T. J. R. Harris, and F. Brown, *Nature* **276**, 298 (1978).
223. L. Pinck and M. Pinck, *FEBS Lett.* **107**, 61 (1979).
224. M. R. Gunn and R. H. Symons, *FEBS Lett.* **109**, 145 (1980).
225. R. Dasgupta and P. Kaesberg, *PNAS* **74**, 4900 (1977).
226. E. C. Koper-Zwarthoff and J. F. Bol, *PNAS* **76**, 1114 (1979).
227. C. J. Houwing and E. M. J. Jaspars, *Bchem* **17**, 2927 (1978).
228. E. Ziff and N. Fraser, *J. Virol.* **25**, 897 (1978).
229. A. Panet, M. Gorecki, S. Bratosin, and Y. Aloni, *NARes* **5**, 3219 (1978).
230. M. Horowitz, S. Bratosin, and Y. Aloni, *NARes* **5**, 4663 (1978).
231. L.-H. Wang, P. H. Duesberg, T. Robins, H. Yokota, and P. K. Vogt, *Virology* **82**, 472 (1977).
232. J. Tal, H. J. Kung, H. E. Varmus, and J. M. Bishop, *Virology* **79**, 183 (1977).
233. D. E. Schwartz, P. C. Zamecnik, and H. L. Weith, *PNAS* **74**, 994 (1977).
234. J. M. Coffin and W. A. Haseltine, *PNAS* **74**, 1908 (1977).
235. R. J. Colonno and A. K. Banerjee, *Cell* **8**, 197 (1976).
236. J. D. Keene, M. Schubert, R. A. Lazzarini, and M. Rosenberg, *PNAS* **75**, 3225 (1978).
237. R. Kamen, *Nature* **221**, 321 (1969).
238. U. Rensing and J. T. August, *Nature* **224**, 853 (1969).
239. A. Steinschneider and H. Fraenkel-Conrat, *Bchem* **5**, 2729 (1966).
240. R. J. Kohl and T. C. Hall, *PNAS* **74**, 2682 (1977).
241. A. L. Haenni and F. Chapeville, *in* "Transfer RNA: Biological Aspects" (D. Söll, J. N. Abelson, and P. R. Schimmel, eds.), p. 589. Cold Spring Harbor Laboratory, Cold Spring Harbor, New York, 1980.
242. B. Oberg and L. Philipson, *BBRC* **48**, 927 (1972).
243. S. Litvak, A. Tarrago, L. Tarrago-Litvak, and J. E. Allende, *Nature NB* **241**, 88 (1973).

244. M. Pinck, S. K. Chan, M. Genevaux, L. Hirth, and H. Duranton, *Biochimie* **54**, 1093 (1972).
245. L. Pinck, M. Genevaux, J. P. Bouley, and M. Pinck, *Virology* **63**, 589 (1975).
246. T. C. Hall, D. S. Shih, and P. Kaesberg, *BJ* **129**, 969 (1972).
247. R. J. Kohl and T. C. Hall, *J. Gen. Virol.* **25**, 257 (1974).
248. R. Salomon and U. Z. Littauer, *Nature* **249**, 32 (1974).
249. I. J. D. Lindley and N. Stebbing, *J. Gen. Virol.* **34**, 177 (1977).
250. A. Prochiantz and A. L. Haenni, *Nature NB* **241**, 168 (1973).
251. S. Joshi, A. L. Haenni, E. Hubert, G. Huez, and G. Marbaix, *Nature* **275**, 339 (1978).
252. S. Litvak, D. S. Carré and F. Chapeville, *FEBS Lett.* **11**, 316 (1970).
253. P. Yot, M. Pinck, A. L. Haenni, H. M. Duranton and F. Chapeville, *PNAS* **67**, 1345 (1970).
254. A. L. Haenni, A. Prochiantz, O. Bernard, and F. Chapeville, *Nature NB* **241**, 166 (1973).
255. D. Lamy, G. Jonard, H. Guilley, and L. Hirth, *FEBS Lett.* **60**, 202 (1975).
256. T. L. German, G. A. De Zoeten, and T. C. Hall, *Intervirology* **9**, 226 (1978).
257. M. Grunstein and J. E. Grunstein, *CSHSQB* **42**, 1083 (1978).
258. L. McReynolds, B. W. O'Malley, A. D. Nisbet, J. E. Fothergill, D. Givol, S. Fields, M. Robertson, and G. G. Brownlee, *Nature* **273**, 723 (1978).
259. G. N. Buell, M. P. Wickens, J. Carbon, and R. T. Schimke, *JBC* **254**, 9277 (1979).
260. J. H. Nunberg, and R. J. Kaufman, A. C. Y. Chang, S. N. Cohen, and R. T. Schimke, *Cell* **19**, 355 (1980).
261. P. Hobart, R. Crawford, L. Shen, R. Pictet, and W. J. Rutter, *Nature* **288**, 137 (1980).
262. O. Hagenbüchle, R. Bovey, and R. A. Young, *Cell* **21**, 179 (1980).
263. M. Shani, U. Nudel, D. Zevin-Zankin, R. Zakut, D. Givol, D. Katcoff, Y. Carmon, J. Reiter, A. M. Frischauf, and D. Yaffe, *NARes* **9**, 579 (1981).
264. N. J. Proudfoot and G. G. Brownlee, *Br. Med. Bull.* **32**, 251 (1976).
265. C. Benoist, K. O'Hare, R. Breathnach, and P. Chambon, *NARes* **8**, 127 (1980).
266. A. G. Porter, P. Fellner, D. N. Black, D. J. Rowlands, T. J. R. Harris, and F. Brown, *Nature* **276**, 298 (1978).
267. H. M. Kronenberg, B. E. Roberts, and A. Efstratiadis, *NARes* **6**, 153 (1979).
268. D. S. Adams, D. Noonan, and W. R. Jeffery, *FEBS Lett.* **114**, 115 (1980).
269. W. E. G. Müller, J. Arendes, R. K. Zahn, and H. C. Schröder, *EJB* **86**, 283 (1978).
270. W. R. Jeffery, *BBA* **521**, 217 (1978).

tRNA-like Structures in the Genomes of RNA Viruses[1]

ANNE-LISE HAENNI,
SADHNA JOSHI, AND
FRANÇOIS CHAPEVILLE

*Institut de Recherche en Biologie
Moléculaire du Centre National de
la Recherche Scientifique
Université Paris VII
Paris, France*

I. Introduction

All structural studies of RNAs from various origins, be they cellular messenger RNAs or viral RNAs, show that these molecules contain nucleotide sequences that are not translated into polypeptides. At the 5' end, besides the "cap" structure generally found in eukaryotic

---

[1] tRNA-like structures that are part of the genomes of certain RNA viruses are not to be confused with bona fide tRNAs that are encapsidated in certain RNA tumor viruses and that act as primer for RNA-dependent DNA polymerase. (See Waters and Mullin, in Vol. 20 of this series.)

Progress in Nucleic Acid Research
and Molecular Biology, Vol. 27

mRNAs and viral RNAs, the untranslated sequence is heteropolymeric and of variable length, from a few nucleotides to a few hundred nucleotides. At the 3' end, a homopolymeric sequence of adenylate residues [poly(A)] of size from about 50 to 200 nucleotides is preceded by a heteropolymeric sequence of variable length, which is also not translated. In bacterial mRNAs, bacteriophage RNAs, and certain eukaryotic and viral mRNAs in which the poly(A) sequence is absent, the heteropolymeric untranslated sequences at the 3' end are always present.

The physiological role of these untranslated heteropolymeric regions is not well understood. In most of the eukaryotic viral systems studied, initiation of polypeptide synthesis is normally restricted to the 5' proximal AUG in the mRNA even if this RNA is polygenic. Consequently, translation is generally limited to the cistron closest to the 5' end of the RNA. The untranslated heteropolymeric region at the 5' end certainly plays an important role in the accessibility of the initiator AUG codon for the ribosome. Regarding the 3' end, the poly(A) sequence seems to protect the mRNA from degradation by exonucleases, and possibly it modulates mRNA transport to the cytoplasm (1). The function of the heteropolymeric regions at that end is likewise unknown. However, the fact that these sequences are highly conserved, as shown for example in a group of plant viruses (2), suggests that they do play an important role. The removal of a part of these regions from the genome of RNA bacteriophages (3, 4) or of RNA viruses (5–8) abolishes infectivity.

The RNA genomes of most plant viruses are devoid of poly(A) stretches, and the lengths of the untranslated heteropolymeric sequences at the 3' end of the RNA can be 200 nucleotides or more.

The discovery in 1970 (9, 10) of the enzymic aminoacylation at the 3' end of turnip yellow mosaic virus (TYMV) RNA in conditions similar to the aminoacylation of tRNAs, and the subsequent extension of this observation to many other RNA viruses, opened new perspectives for the study of the physiological role of these untranslated regions at the 3' end of viral RNAs.

In this review, we summarize the results obtained with different viral RNAs that accept an amino acid and are recognized by various tRNA-specific enzymes. For a number of these viral RNAs, the nucleotide sequence of the amino-acid-acceptor regions has been determined and the structures have been compared. The most surprising outcome of these studies is that, apart from the C-C-(A) at the 3' end, these sequences do not contain, in an appropriate position, the "invariable" nucleotides generally found in tRNAs; furthermore the secondary structures constructed from these sequences do not resemble the classical cloverleaf model of tRNAs. This leads to a rather important conclusion concerning the relationships between the structure and the function of nucleic acids: Different primary and secondary structures of two nucleic acid molecules, such as tRNAs and certain viral RNAs, can be recognized efficiently by the same enzyme systems (tRNA-specific enzymes) that play a central role in the transfer of genetic information.

Two review articles have been published on the tRNA-like structures in viral RNA genomes (11, 12).

II. Aminoacylation of Viral RNAs

Most of the information concerning the aminoacylation of viral RNAs comes from the study of plant RNA viruses.

The general conditions of the aminoacylation of viral RNAs first used for the valylation of TYMV RNA are similar to those for tRNAs (9, 10, 13). Extensive analyses of the product formed showed that the 2'- or 3'-hydroxyl group of the adenosine at the 3' end of the RNA forms an ester bond with the carboxyl group of valine (9, 10).

In all cases examined, the aminoacyl-tRNA synthetase of eukaryotic origin catalyzes the reaction. Even though no exhaustive compara-

TABLE I
In Vitro AMINO ACID ACCEPTOR ACTIVITY OF VIRAL RNA GENOMES

Virus group	Virus	Amino acid bound	References
Plant viruses			
Tymovirus	Turnip yellow mosaic virus (TYMV)	Valine	9, 10
	Cacao yellow mosaic virus (CYMV)	Valine	14
	Eggplant mosaic virus (EMV)	Valine	14, 15
	Okra mosaic virus (OMV)	Valine	14
	Wild cucumber mosaic virus (WCMV)	Valine	16
Tobamovirus	Tobacco mosaic virus (TMV)[a]	Histidine	17–19
	Cowpea strain of TMV (C$_c$TMV)	Valine	20
Bromovirus	Brome mosaic virus (BMV)	Tyrosine	13, 21
	Broad bean mottle virus (BBMV)	Tyrosine	13
	Cowpea chlorotic mottle virus (CCMV)	Tyrosine	13
Cucumovirus	Cucumber mosaic virus (CMV)	Tyrosine	13
Animal viruses			
Picornavirus	Mengovirus	Histidine	22
	Encephalomyocarditis virus (EMCV)	Serine	23

[a] The TMV strains tested were U$_2$, vulgare, Holmes ribgrass (HRG), and dahlmensis (15–17) and Judy Pride (R. Giégé, personal communication).

tive studies have been performed, from the data available it seems likely that the viral RNAs behave similarly to the cytoplasmic tRNAs of eukaryotes in their capacity to recognize aminoacyl-tRNA synthetases of various origins. Only in a few cases have the viral RNA and the corresponding eukaryotic cytoplasmic tRNAs been esterified with the bacterial enzymes. Such, for example, is the case with host tRNA^{Val} and TYMV RNA. This parallel behavior is in accordance with the fact that these viruses develop in the cytoplasm and suggests that their genomes might be esterified *in vivo*. With one exception among plant viruses, the RNAs of viruses of the same group accept the same amino acid. Moreover, in the case of the multicomponent viruses that can be aminoacylated, each RNA component is esterified with the same amino acid.

Table I lists the viruses whose RNAs can be aminoacylated, the group to which these viruses belong, and the amino acid accepted (9, 10, 13–23).

A. Plant Viruses

1. TYMOVIRUSES

The icosahedral viruses of this group contain a genomic RNA of 2×10^6 daltons. In TYMV, EMV, and OMV, a subgenomic RNA of about 0.24×10^6 daltons, which is also present at the 3' end of the genomic RNA, is also encapsidated; it codes for the viral coat protein and is therefore often referred to as the "coat protein mRNA."

In the first experiments on the aminoacylation of TYMV RNA (9, 10), an *Escherichia coli* enzyme preparation devoid of tRNAs was used in the presence of ATP and a mixture of amino acids. Valine was the only amino acid bound to the viral RNA, and up to 80% of the viral RNA molecules could be aminoacylated. None of the other triphosphonucleosides could replace ATP. It was shown that the valyl-tRNA synthetase is responsible for the reaction. The following results unambiguously demonstrated that the carboxyl group of valine esterifies the 2'- or 3'-hydroxyl group of the adenosine at the 3' end of the viral RNA.

1. The amino group of the valine is free and can be acetylated chemically.
2. The chemical properties (i.e., half-life time) of the bond between valine and the RNA are similar to those between valine and tRNA.
3. Pancreatic RNase or snake venom phosphodiesterase digestion of the valyl-RNA yields valyl-adenosine or valyl-AMP, respectively.

The analyses of the RNase T1 digests of the viral valyl-RNA compared to those of valyl-tRNAs from the host cells yielded different valyl-oligonucleotides. This excludes the involvement in the charging reaction of a cellular tRNA that would somehow be linked to the viral RNA.

By sucrose gradient analyses of the aminoacylated viral RNA, a predominant product containing valine and corresponding to aminoacylated genomic RNA as well as a product of lower molecular weight also containing valine were observed (9). This latter product must correspond to valylated coat protein mRNA, since later experiments demonstrated that the subgenomic RNA can indeed also be efficiently aminoacylated by valine (24). The valyl-tRNA synthetases of various origins—yeast, plant and animal—also catalyze the aminoacylation reaction of TYMV RNA (13, 25). With purified yeast valyl-tRNA synthease, the kinetic parameters (K_m and rate constants) for the esterification of TYMV RNA are very similar to those observed for yeast valine tRNA (24).

The aminoacylation of TYMV RNA has been studied *in vivo* by injecting the viral RNA into *Xenopus laevis* oocytes (26). The injected TYMV RNA (total or coat protein mRNA) was esterified with valine as efficiently as injected *E. coli* tRNA^{Val-1}. Similar studies with the homologous system (Chinese cabbage leaves) suggest that the viral RNA is valylated also in the infected plant (S. Joshi, unpublished results). However, the fact that the viral RNA in the virion is not esterified suggests that such esterification is only transient or concerns only a minor fraction of the viral RNA population. One can also postulate that, *in vivo*, a small part of the viral RNA population is fragmented to yield lower molecular weight valyl-RNA possibly involved in a biological activity, such as the regulation of RNA replication or translation; indeed an RNA fragment of 4.5 S (27; see below) from the 3' end of the viral RNA can accept valine *in vitro*.

The RNAs of four other viruses of the tymovirus group also accept valine under conditions similar to those used for TYMV RNA (Table I). These are CYMV (14), EMV (14, 15), OMV (14), and WCMV (16).

2. Tobamoviruses

Extensive studies on the structural, morphological, and biological properties of TMV have been performed. This virus is composed of rod-shaped particles containing a single RNA of 2×10^6 daltons. The C$_r$TMV strain engenders rods of various sizes in infected tissues, including a short rod containing the coat protein mRNA (20).

Shortly after the discovery of the valylation of TYMV, it was shown that, with rabbit liver or yeast (but not *E. coli*) enzyme preparations,

TMV RNA can be acylated with histidine (*17, 18*). There appear to be differences in the histidine acceptor capacities of the RNAs obtained from different strains of TMV (*19*). The four strains studied can be classified in two groups. The RNAs from the vulgare and U_2 strains have an acceptor capacity of approximately 0.4 mole of histidine per mole of RNA. The RNAs of the other two strains, dahlmensis and HRG (Table I), are much poorer histidine acceptors (~0.1 mole per mole of RNA). These differences are apparently due to differences in the folding of the polynucleotide structure: heating of the RNA of the HRG strain to 80°C in advance increases the amount of RNA molecules capable of accepting histidine from 0.1 to 0.4 mole per mole of RNA (*19*). Lack of stoichiometry in the aminoacylation in all the strains studied could arise from inadequate secondary or tertiary structures, from partially degraded RNA molecules, and/or from suboptimal esterification conditions. Close to 100% aminoacylation with the RNA of the Judy Pride strain of TMV has been observed (R. Giégé, personal communication).

A surprising result was obtained with C_cTMV: instead of accepting histidine, the RNA of this strain is aminoacylated with valine (*20*). Among the plant viruses, this is the only case in which the RNAs of viruses from the same group accept different amino acids. (See Addendum, A.)

3. BROMOVIRUSES AND CUCUMOVIRUSES

The general characteristic of these viruses is that they are multicomponent. Brome mosaic virus (BMV), the representative of the bromoviruses, encapsidates four RNAs, numbered 1 to 4 in order of decreasing mass (1.1, 1.0, 0.7, and 0.3×10^6 daltons, respectively). RNAs 1, 2, and 3 make up the viral genome, whereas RNA 4 is a subgenomic RNA coding for the coat protein; it comes from the 3' end of RNA 3. The four RNAs are contained in three virions designated H, M, and L. Virion H contains RNA 1, virion M contains RNAs 3 and 4, and virion L contains RNA 2. All the virions have the same complement of 180 identical coat-protein subunits. All three virions are needed for infectivity, but only RNAs 1, 2, and 3 are required. The structure of cucumber mosaic virus, representative of the cucumovirus group, is similar to that of the bromoviruses. It also contains three genomic RNAs and a subgenomic coat protein mRNA.

Enzyme preparations from bean seed cotyledons or from wheat germ can aminoacylate the RNAs of three different viruses of the bromovirus group, BMV, BBMV, and CCMV (*13, 21*), and of one virus of the cucumovirus group, CMV (*13*) with tyrosine (Table I) to the extent of about 0.7 mole per mole of RNA (*13*). The four RNA molecules of different sizes that compose the genome of each of these viruses can be aminoacylated. If the 3′ end of BMV RNA is chemically modified, the RNA no longer accepts tyrosine (28). (See Addendum, B.) Finally, it is interesting that the nonencapsidated satellite RNA in BMV and CMV, referred to as "RNA 5", cannot be aminoacylated (mentioned in 11). (See Addendum, C.)

B. Animal Viruses

The aminoacylation studies of viral RNAs require substantial amounts of RNA, which are easy to obtain from plant viruses. In general, this is not the case with animal viruses, which probably explains the fact that the aminoacylation capacity of only a few of them have been studied.

Mouse liver aminoacyl-tRNA synthetases can acylate menogovirus RNA with histidine to the extent of about 0.2 mole of histidine per mole of RNA (22). The size of the histidyl-RNA is somewhat below 16 S, whereas that of the genomic RNA is about 30 S. Since a part of the mengovirus RNA population contains a poly(A) stretch at its 3′ end (29, 30), esterification with the amino acid seems to require prior removal of this homopolymeric region; alternatively, esterification might be restricted to poly(A)-deficient RNA molecules. In either situation, prior fragmentation of the viral RNA by nucleases present in the synthetase preparations might be necessary. If such nucleolytic splitting is necessary for an RNA fragment to be esterified, the nuclease(s) implied must have a certain specificity, either for highly exposed regions in the RNA, or for the sequence close to the 3′ end of the resulting aminoacylatable fragment.

A second viral RNA whose esterification capacity has been studied is that of EMCV (23). Using E. coli or beef or rabbit liver synthetase preparations, this RNA can be acylated with serine, the extent of aminoacylation being between 0.024 and 0.08 mole per mole of EMCV RNA. As with mengovirus RNA, the esterified material is of lower molecular weight than the genomic RNA. EMCV RNA also contains a poly(A) stretch at its 3′ end (31). Periodate oxidation completely abolished esterification of tRNA but had no effect on the serylation of the viral RNA (23), which suggests that the 3′ end of the viral RNA is not the site of the aminoacylation reaction, but rather that specific cleavage of the genome is required to liberate the regions of the RNA recognized by the aminoacyl-tRNA synthetase.

C. Conclusions

The observations with the two animal viruses discussed above is at variance with those made in plant viruses, since in the latter aminoacylation occurs at the 3′ end of the viral RNA without prior fragmentation.

Not all the genomes of plant RNA viruses can be aminoacylated. Unsuccessful attempts have been reported for alfalfa mosaic, pea enantiation mosaic, southern bean mosaic, tobacco streak, tobacco rattle (mentioned in *11*), and satellite tobacco necrosis viruses (*17*), and citrus exocortis viroid (*32*). Attempts to aminoacylate RNAs from the bacteriophages R17 (*33*), Qβ (*17, 33*), MS2 (*33*) and PP7 (mentioned in *11*) have been unsuccessful. Finally, neither poliovirus RNA (*17*) nor foot-and-mouth disease virus RNA (*34*) could be aminoacylated.

In conclusion, the observation (see Table I) that viral RNAs of high molecular weight can behave as tRNAs in the presence of aminoacyl-tRNA synthetases was unexpected. The first report (*9, 10*) on the valylation of TYMV RNA was thought to be an isolated case, due probably to an unspecific phenomenon. Further studies showing that the RNAs of many viruses behave the same way, and that, in general, the genomes of the viruses within a given group are esterified with the same amino acid, suggest that this hides some important biological function.

III. Interaction of Viral RNAs with Other tRNA-Specific Enzymes

In protein-synthesizing systems, tRNAs react with several specific enzyme systems other than aminoacyl-tRNA synthetases. During the maturation of their precursors, they also interact with enzymes that specifically modify certain nucleotides or complete the 3′ terminal C-C-A sequence. A series of experiments was performed to define to what extent these tRNA-specific enzymes react with the viral RNAs.

A. tRNA Nucleotidyltransferase

This enzyme is involved in the terminal addition of two cytidylate and one adenylate residues to the 3′ end of tRNA precursors or of tRNAs deprived of their C-C-A end after exonuclease treatment.

With TYMV RNA, when highly purified valyl-tRNA synthetase was used instead of the partially purified *E. coli* extracts, valylation did not occur. Addition of tRNA nucleotidyltransferase reestablished valylation (*10, 35*); Table II summarizes these results. Sequence data later showed that TYMV RNA isolated from the virion is terminated by C-C (*36, 37*) and that the tRNA nucleotidyltransferase is needed for the addition of a terminal adenylate residue prior to esterification. The fact that TYMV RNA injected into *X. laevis* oocytes can be esterified with

TABLE II
ACCEPTOR ACTIVITY OF VARIOUS RNAs FOR [^{14}C]VALINE[a,b]

Enzymes added	E. coli tRNA (cpm/μg RNA)	Cabbage tRNA (cpm/μg RNA)	TYMV RNA (cpm/μg RNA)
DEAE-enzyme preparation	425	340	56
Valyl-tRNA synthetase	406	378	5
tRNA nucleotidyltransferase and valyl-tRNA synthetase	375	279	53

[a] From Yot et al. (10).
[b] Escherichia coli enzyme preparations were used.

valine indicates that, in vivo also, tRNA nucleotidyltransferase can adenylate the RNA, thereby permitting valylation (26).

In OMV RNA, the terminal adenosine is also absent, and its addition is needed for acylation (38); in EMV, CYMV, and WCMV it is absent in at least a part of the RNA population (39, 40).

In the other plant viruses whose RNAs accept amino acids, the addition of terminal nucleotides is not necessary; these RNAs are terminated by C-C-A (see below). However, if the C-C-A terminus is removed, the E. coli tRNA nucleotidyltransferase catalyzes its addition (41, 42). Likewise, if TYMV RNA is first treated with snake venom phosphodiesterase (36), two molecules of cytidylate and one of adenylate can subsequently be added per RNA molecule by tRNA nucleotidyltransferase. Thus, the genomes of all the plant RNA viruses that can be aminoacylated are recognized by the RNA nucleotidyltransferase.

The genomes of the RNA bacteriophages Qβ, R17 and MS2 terminate at their 3' end with the sequence C-C-A. If such RNAs are first incubated with commercial snake venom phosphodiesterase, close to two cytidylate and one adenylate residues can subsequently be added per RNA molecule with the tRNA nucleotidyltransferase (33). This suggests that, even if these RNAs cannot be aminoacylated (see above), they contain certain features common to tRNAs recognized by tRNA nucleotidyltransferase.

B. tRNA Methyltransferases

Except for the 5' terminal "cap" structure, plant viral RNAs are not methylated nor do they contain modified nucleotides. Attempts have been made to introduce a methyl group into certain plant viral RNAs. Using a tRNA (uracil-5)-methyltransferase (EC 2.1.1.35) from E. coli (43, 44), a uracil residue in the oligonucleotide U-U-C-G of TMV RNA has been methylated (*44*); this methylation site is similar to that of the usual position of T in the T-ψ-C-G loop of tRNAs. BMV RNA could also be methylated under these conditions, but the position of methylation within the RNA molecule is unknown (mentioned in *11*).

In TYMV RNA, one or two methyl groups could be added per RNA molecule by a tRNA (cytosine-5)-methyltransferase (EC 2.1.1.29) of mammalian origin, but the position of methylation within the genome was not determined (*45*).

C. "RNase P"

Analyses on polyacrylamide gels of the aminoacylation products of TYMV RNA obtained with crude enzymic extracts revealed a lower molecular weight (4.5 S) RNA population bearing valine. The formation of this fragment was due to the presence of nucleases. If the viral RNA was first submitted to the action of the enzymic extracts, the 4.5 S fragment could subsequently be aminoacylated (*27*).

Enzymic preparations from *E. coli* ribosomes containing RNase P, which is involved in the processing of tRNA precursors (*46*), are also capable of yielding a 4.5 S fragment from the 3' end of the viral RNA (*27*). A similar fragment was also found using plant extracts (our unpublished results), or *in vivo* after injection of the viral RNA into *X. laevis* oocytes (*26*). It is not known whether this specific splitting is due to RNase P and/or to other endonucleases acting on a highly exposed sequence of nucleotides in the RNA leading to a fragment of about 110 nucleotides in length from the 3' end of the viral RNA.

D. Elongation Factors

The elongation factors from *E. coli* and wheat germ have been used to examine their interaction with viral RNAs and GTP. Only the aminoacylated species could form ternary complexes. Both TMV histidyl-RNA and TYMV valyl-RNA interact stoichiometrically with GTP and purified wheat germ EF-1 (*18*). A similar ternary complex was observed with TYMV valyl-RNA, GTP, and purified *E. coli* EF-T (*47*). In both series of experiments, the Millipore filtration technique was used for the detection of the ternary complex. Using BMV tyrosyl-RNA and the Sephadex filtration technique, a ternary complex containing tyrosyl-RNA, EF-1 from wheat germ, and GTP could not be isolated, although such a complex was detected by the Millipore assay (*48*). This can be explained by a lower stability of such ternary complexes involving viral RNAs rather than tRNAs.

E. Peptidyl-tRNA Hydrolase

This enzyme hydrolyzes the ester linkage in all N-substituted aminoacyl-tRNAs except that of Met-tRNA^{fMet} (49–51). Its role *in vivo* is not completely elucidated. It probably acts as a scavenger enzyme by hydrolyzing peptidyl-tRNAs of unfinished polypeptide chains accidentally released from ribosomes. The N-acetylated valyl-RNA of TYMV is a good substrate for the *E. coli* peptidyl-tRNA hydrolase (10); it yields acetylvaline with the same kinetic parameters as does N-acetylated valyl-tRNA.

F. Ribosomal Systems

Using TYMV valyl-RNA in an *E. coli* ribosome-dependent protein-synthesizing system, an apparent but poor valine incorporation into the synthesized polypeptide chains was detected (52). In these experiments, valinol-AMP was used as inhibitor of the valyl-tRNA synthetase, which would otherwise catalyze the transfer of valine from the valyl-RNA of TYMV onto the tRNA^{Val} present in the incubation medium. However, it was not checked whether a direct transfer from valyl-RNA to tRNA^{Val} occurred and whether the low incorporation into polypeptides observed was not due to such a transfer. More recently, data obtained in our laboratory suggest that this was probably the case. Using a wheat-germ extract and either BMV tyrosyl-RNA (53) or EMV valyl-RNA (54), no transfer of the amino acid moiety into polypeptides was detected.

It thus appears that the viral RNAs recognized by several tRNA-specific enzymes cannot be used by ribosomal systems for polypeptide synthesis. Further studies are necessary to define whether the viral RNAs can compete with normal tRNAs during translation, and whether they are able to donate their amino acid not for elongation, but rather for termination, of polypeptide chains. Indeed, it is known that aminoacylated fragments of tRNAs and even aminoacyl-A can act in this way (54a).

G. Conclusions

The fact that the RNAs of several viruses not only can be specifically aminoacylated but also can interact with other tRNA-specific enzymes or factors leads to the conclusion that they must have structures similar to those of tRNAs. Consequently, these regions in such viral RNA genomes are commonly referred to as "tRNA like structures."

As viral RNA genomes isolated from the virions are not aminoacylated, as they contain no modified nucleotides, and as in some cases they are devoid of a 3′ terminal adenosine residue, they must not be readily accessible to tRNA-specific enzymes *in vivo*, probably owing to rapid encapsidation. One cannot exclude the possibility, however, that a part of the RNA population escapes encapsidation and is recognized *in vivo* by these enzymes.

IV. Nucleotide Sequences of the Amino-Acid-Accepting Regions of Viral RNAs

The nucleotide sequence of virtually all tRNA molecules can be drawn in a hydrogen-bonded "cloverleaf" structure. The existence of this structure, further folded into a tertiary structure, has been proved by X-ray diffraction analyses.

The interaction of viral RNAs with tRNA-specific enzymes suggested that a similarity might exist in the nucleotide sequences of the viral RNAs and tRNAs. If such sequence similarities were not observed, one would expect that the tRNA-like structures should at least be able to adopt a cloverleaf-like conformation, thought to be necessary for interaction with various enzymes or factors.

The sequences of the 3′ regions of several plant viral RNAs reacting with tRNA-specific enzymes have been determined (see below). Even ignoring base modifications, sequence identities of more than five nucleotides are usually scarce, and, even if present, they do not always occupy sequentially similar locations in the tRNA-like structures and in the corresponding tRNA. Likewise, nucleotides normally present in precise positions in tRNAs cannot be found in these tRNA-like structures, except for the 3′ C-C-A terminus. Finally, even excluding modifications, in only a few cases can minor resemblances to the cloverleaf model be found.

The fact that the tRNA-like sequences do not contain modified nucleotides leads to the extrapolation that these modifications are not needed for recognition by the tRNA-specific enzymes (55). A direct demonstration of this feature could not previously be obtained because of the impossibility of purifying such unmodified tRNAs from cells.

A. Tymovirus RNAs

The sequence of the 3′-terminal, 112-nucleotide-long fragment obtained after "RNase P" digestion of TYMV RNA (55), extended (37) into the coat protein gene, which is adjacent to the tRNA-like struc-

ture, has been established. More recently (56), the complete nucleotide sequence of the TYMV coat protein mRNA has been elucidated. Figure 1 shows a putative secondary structure of the TYMV
RNA 3' fragment, optimized for base-pairing, which presents certain
features of the cloverleaf model (55, 57). It is worth indicating that the
termination codon (UAA) of the coat-protein gene precedes the tRNA-
like structure. Four other termination codons in phase with the UAA
triplet appear in the tRNA-like region; there are no out-of-phase termination codons and no AUG. A GUG triplet lies close to the 3' end.
Consequently, the tRNA-like structure is in a noncoding region. As far
as its resemblance to tRNAs is concerned, other than the A-C-C-(A)
end, the only significant homologies reside in the anticodon stem and
loop regions, with an appropriate valine anticodon (CAC) centered in
the loop.

When valyl-RNA of TYMV is incubated with an *E. coli* extract, a
valyl-RNA fragment of less than 4 S is also liberated. This fragment of
about 50–60 nucleotides has lost its capacity to be aminoacylated (S.
Joshi, unpublished results), indicating that the region between nucleotides 50–60 and 110 must be important for recognition by tRNA-
specific enzymes.

The sequence of the 58 nucleotides at the 3' end of EMV RNA has
been established (39), but the length of this sequence is insufficient to
attempt to build a cloverleaf structure. Only few sequence identities

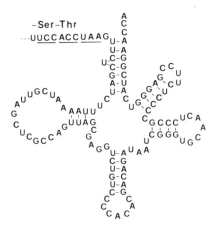

FIG. 1. A possible secondary structure for the turnip yellow mosaic virus. tRNA-like
fragment. The last two codons of the coat protein gene corresponding to serine and
threonine and the adjacent termination codon are underlined. From Silberklang *et al.*
(55).

are found when this sequence is compared to that of yeast tRNA^{Val-1}; there are more similarities between this sequence and the corresponding region in TYMV RNA.

B. Tobamovirus RNAs

Figure 2 shows a possible secondary structure of the 3′ noncoding region of TMV RNA in which the last 125 nucleotides are folded into a possible cloverleaf-type configuration (58, 59). The resemblance to an authentic tRNA cloverleaf is rather poor. For instance, the stems and loops are much longer than in tRNAs, and no histidine anticodon can be appropriately positioned in a loop. Few significant sequence similarities between various parts of the viral RNA molecule and authentic tRNAs specific for histidine can be found: a 13-nucleotide-long sequence identity is found in the viral RNA and in the corresponding tRNAs of *E. coli* and *Salmonella typhimurium*; it comprises the tetranucleotide U-U-C-G characteristic of the TψC loop of tRNAs.

A fragment of 47 nucleotides from the 3′ end of the RNA of the green tomato atypical mosaic virus strain of TMV has been sequenced

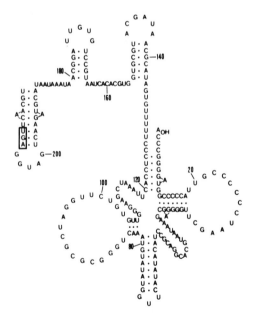

FIG. 2. Possible secondary structure for the TMV RNA 3′-terminal region. The termination codon of the coat protein gene adjacent to this region is boxed. From Guilley *et al.* (59).

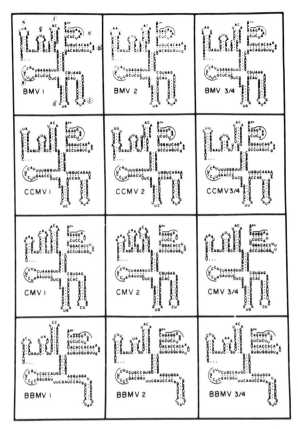

FIG. 3. Proposed secondary structure for the 3'-terminal region of the RNAs of brome mosaic virus (BMV), cowpea chlorotic mottle virus (CCMV), cucumber mosaic virus (CMV), and broadbean mottle virus (BBMV). Hairpins are labeled with lowercase letters as indicated in the BMV RNA 1 structure. The overlined sequences are complementary. From Ahlquist *et al.* (2).

(60). It bears little resemblance with the wild-type strain, although it retains the same sequence identities with tRNA[His] as does TMV RNA.

C. Bromovirus and Cucumovirus RNAs

Extensive structural studies of the 3' noncoding regions of viruses whose RNAs accept tyrosine have been reported (2, 61–64). Figure 3 shows the possible secondary structures proposed for the first 200–260 nucleotides from the 3' end of the various RNA molecules isolated from BMV, BBMV, CCMV, and CMV (2). All these molecules contain at their 3' end a sequence of 7 or 8 nucleotides found in the same position in yeast tyrosine tRNAs. The BMV RNA fragments also contain an 11-nucleotide-long sequence identical to the one positioned in the anticodon loop and stem of yeast tRNA^{Tyr}. However, these two sequences are separated by 27 nucleotides in tRNA^{Tyr} but by only five nucleotides in the BMV RNA fragments.

The fragment of 65 nucleotides from the 3' end of BMV RNA cannot be aminoacylated (61), whereas this is the case for the 161-nucleotide-long fragment (65). Consequently, regions between nucleotides 65 and 161 are necessary for synthetase recognition. Since hairpin "d" (Fig. 3) comprising nucleotides 80 to 100 is missing from BBMV RNA, only a part of the sequence between nucleotides 65 and 161 is needed for recognition (2). Hairpin "c" of BMV and CCMV RNAs contains a tyrosine anticodon. However, BBMV and CMV RNAs lack such an anticodon in this hairpin (Fig. 3).

The comparison of the noncoding sequence of 200–260 nucleotides from the 3' end of the different RNA components of a given virus shows that these sequences have been very highly conserved during evolution even though the coding regions preceding them can be very different (61).

D. Conclusions

The sequence data on the amino-acid-accepting noncoding regions of the RNAs of various plant viruses show very little similarities to tRNAs. Moreover, the secondary structures of these regions do not fit into a classical cloverleaf conformation. Consequently, neither primary structure nor cloverleaf folding appears to be essential for recognition by tRNA-specific enzymes. One must therefore assume that tertiary foldings unrevealed by cloverleaf base-pairs and/or enzyme-induced conformational changes determine the recognition features of these molecules for tRNA-specific enzymes. This leads to rather important general conclusions in the field of protein–nucleic acid interactions, showing how difficult it is to speculate on such interactions on the basis only of primary and secondary structures.

Since, in most of the cases studied, the aminoacylation of plant viral RNA is efficient, the 3'-terminal region in these molecules must be readily accessible for interaction with the tRNA-specific enzymes. In TYMV genomic RNA (66) and in BMV RNA 3 (62) the 5' end of the viral RNA has long sequences complementary to the 3'-terminal regions possessing the tRNA-like structures. Thus, if base-pairing between the 5' and the 3' ends of the viral RNAs exists *de facto*, the tRNA-specific enzymes or the extracts containing these enzymes should somehow destabilize this base-pairing. Furthermore, the fact that an isolated fragment of about 100 nucleotides from the 3′ end of these viral RNAs can interact with tRNA-specific enzymes indicates that distal parts of the RNA molecule do not participate in the formation of the tRNA-like structures recognized by these enzymes.

In multicomponent viruses, the different RNA components coding for different proteins contain a 3′ amino-acid-accepting region whose sequence is very highly conserved. All the sequence data obtained from the 3′ terminal noncoding region from "nonchargeable" viral RNAs indicate that here again this part of the genome is highly conserved. The biological significance of this conservation remains to be elucidated.

V. Possible Role of tRNA-like Structures in Viral RNA Genomes

The significance of the presence of tRNA-like structures in viral RNA genomes is unknown at the present time, and only speculations are possible. Indications have been obtained that the RNAs of BMV (70) and TYMV (our unpublished results) are acylated *in vivo*. However, the fact that in the virion the RNA is not acylated suggests that acylation is only transient, and/or that only a part of the viral RNA population is involved in this process. Conceivably, a part of the viral genome might also be sacrificed, yielding a 3′-terminal fragment that would be aminoacylated, and as such would play a well-defined regulatory function in viral RNA replication or in viral protein synthesis.

In RNA bacteriophages, two protein elongation factors, ET-Tu and EF-Ts, make up part of the RNA replicating system. Since the EF-Tu factor interacts with aminoacyl-tRNAs, it was suggested (18, 67) that the tRNA-like structures in plant viral RNAs might play a regulatory role in replication by interacting with a putative elongation factor that would be a part of the replicase. At the present time, there is no experimental evidence to support or reject this hypothesis.

As mentioned above, the 5′-terminal regions of TYMV genomic RNA (66) and of BMV RNA 3 (62) possess long sequences complementary to the 3′ end of the viral RNA. If such base-pairing occurs, it could modulate the accessibility of ribosomes to the 5′ end of the viral RNA, thereby hindering translation of the genomic RNA in favor of that of the subgenomic RNA. It is also conceivable that, since during replication this sequence complementarity leads to sequence homology near the 3′ end of both "+" and "−" strands of the viral RNA, this sequence could compose the recognition site for the replicase or for one of its subunits.

At the translational level, an aminoacylated tRNA-like fragment could play a role in the regulation of viral or cellular protein synthesis by blocking the elongation step. Most of the tRNA-like structures have no proper anticodon loop and stem nor the corresponding anticodon. It is therefore not conceivable that the aminoacylated structure can be appropriately positioned on the A site of the ribosome. However, as in the case of puromycin, an incomplete positioning might be sufficient for the transfer of the growing polypeptide chain onto the aminoacyl-tRNA-like structure, thereby leading to the release of the polypeptide. If this were the case, one would expect such a mechanism to be specific for one protein or for a set of proteins, and not to be general; it is not easy to visualize how such a specificity could be established.

tRNA-like structures may play a regulatory role at other levels than in replication or translation. Indeed, tRNAs are known to be pleiotropic; they are involved in processes such as the N-terminal addition of an amino acid to preformed polypeptide chains, the initiation of reverse transcription in oncornaviruses (68), the regulation of the histidine operon in *S. typhimurium*, and the peptide synthesis of bacterial cell walls. One can therefore envisage the possibility that, in virus-infected cells, tRNA-like structures could act at a level distant from replication or translation but connected metabolically with one of these steps. Systematic studies of different metabolic pathways in virus-infected cells might lead to the discovery of the reactions in which such structures are involved.

ACKNOWLEDGMENTS

This work was supported in part by a grant from the Ecole Pratique des Hautes Etudes and in part by a grant from the Action Thématique Programmée: Phytopathologie (No. 3608). The article was written while S. J. was holder of an EMBO Long Term Fellowship.

REFERENCES

1. U. Z. Littauer and H. Soreq, this volume.
2. P. Ahlquist, R. Dasgupta, and P. Kaesberg, *Cell* **23**, 183 (1981).
3. K. Kamen, *Nature* **221**, 321 (1969).
4. U. Rensing and J. T. August, *Nature* **224**, 853 (1969).
5. A. Steinschneider and H. Fraenkel-Conrat, *Bchem* **5**, 2735 (1966).
6. R. Salomon, I. Sela, H. Soreq, D. Giveon, and U. Z. Littauer, *Virology* **71**, 74 (1976).
7. R. Salomon, M. Bar-Joseph, H. Soreq, I. Gross, and U. Z. Littauer, *Virology* **90**, 288 (1978).
8. R. J. Kohl and T. C. Hall, *PNAS* **74**, 2682 (1977).
9. M. Pinck, P. Yot, F. Chapeville, and H. Duranton, *Nature* **226**, 954 (1970).
10. P. Yot, M. Pinck, A. L. Haenni, H. M. Duranton, and F. Chapeville, *PNAS* **67**, 1345 (1970).

11. T. C. Hall, *Int. Rev. Cytol.* **60**, 1 (1979).
12. A. L. Haenni and F. Chapeville, *in* "tRNA: Biological Aspects" (D. Söll *et al.*, eds.), p. 539. Cold Spring Harbor Laboratory, Cold Spring Harbor, New York, 1980.
13. R. J. Kohl and T. C. Hall, *J. Gen. Virol.* **25**, 257 (1974).
14. M. Pinck, S. K. Chan, M. Génevaux, L. Hirth, and H. Duranton, *Biochimie* **54**, 1093 (1972).
15. M. Pinck and T. C. Hall, *Virology* **88**, 281 (1978).
16. L. Pinck, M. Génevaux, J. P. Bouley, and M. Pinck, *Virology* **63**, 589 (1975).
17. B. Öberg and L. Philipson, *BBRC* **48**, 927 (1972).
18. S. Litvak, A. Tarrago, L. Tarrago-Litvak, and J. E. Allende, *Nature NB* **241**, 88 (1973).
19. E. Carriquiry and S. Litvak, *FEBS Lett.* **38**, 287 (1974).
20. R. N. Beachy, M. Zaitlin, G. Bruening, and H. W. Israel, *Virology* **73**, 498 (1976).
21. T. C. Hall, D. S. Shih, and P. Kaesberg, *BJ* **129**, 969 (1972).
22. R. Salomon and U. Z. Littauer, *Nature* **249**, 32 (1974).
23. I. J. D. Lindley and N. Stebbing, *J. Gen. Virol.* **34**, 177 (1977).
24. R. Giégé, J. P. Briand, R. Mengual, J. P. Ebel, and L. Hirth, *EJB* **84**, 251 (1978).
25. P. Yot, Ph.D. Thesis, University of Paris 7 (1970).
26. S. Joshi, A. L. Haenni, E. Hubert, G. Huez, and G. Marbaix, *Nature* **275**, 339 (1978).
27. A. Prochiantz and A. L. Haenni, *Nature NB* **241**, 168 (1973).
28. D. S. Shih, P. Kaesberg, and T. C. Hall, *Nature* **249**, 353 (1974).
29. P. Perez-Bercoff and M. Gander, *Virology* **80**, 426 (1977).
30. U. Z. Littauer, H. Soreq, and P. Cornelis, *Enzyme Regul. Mech. Action Proc. FEBS Meet.* **60**, 233 (1960).
31. J. S. Emtage, N. H. Carey, and N. Stebbing, *EJB* **69**, 69 (1976).
32. T. C. Hall, R. K. Wepprich, J. W. Davies, L. G. Weathers, and J. S. Semancik, *Virology* **61**, 486 (1974).
33. A. Prochiantz, C. Bénicourt, D. Carré, and A. L. Haenni, *EJB* **52**, 17 (1975).
34. N. K. Chatterjee, H. L. Bachrach, and J. Polatnick, *Virology* **69**, 369 (1976).
35. S. Litvak, D. Carré, and F. Chapeville, *FEBS Lett.* **11**, 316 (1970).
36. S. Litvak, L. Tarrago-Litvak, and F. Chapeville, *J. Virol.* **11**, 238 (1973).
37. J. P. Briand, G. Jonard, H. Guilley, K. Richards, and L. Hirth, *EJB* **72**, 453 (1977).
38. M. Génevaux, M. Pinck, and H. M. Duranton, *Ann. Microbiol. (Paris)* **127A**, 47 (1976).
39. J. P. Briand, K. E. Richards, J. P. Bouley, J. Witz, and L. Hirth, *PNAS* **73**, 737 (1976).
40. M. Génevaux, Ph.D. thesis, University of Strasbourg, 1974.
41. C. Bénicourt and A. L. Haenni, *FEBS Lett.* **45**, 228 (1974).
42. P. Busto, E. Carriquiri, L. Tarrago-Litvak, M. Castroviejo, and S. Litvak, *Ann. Microbiol. (Paris)* **127A**, 39 (1976).
43. K. Marcu and B. Dudock, *BBRC* **62**, 798 (1975).
44. J. Lesiewicz and B. Dudock, *BBA* **520**, 411 (1978).
45. A. L. Haenni, C. Bénicourt, S. Teixeira, A. Prochiantz, and F. Chapeville, *FEBS Proc. Meet.* **39**, 121 (1975).
46. S. Altman and J. D. Smith, *Nature NB* **233**, 35 (1971).
47. A. L. Haenni, A. Prochiantz, and P. Yot, *Lipmann Symp. Energy, Regul. Biosynth. Mol. Biol.*, p. 264 (1974).
48. M. Bastin and T. C. Hall, *J. Virol.* **20**, 117 (1976).
49. F. Cuzin, N. Kretchmer, R. E. Greenberg, R. Hurwitz, and F. Chapeville, *PNAS* **58**, 2079 (1967).
50. F. Chapeville, P. Yot, and D. Paulin, *CSHSQB* **34**, 493 (1969).
51. H. Kössel and U. L. RajBhandary, *JMB* **35**, 539 (1968).

52. A. L. Haenni, A. Prochiantz, O. Bernard, and F. Chapeville, *Nature NB* **241**, 166 (1973).
53. J. M. Chen and T. C. Hall, *Bchem* **12**, 4570 (1973).
54. T. C. Hall, M. Pinck, Y. Ma, H. M. Duranton, and T. L. German, *Virology* **97**, 354 (1979).
54a. A. A. Krayevsky and M. K. Kukhanova, *This Series*, Vol. 23, p. 2 (1979).
55. M. Silberklang, A. Prochiantz, A. L. Haenni, and U. L. RajBhandary, *EJB* **72**, 465 (1977).
56. H. Guilley and J. P. Briand, *Cell* **15**, 113 (1978).
57. A. Prochiantz, Ph.D. thesis, University of Paris 7 (1976).
58. H. Guilley, G. Jonard, and L. Hirth, *PNAS* **72**, 864 (1975).
59. H. Guilley, G. Jonard, B. Kukla, and K. E. Richards, *NARes* **6**, 1287 (1979).
60. D. Lamy, G. Jonard, H. Guilley, and L. Hirth, *FEBS Lett.* **60**, 202 (1975).
61. R. Dasgupta and P. Kaesberg, *PNAS* **74**, 4900 (1977).
62. R. Dasgupta, P. Ahlquist, and P. Kaesberg, *Virology* **104**, 339 (1980).
63. R. H. Symons, *NARes* **7**, 825 (1979).
64. M. R. Gunn and R. H. Symons, *FEBS Lett.* **115**, 77 (1980).
65. M. Bastin, R. Dasgupta, T. C. Hall, and P. Kaesberg, *JMB* **103**, 737 (1976).
66. J. P. Briand, G. Keith, and H. Guilley, *PNAS* **75**, 3168 (1978).
67. T. C. Hall and R. K. Wepprich, *Ann. Microbiol. (Paris)* **127A**, 143 (1976).
68. L. C. Waters and B. C. Mullin, This Series, Vol. 20, 131 (1977).
69. T. Meshi, T. Ohno, H. Iba, and Y. Okada, *Mol. Gen. Genet.*, in press (1981).
70. L. S. Loesch-Fries, P. A. Kiberstis, and T. C. Hall, Fifth International Congress of Virology, Strasbourg, W20/04 (1981).
71. A. A. Agranovsky, V. V. Dolja, V. G. Gorbulev, Y. V. Kozlov, and J. G. Atabekov, *Virology* **113**, 174 (1981).

ADDENDUM

A. The sequence of over 1000 nucleotides from the 3' end of C_cTMV RNA has recently been determined (69). The sequence of the tRNA-like region of the RNA reveals strong (55%) identity with the corresponding region in TYMV RNA; only the last 7 nucleotides proximal to the 3' end are common to C_cTMV and TMV vulgare RNAs.

B. Interestingly, all 4 BMV RNAs can be tyrosylated *in vivo* (70) upon infection of barley protoplasts with the viral RNA.

C. Barley stripe mosaic virus (BSMV), representative of this group of viruses, has a functionally divided genome whose RNA components are numbered from 1 to 4 (1.40–1.50, 1.17–1.24, 1.04–1.20, and 0.93–1.05 × 10^6 daltons, respectively). The genome presents unusual variability, since the number of RNA components varies from 2 to 4 depending on the strain, and since, in a given four-component strain, the number of genetic components can be changed by the loss of RNA 3 and/or RNA 4 by transferring of the virus at large dilutions. It has recently been shown, using a wheat germ extract, that all the RNA components of BSMV strains harbor either two or three components, and that the total RNA of a four-component strain can be tyrosylated at their 3' ends (71). Surprisingly, the tRNA-like structure in the viral RNA is generally preceded by a poly(A) stretch.

Mechanism of Interferon Action: Progress toward Its Understanding

GANES C. SEN

*Memorial Sloan-Kettering Cancer
    Center
New York, New York*

105

Progress in Nucleic Acid Research
and Molecular Biology, Vol. 27

I. Introduction[1]

A. The Interferon System

Interferons were discovered by Isaacs and Lindenmann in 1957
(1), who observed that, upon exposure to heat-inactivated influenza
virus, chicken chorioallantoic membranes would release a substance
in the surrounding fluid that, when added to the culture medium of
other cells, inhibited the replication of a variety of viruses in these
cells. Since it interfered with virus replication, they named the substance "interferon." Interferons were later characterized as glycoproteins.

To this day, a protein is identified as an interferon mainly by virtue
of its broad antiviral activity. However, studies on the action of interferons over the last 20 years reveal that interferons have numerous other
biological activities besides their antiviral actions. Probably the "interferon system," constituting the processes of interferon synthesis and
interferon action, is operative in all vertebrates, serving as the first line
of defense against natural viral infections. Moreover, interferons probably play an important role in the immune system. The discovery that
interferons have potent antitumor effects in animals has created hope
that they may be of therapeutic use, not only against viral infections,
but also against various forms of cancer.

Interferons are synthesized in vertebrate cells in response to various inducers. They are secreted out of the cells, interact with other
cells, and thereby render them incapable of supporting virus replication. For historical reasons, most of the studies on interferons have
focused on their antiviral actions, and they are assayed by virtue of
their antiviral activities. Since interferons are extremely potent, the
assays are very sensitive. In cell culture, as low as 3×10^{-14} M interferon may impair virus replication. Many effects of interferon on cellular metabolism are reversible. These effects are slowly dissipated once
the interferon is removed. In general, interferons are host-specific;
i.e., they are the most active in cells of the species in which they were
synthesized.

Studies on the interferon system can be classified broadly into two
groups: studies on interferon biosynthesis, and studies on interferon
actions. The main focus of this article is on some aspects of the latter.

[1] Abbreviations used: cDNA, complementary DNA; ssRNA, single-stranded RNA;
dsRNA, double-stranded RNA; EAT, Ehrlich ascites tumor; VSV, vesicular stomatitis
virus; EMCV, encephalomyocarditis virus; SV40, simian virus 40; MSV, murine sarcoma
virus; MLV, murine leukemia virus; MuMTV, murine mammary tumor virus.

Specifically, I discuss what we know about the mechanism of the antiviral action of interferons and the biochemical changes brought about by interferon treatment of cells not infected with viruses. Friedman (2), Baglioni (3), Revel (4), Williams and Kerr (5), and Lengyel *et al.* (6), among others, have reviewed portions of this topic in the recent past. I also discuss briefly some other aspects of the interferon system and refer to existing review articles on those topics. The books by Finter (7) and Stewart (8) are recommended for general reading.

B. Interferon Biosynthesis

Interferons are a family of glycoproteins with apparent molecular weights of about 15,000 to 35,000, all characterized by their antiviral properties. One organism or even a single cell may produce several types of interferon (9). At least three types of human interferons have been described; the type synthesized depends on the nature of both the inducer and the producing cell (10). By techniques of somatic cell genetics, human interferon genes on three different chromosomes have been identified (11, 12). Studies on interferon gene cloning and sequencing indicate a probability that there are many nonidentical genes for each type of interferon (13).

Most of the studies on interferon biosynthesis have been carried out with cells in tissue culture. Under normal growth conditions, most cells do not make interferon. However, spontaneous interferon production in cells from the hemopoietic system has been described (14). When cells not producing interferons (or producing them at a very low level) are treated with certain agents ("interferon inducers"), the interferon biosynthetic pathways are activated. A large number of natural or synthetic substances induce interferon synthesis. These include viruses, other microorganisms, bacterial and fungal products, natural and synthetic polynucleotides, various substances of low molecular weight, and mitogens (8). The discovery of interferons resulted from using influenza virus as inducer. It has since been shown that practically all viruses can induce interferon under appropriate conditions. However, these conditions vary widely. Most RNA viruses, either single- or double-stranded, are efficient interferon inducers, and most *in vitro* studies have utilized either myxoviruses or arboviruses. The important discovery that double-stranded RNAs from a wide variety of sources are potent interferon inducers opened up a search for the ideal interferon inducer that took the form of testing various synthetic double-stranded polynucleotides (dsRNA). It has been postulated that induction of interferon synthesis by dsRNA and by virus infection follow a common pathway. A case can be made for the hypothesis that virus infection causes the synthesis of dsRNA as a side product or as an intermediate of the virus life cycle, and that this intracellular dsRNA is the active trigger for the induction of interferon synthesis (15).

Induction of interferon synthesis by any inducer needs active gene expression. For this reason, interferon biosynthesis is inhibited by treatment of cells with actinomycin D (16) or by enucleation of the cells (17) before induction. Increased amounts of interferon mRNAs are synthesized in the nuclei of induced cells. The newly synthesized interferon mRNAs travel to the cytoplasm and are translated on membrane-bound polysomes (18). The mature interferon molecules are secreted from the cells after various posttranslational modifications, including removal of a signal peptide and glycosylation. Interferon mRNAs can be isolated from cells induced for interferon synthesis, and can be translated into interferons in cells from other organisms. Both mouse and human interferon mRNAs have been introduced into heterologous cells under proper conditions, and the corresponding interferons have been synthesized in these cells. Since interferons are relatively species-specific, it was possible to establish that the newly synthesized interferons are coded for by the incoming heterologous mRNA, but not by mRNAs transcribed from the recipient cell-genome. Interferon mRNAs can also be translated in cell-free protein-synthesizing systems or in frog oocytes (reviewed, in 19).

The synthesis of interferons in the induced cells is a highly regulated phenomenon. In many cell systems, treatment of cells with a low level of interferons before induction generally enhances subsequent interferon production, a phenomenon called "priming" (20). The molecular mechanism of priming is unknown. There is correlation between the sensitivity of a particular cell line to the antiviral action of interferon and its ability to become primed (21). An opposite phenomenon, called "blocking", is observed in interferon-producing cells (22). In these cells, which have been producing interferon, or in cells treated in advance with a high concentration of crude interferon, the continued presence of an inducer does not lead to continued production of interferons. Human fibroblasts, exposed to poly(I) · poly(C), synthesize interferon for 3–4 hours; the synthesis then ceases. The cause of this cessation of interferon synthesis is not clear. Treatment of mouse cells with pure mouse interferons does not inhibit subsequent poly(I) · poly(C)-induced interferon synthesis in these cells (23). Therefore, it seems that interferon itself does not exert a negative feedback on its own biosynthesis; rather it is the synthesis of some other molecules triggered by the induction process that shuts off interferon synthesis. This substance was presumably present in the crude interferon preparations that caused the blocking effects.

The block to interferon synthesis operates at a posttranscriptional level by selectively inactivating interferon mRNA molecules. The $(2'-5')A_n$ system (see Section VII,C) does not seem to be involved in this shutoff (23a). The causative agent is species-specific. Isolated human or hamster interferon mRNA artificially introduced into human or hamster cells is translated into the respective species of interferon; further, human interferon mRNA is translated in normal human and hamster cells and in "blocked" hamster cells, but not in "blocked" human cells (24). Conversely, hamster interferon mRNA is translated in normal human, normal hamster, and "blocked" human cells, but not in "blocked" hamster cells. [The "blocked" cells were prepared by inducing interferon production with poly(I) · poly(C) and waiting for 3–4 hours, at which time production was shut off (24).]

The speculation that a repressor of interferon synthesis accumulates in the induced cell gets further support from the "superinduction" phenomenon (25). When applied at suitable intervals and dosages after the onset of induction, various inhibitors of protein and RNA synthesis, alone or in combination, can increase interferon production induced by poly(I) · poly(C). These inhibitors presumably inhibit synthesis of the repressor system that incapacitates the interferon mRNAs. This allows continued translation of interferons from the pool of interferon mRNAs already accumulated in the induced cells. There appears to be an enhanced level of interferon mRNA in the superinduced cells as compared to the ordinary induced cells, which indicates that the repressor system causes irreversible inactivation of the interferon mRNA molecules (26, 27). It is curious that the superinduction phenomenon has not been observed in virus-induced interferon biosynthesis.

C. Double-Stranded RNA and the Interferon System

Double-stranded RNAs play a central role in the interferon system. Added to the cell culture medium, they can induce interferon synthesis. It has been postulated, with some experimental support, that induction of interferon synthesis by viral infection is also mediated through double-stranded RNA (15). At the other end of the spectrum, some interferon-treated cells are highly sensitive to the cytopathic effects of dsRNA (28). In interferon-treated cells, a number of enzymes whose action depends on the presence of dsRNA are synthesized, which implies a role for dsRNA in the mechanism of action of interferons.

Quantitatively, dsRNA is not a major constituent of the eukaryotic cell. Although the demonstration of its presence in the nuclei of HeLa, ascites, human lymphocytes, and Vero and mosquito cells has been claimed, the experimental evidence in most of these cases is not compelling (29). Usually, dsRNA can be extracted from these cells upon deproteinization. However, these complementary RNA strands may not exist in a double-stranded form *in vivo*. Poly(A)-containing RNAs isolated from the nuclei or cytoplasm of Chinese hamster ovary cells are hydrogen-bonded to RNAs 90–100 nucleotides long (30). Whether they remain so hydrogen-bonded *in vivo* is yet to be shown.

A whole class of animal viruses has dsRNA as its genetic material, and dsRNA has been shown to be produced as an intermediate in the life cycles of other viruses. Partially double-stranded RNA molecules about 18 S in size were first isolated from poliovirus-infected HeLa cells (31). Formation of partially double-stranded replicative intermediates seems to be a general characteristic of the life cycle of RNA viruses. The formation of viral dsRNA in EMC-infected cells has been demonstrated by cross-linking complementary strands of EMC RNA in intact cells with a psoralen derivative (31a). Complementary RNA molecules are also present in cells infected with such DNA viruses as vaccinia virus and adenovirus (32, 33).

In tissue-culture cells, the most notable biological effect of dsRNA is the induction of interferon synthesis. It is claimed (34) that dsRNA has inhibitory effects on cellular protein synthesis in whole cells. L cells treated with interferon are more susceptible to the cytotoxic effects of poly(I) · poly(C) than are untreated cells (28). This cytotoxic effect is preceded by morphological changes in mitochondria, nuclei, and endoplasmic reticulum (35). An interferon-resistant subline of L cells is 20 times less sensitive to the toxic effects of dsRNA (35).

dsRNA inhibits protein synthesis in cell-free systems from a variety of cell lines. However, the extent of inhibition varies over a wide range. Two of the most well-studied systems where dsRNA inhibits protein synthesis very strongly are rabbit reticulocyte lysates and cell-free extracts made from interferon-treated cells. As discussed in detail in Section VII, recent studies reveal a remarkable similarity between these two systems regarding the molecular mechanism of dsRNA-mediated inhibition of protein synthesis. It was first demonstrated in 1971 that cytoplasmic extracts of poliovirus-infected HeLa cells contain a substance that inhibits initiation of protein synthesis *in vitro* in rabbit reticulocyte lysates (36). This substance was purified and identified as poliovirus dsRNA. Similar results were obtained from cells infected with Sindbis virus. Synthetic dsRNAs and dsRNAs isolated from microbial sources have similar effects. Surprisingly, dsRNA inhibits peptide chain initiation only at a very low concentration (1–100 ng/ml). The nature of the inhibition of peptide chain initiation in rabbit reticulocyte lysate under several other conditions (absence of hemin, presence of oxidized glutathione, application of high pressure, etc.) is very similar to the dsRNA effect. Ochoa and deHaro (37) have reviewed this field.

The structural requirements of the dsRNA needed for its action as an interferon-inducer and its action as an inhibitor of protein synthesis in cell-free systems have been compared (38, 39). Using rabbit reticulocyte lysates as the assay system for protein synthesis inhibition, it appears that natural dsRNAs are extremely potent inhibitors of protein synthesis (38). So is the synthetic alternating copolymer poly(A-U). However, homopolynucleotides such as poly(A) · poly(U), poly(I) · poly(C), poly(I) · poly(br^{5}C), and poly(I) · poly(s^{2}C) are poor inhibitors of protein synthesis. In contrast, the latter synthetic double-stranded polynucleotides are much better interferon inducers, compared to the natural dsRNAs, in rabbit kidney cells. The data (38) indicate that although in some aspects, e.g., molecular size, the structural requirements of dsRNA for the two effects are similar, the fine structural requirements of dsRNA for optimum effect in the two actions are quite different.

Using EMCV RNA translation in extracts made from interferon-treated L cells as the assay of inhibition of protein synthesis by dsRNA, it was found that extracts from interferon-treated cells were 10,000 times more sensitive to the action of poly(I) · poly(C) than extracts from control cells (39). But extracts from control and interferon cells were equally sensitive to natural dsRNAs, such as *Penicillium chrysogenum* dsRNA at the same concentration as the poly(I) · poly(C). Of 46 different synthetic dsRNA tested, only 6 could induce differential inhibition of protein synthesis in extracts of treated cells. There were also differences observed in structural requirements of a dsRNA for being a good inhibitor of protein synthesis and for being a good inducer of interferon synthesis. Poly(I) · poly(br^{5}C), a potent inducer of interferon, was completely inactive as an inhibitor of protein synthesis. On the other hand, three triple-helical nucleic acids were potent inhibitors of protein synthesis in the cell-free system, but were inactive as inducers of interferons in L cells (39).

II. Interferon Proteins and Interferon Genes

At least three types of human interferons, as classified by the lack of immune cross-reactivity and other properties, have been identified: interferon$_{Le}$ (leukocyte interferon, or α interferon), interferon$_F$ (fibroblast interferon or β interferon), and immune interferon (type II interferon, or γ interferon) (10). Similarly, more than one type of interferon has been identified in the mouse system. Within one type, there are many molecular species varying in molecular weights. The latter heterogeneity could be due to nonuniform posttranslational proteolytic cleavage and glycosylation or to genuine differences in amino acid sequences.

In spite of their enormously high biological activity and unusual stability to acid pH and to treatment with dodecyl sulfate (8), the purification of interferons has been difficult, mainly because the quantity of interferons produced by any cell is very low. Only recently mouse (40, 41) and human (42–44) interferons have been purified to apparent homogeneity. Even "pure" interferons have a range of molecular weights due to nonuniform glycosylations. The sugars are most likely not needed for the action of interferons.

New developments in automated amino-acid-sequence analysis techniques have made possible the determination of partial amino-acid sequences from the amino terminal on picomole quantities of pure interferons (45–47), but even these techniques have been outpaced by modern fast DNA sequencing techniques coupled with recombinant DNA technology.

In the last 2 years, several groups have cloned interferon cDNAs, isolated interferon genes, determined their structures, and produced relatively large quantities of interferon in *Escherichia coli* through the use of suitable recombinant DNA techniques (48–52). From the complete nucleotide sequences of the cDNA inserts (13, 49, 51), the complete amino-acid sequences of human fibroblast and leukocyte interferons could be predicted. The complete sequence of human fibroblast interferon cDNA was also obtained using a novel technique of priming the cDNA synthesis with a synthetic oligonucleotide complementary to the region of interferon mRNA coding for the amino-terminal amino acids (52). The sequence obtained agrees with the complete sequence obtained by the others (49, 51).

Interferon gene and cDNA sequencing data provide the sequence of the putative signal peptide at the amino terminal of the primary translation product of the interferon mRNAs. In the case of fibroblast interferon, the length of the signal peptide is 21 amino acids, and in the case of one leukocyte interferon, it is 23 amino acids (or, less likely, 15). Only at positions 1, 7, and 11 do the two signal peptides have the same amino acids. The DNA sequencing data revealed that human fibroblast interferon mRNA contains about 200 untranslated nucleotides at the 3′ end and an undetermined number of nucleotides at the 5′ end. For one human leukocyte interferon mRNA, there are at

TABLE I
PARTIAL AMINO-ACID SEQUENCES OF DIFFERENT SPECIES OF INTERFERONS[a]

Position from amino terminal	Mouse A and B[b]	Human fibro-blast[c]	Mouse C[d]	Human lympho-blastoid[b]	Human leukocyte[d]
1	Ile	Met	Ala	Ser	Cys
2	Asn	Ser	Asp —— Asp —— Asp		
3	Tyr —— Tyr		Leu —— Leu —— Leu		
4	Lys	Asn	Pro —— Pro —— Pro		
5	Gln	Leu	Gln —— Gln		Glu
6	Leu —— Leu		Thr —— Thr —— Thr		
7	Gln	Gly	Tyr	His —— His	
8	Leu	Phe	Asn	Ser —— Ser	
9	Gln	Leu	Leu —— Leu —— Leu		
10	Glu	Gln	Gly —— Gly		Asp
11	Arg —— Arg		Asn —— Asn —— Asn		
12	Thr	Ser	Lys	Arg —— Arg	
13	Asn	Ser	Gly	Arg —— Arg	
14	Ile	Asn	Ala —— Ala		Thr
15	Arg	Phe	Leu —— Leu —— Leu		
16	Lys	Gln	Lys	Ile	Met
17	?	Cys	Val	Leu —— Leu	
18	Gln —— Gln		Leu —— Leu —— Leu		
19	Glu	Lys	Ala —— Ala —— Ala		
20	Leu —— Leu		Gln —— Gln —— Gln		
21	Leu —— Leu				Met
22	Glu	Trp			Ser
23	Gln —— Gln				Arg
24	Leu —— Leu				Ile

[a] Amino-acid sequence homologies are emphasized by horizontal lines.
[b] Sequence is determined by direct amino-acid sequencing.
[c] Complete sequence is determined by DNA sequencing; sequence up to position 13 is also determined by direct amino-acid sequencing.
[d] Complete sequence is determined by DNA sequencing.

least 56 nucleotides at the 5' end, and 242 nucleotides at the 3' end, that are not translated.

Partial amino-acid sequences of various types of interferons are compared in Table I. Mouse interferon A and B have identical sequences up to the first 24 amino acids from the amino terminal (position 17 is unidentified). Mouse interferon C has a completely different partial sequence; out of the first 20 amino acids, only positions 5 and 16 have the same amino acids in A, B, and C. There is considerable sequence homology between mouse A and B and human fibroblast interferons. Out of the first 24 positions, 8 are the same. It is more striking to compare the sequences of type C and human lymphoblastoid (or leukocyte) interferons. Out of the first 20 positions, 13 are the same. These similarities indicate that the interferon genes have been reasonably conserved in evolution.

Although very similar, human lymphoblastoid and human leukocyte interferons are the products of two different genes. Out of the first 20 amino acids, 5 are different for the two species. Human fibroblast interferon is distinctly different from both lymphoblastoid and leukocyte interferons. Out of the first 24 positions, only one amino acid at position 9 is common among them. Comparison of the complete coding sequences of two cloned cDNAs of leukocyte and fibroblast interferons indicated homologies of 45% at the nucleotide level and 29% at the amino-acid level. However, the longest stretch of the same nucleotide sequence is only 13 nucleotides, indicating that the two mRNAs coding for the two kinds of interferons are not the products of the same gene that are only spliced differently. When the derived amino-acid sequences of the two kinds of interferons are compared, three or four main domains of homology can be distinctly discerned. Those domains may be responsible for important common functions of the two proteins. It was concluded (53) that the two genes coding for these two subspecies of human fibroblast and leukocyte interferons were derived from a common ancestor.

Interferon genes are members of multigene families. There are at least ten α interferon genes and more than one human β interferon gene (48, 51, 53a). At least eight α interferon genes and one β interferon gene are located on human chromosome 9 (53b). Some of these genes are also closely linked (53c,d). Two α-interferon genes are separated by 12,000 nucleotides, and two others are only 5000 nucleotides apart. Different α-interferon genes have 85–95% sequence homology. All the interferon genes whose structures have been determined so far lack any introns either in the coding or in the noncoding regions.

Large quantities of interferons have been produced in *E. coli* containing plasmids or λ vectors with interferon cDNA inserts to which bacterial transcription promoter signals have been added at suitable positions. Interferons produced by *E. coli* are not glycosylated, and they often contain the signal peptides that are cleaved during secretion of interferons by eukaryotic cells. Nonetheless, interferons produced in bacteria are biologically active and mimic natural interferons in all biological functions tested so far (53e, 53f). Since various activities are exhibited by a cloned protein species, this also establishes the fact that all these activities are due to one single species of interferon.

Different α interferons have different degrees of species specificity. Human α-1 interferon is 10–20 times more active on bovine cells than on human cells, whereas α-2 interferon is only half as active on bovine cells as on human cells. Hybrid interferon molecules containing the NH_2-terminal half of α-1 and carboxy terminal half of α-2, or vice versa, have been manufactured in *E. coli*. These hybrid molecules have activity spectra different from that of either parent (53g).

III. Various Activities of Interferons

Interferon was discovered through its antiviral effect. This effect is the one aspect that has been studied the most, and is understood to a certain degree. However, interferon has a multitude of other effects. For example, it slows cell multiplication, increases cell size and volume, affects subcellular microfilament organization and fibronectin distribution (54); it changes cell motility and the electrophoretic mobility of the cells; it enhances the expression of certain surface antigens; it has significant effects on the immune system, and it has antitumor activities (8). Interferons inhibit mitogen-induced DNA synthesis in lymphocytes (54a) and epidermal growth-factor-induced DNA synthesis in quiescent fibroblasts (54b). They also inhibit cellular differentiation *in vitro* (54c,d) and alter the compositions of cellular phospholipids (54e). These effects are less dramatic than the antiviral effects but may have profound biological significance nonetheless. A detailed discussion of these effects is beyond the scope of this review, but the concept that interferon should be looked at as a hormone having numerous effects in a multicellular higher organism, not as a convenient antiviral chemical, is worth emphasizing.

The effects of interferons on the immune system were reviewed in 1980 (55). The immunosuppressive activities of interferons and the enhanced recruitment of natural killer cells in response to interferons are subjects of intensive research at the present moment. The discovery of the antitumor activities of interferon has created great expectations for possible clinical use of interferon as an antineoplastic drug (56). The initial limited clinical trials are promising, and research efforts in this direction have gained such momentum that it is already overshadowing research on the antiviral effects of interferon.

Some of the non-antiviral effects of interferons require interferons at a much higher dose than what is needed for its antiviral effects. This is one of the reasons why there was a lingering suspicion that the nonantiviral effects arose from impurities present in partially purified interferon preparations. However, once interferons were purified to homogeneity, and their antiviral effects were used for biological assays, it was quickly established that almost all of the non-antiviral activities tested came from interferon itself (23). The recognition of interferons as hormone-like biological agents with pleiotropic effects on target cells also led to the realization that probably no unique mechanism of interferon actions exists. The manifestations of different effects may be brought about by independent or partially overlapping pathways of interferon actions. This notion is consonant with the discovery of a variety of biochemical changes that ensue upon treating cells with interferon. Historically, all these biochemical changes were observed in interferon-treated cells and in extracts made from interferon-treated cells in the course of elucidating the mechanisms of the antiviral actions of interferons. However, many of these changes may not contribute at all to this end, but may be primarily responsible for some non-antiviral effects.

IV. Establishment of the Antiviral State

Interferons inhibit viral replication by inducing the synthesis of "antiviral substances" in cells that have come in contact with interferons. The antiviral state is reversible, and it decays after the interferons have been removed. The nature of the interactions between interferons and cells is poorly understood. Though there has been no direct demonstration as yet, it is generally believed that there are specific receptors for interferons on cell surfaces. It has been claimed (57) that, for interferons to be active, they have to interact with specific receptors on the external side of the cell membrane. Thus, cells synthesizing interferon will not be in an antiviral state unless interferon is allowed to be secreted so that it can interact with the outside of the cell membrane. Whether interferons act only on the cell surface or are also internalized is an open question. With the availability of pure radiolabeled interferons, answers to the above questions should be forthcoming shortly.

Interferons probably first bind to gangliosides on the cell membrane (58). However, the specificity of binding is not exerted through gangliosides, as mouse interferon binds to gangliosides on human cells but does not induce the antiviral effects. The specificity of interferon binding may be controlled through some glycoproteins on the cell surface that may constitute the interferon receptors (59). After exposure of the cells to interferons, it takes a few hours before the antiviral state develops (60). Active metabolic processes are needed for establishment of the antiviral state, as cells kept at 4° and treated with interferon do not develop the antiviral state unless they are brought back to 37°. Both RNA synthesis and protein synthesis are needed after interferon treatment to develop the antiviral state. These conclusions were first drawn by using the RNA synthesis inhibitor actinomycin D (61) and the protein synthesis inhibitor cycloheximide (62). Further support came from studies (using enucleated cells) showing that the presence of an active nucleus is needed for the establishment, but not the maintenance, of the antiviral state (63). How many genetic loci are involved in the establishment and regulation of the antiviral state is not known. In human cells, sensitivity to interferon is dependent on genes located on chromosome 21 (64). Mouse cells are not sensitive to human interferons, but a human–mouse somatic cell hybrid in which chromosome 21 is the only detectable human genetic material is sensitive to human interferons (65). Antibodies prepared in mice against such hybrid cells containing chromosome 21 can block interferon actions on human cells (66). This indicates that genes on chromosome 21 code for cell-surface components specifically needed for interferon action. Those components may be the interferon receptors. It now appears that mouse chromosome 16 carries genes for sensitivity to mouse interferon action (67).

Blalock and Baron (68) believe that there is an intermediate step between the action of interferon on the cell surface and the synthesis of the components of the antiviral state. According to them, in this step secondary molecules (of unknown molecular nature) participate. They provided interesting experimental evidence in support of this notion. They found that while human amnion or baby hamster kidney cells are not sensitive to mouse interferons by themselves, cocultivation of either of these cells with sensitive mouse L cells in the presence of mouse interferon results in a marked inhibition of virus replication in the nonmurine cells. Presumably this is achieved through the "transfer of viral resistance" from the mouse cells to the others. Cell-to-cell contact is needed for this transfer, and anti-human interferon present in the medium cannot prevent this transfer. There is also some evidence in support of the transferred molecules not being the membrane receptors of interferon, or the mRNA coding for antiviral proteins, or the antiviral proteins themselves (69). These intriguing results remain to be confirmed by other investigators.

V. Antiviral Effects as Studied with Intact Virus-Infected Cells

Interferon treatment of cells makes them incapable of supporting the replication of a variety of viruses whose life cycles are distinctly different. However, the degree of inhibition of virus replication varies from virus to virus. The dose of interferon and the multiplicity of infection are also important parameters in this respect. Since there is no unique metabolic step that is used by all viruses, but is not used by their host cells, it is hard to imagine that interferon would have a single mode of antiviral action. Discoveries of a multitude of biochemical changes caused by interferon treatment of uninfected cells support the idea that interferons inhibit the replication of viruses in a number of ways. The particular step in the life cycle of a virus affected by interferon treatment would depend on the mode of replication of the virus itself as well as on the nature of host–virus interactions.

Several virus systems have been used extensively to discern the specific virus function affected by interferon treatment. These studies have been difficult to interpret, in general, because of two fundamental limitations. For most viruses, the details of their life cycles and the nature of their interactions with their hosts are not well understood. Second, virus replication is a repetitive process resulting in a great amplification of the number of infectious viral particles produced compared to the number of incoming infecting particles. A block in any viral function affects other viral functions too. For example, less viral protein synthesis may be caused by direct inhibition of protein synthesis, or it may be a consequence of less availability of viral mRNAs. Similarly, less mRNA synthesis could be a direct effect, or it could be a consequence of less viral RNA polymerase being synthesized. These considerations make it very difficult to identify the primary locus of interferon action even for a given cell–virus system and to establish a cause-and-effect relationship among various viral functions impaired by interferon action. However, I discuss the information available on the mode of action of interferon against the replication of a few well-studied representative viruses. Studies on many other viruses exist, but are not covered here in detail.

A. Nontumor Viruses

Reovirus. Reoviruses have 10 segmented dsRNAs as their genome (*70*). The 10 segments code for 10 mRNAs, which are translated into 10 reoviral proteins. These 10 proteins constitute the two outer coats of reoviruses. Reoviruses multiply in the cytoplasm of host cells. After penetration into the cell, the reovirions are converted into subviral particles by the removal and cleavage of some of their outer coat proteins. This results in the activation of various enzymes associated with the virions. The actions of these enzymes—the RNA transcriptase, the capping enzyme, and the RNA methylases—give rise to mature reo mRNAs. The capped and methylated reo mRNAs are translated into viral proteins. These proteins assemble into particles, every one of which also contains one of each of the 10 species of reo mRNAs. Within the particles, the complementary negative strands of the 10 mRNAs are synthesized, making them double-stranded. The resulting provirions can either resynthesize more reo mRNAs, and thereby amplify the yield of virus replication, or can bind more caspid proteins and thereby mature into infectious virions.

The replication of reovirus in mouse L cells or EAT[1] cells is sensitive to interferon. A concentration of interferon sufficient to decrease the virus yield by over 95% does not affect any of the following steps in reovirus replication: the binding of the virus to cells, the penetration of the virus into the cells, and the conversion of the virions into subviral particles (71, 72). Moreover, the dsRNA and protein compositions of subviral particles formed in interferon-treated cells are indistinguishable from the dsRNA and protein compositions of subviral particles formed in control cells. However, when these subviral particles were used to synthesize reoviral mRNA *in vitro*, there were distinct differences (72). The subviral particles isolated from interferon-treated cells made reo mRNAs of shorter size as compared to those made by subviral particles from control cells (see Section VIII,A).

Under conditions of 95% inhibition of reovirus yield, there was 80% decrease in double-stranded reoRNA and about 60% decrease in single-stranded reo RNA accumulation in interferon-treated L cells. Although cellular protein synthesis is not inhibited early in infection in interferon-treated reovirus-infected cells, the accumulation of reoviral proteins is severely reduced in such cells (73). Because of the complications resulting from the amplification of viral mRNA synthesis by the provirions, these results were not enough to identify the primary interferon-sensitive step in the reovirus replication cycle. Wiebe and Joklik (71) presented data in support of the hypothesis that the translation of early reovirus mRNAs, particularly those that code for polypeptide λ1, is the key step affected by interferon treatment. However, alternative interpretation of their data could not be eliminated. Lengyel *et al.* (6) on the other hand, have data in support of an accelerated turnover rate of reo mRNAs in the interferon-treated cells (see Section VIII,A).

Vesicular Stomatitis Virus. VSV, an enveloped virus, has a single-stranded RNA as its genomic material (74). The genomic RNA is not the mRNA, but it is transcribed into five mRNAs that code for the five structural proteins of VSV. The virions have several associated enzymic activities that are needed for viral RNA synthesis. Replication of VSV is highly sensitive to interferon treatment of various host cells. In interferon-treated VSV-infected cells, the accumulation of both viral RNA and viral proteins is decreased.

Inhibition of primary transcription of VSV RNA has been demonstrated in interferon-treated chick, mouse, human, and monkey cells. However, in most of these studies, cycloheximide was used to inhibit protein synthesis, thereby restricting the viral transcription process to only primary transcription from the incoming infectious virions. Since inhibitors such as cycloheximide may also affect processes other than protein synthesis, and since complete inhibition of protein synthesis is never achieved, unambiguous interpretations of these results are difficult. To overcome these problems, a temperature-sensitive mutant of VSV that produces only parentally derived transcripts at the nonpermissive temperature was employed (75). The results suggest that, in interferon-treated monkey cells, the rate of primary transcription of VSV is reduced. But synthesized mRNAs have similar sizes and similar half-lives in control and treated cells. From these results, interferon seems to have a direct effect on viral RNA transcription in this system. The particular stage of VSV replication cycle affected by interferon treatment may depend on the host cell. According to Thacore's data, interferon treatment of human cells caused inhibition of primary transcription of VSV, whereas in simian cells, viral translation was impaired (76).

A remarkable observation regarding the effect of interferon treatment on VSV production by Ly cells was that, although there was a 100-fold inhibition in the titer of infectious virus production by interferon-treated cells, the production of VSV, as measured by particle-associated RNA, nucleocaspid protein, or transcriptase activity, was inhibited at most by 5- to 10-fold (77). In other words, interferon treatment caused the production of a large number of noninfectious VSV particles. These noninfectious VSV particles contain a reduced amount of the glycoprotein G and the matrix protein M. When examined by electron microscopy, the bullet-shaped VSV particles produced by interferon-treated cells had a smaller number of spikes on their surfaces. These spikes are composed of the G protein, and their absence is most probably the cause of the noninfectivity of these virus particles. These particles contain only full-size 42 S RNA as their genomic material, and they do not interfere with the growth of wild-type VSV in Ly cells. The production of such noninfectious virus particles by interferon-treated cells is well documented for murine retroviruses (see Section V,C).

Vaccinia Virus. Vaccinia virus is a double-stranded DNA virus (78) that contains a virion-associated RNA polymerase and multiplies in the cytoplasm. Vaccinia virus infection results in a quick shutoff of host protein synthesis. On entering the cell, the outer envelope of the virion is removed and the virus core is liberated into the cytoplasm. The viral RNA polymerase is activated, and the viral mRNAs are synthesized. Viral DNA is subsequently released from the cores, and DNA replication ensues. The effects of interferon treatment on vaccinia virus replication are to inhibit the second-stage uncoating and DNA synthesis. The viral RNA synthesis is actually enhanced. All these effects are most probably caused by a primary effect on viral protein synthesis. Translational inhibition is caused by reduced rates of both initiation and elongation of the peptide chains (79). Discoveries of dsRNA-dependent pathways of inhibition of protein synthesis in cell extracts made from interferon-treated cells, and the fact that complementary RNA strands are produced in vaccinia virus-infected cells, should stimulate renewed interest in using this virus as a model for studying antiviral actions of interferons.

I have discussed here in brief the effects of interferon on the multiplication of three viruses whose life cycles are distinctly different. As is obvious from this discussion, for each of these viruses, although interferon has been shown to block one particular stage of the virus replicative cycle more severely than others, no unifying mechanism of antiviral action of interferon is apparent from these studies. Notwithstanding the technical difficulties in designing the right experiments, it is quite possible that no such unique mechanism exists and interferon inhibits virus multiplication by a variety of attacks at several stages of the viral life cycle.

B. DNA Tumor Viruses

In this section I discuss exclusively the effects of interferon on the replication of simian virus-40 (SV40)[1] a tumor virus containing a small double-stranded circular DNA as its genome.[2] SV40 lytically infects monkey cells, its permissive host, but transforms rodent cells that do not produce virus. During lytic infection, after uncoating, the viral DNA is transcribed in the nucleus of the infected cell by a cellular RNA polymerase. During this early phase, the early genes, constituting about 50% of the genome, are transcribed into early SV40 mRNAs. These mRNAs code for early SV40 proteins, including the large T and the small t antigens. T antigens binds to SV40 DNA and is probably involved in the initiation of DNA replication. In SV40-infected monkey cells, viral DNA replication begins about 20–24 hours after infection. Transcription of the late region of the genome starts at the same

[2] See article on SV40 by Das and Niyogi in Vol. 25 of this series.

time. The late mRNAs translate into SV40 VP-1, VP-2, and VP-3 proteins. It takes about 72 hours to complete the viral lytic cycle (80).

Two kinds of protocol have been followed for studying the effects of interferon on SV40 replication in monkey cells. In the conventional protocol, cells are treated with interferon first and infected with the virus later. But Yakobson et al. (81) took advantage of the long replication cycle of SV40 and developed a protocol in which the cells are treated with interferon 24 hours after the SV40-infection had started. A considerable amount of information has been gathered on the effects of interferon on SV40 replication, using these two approaches.

Interferon pretreatment inhibits the synthesis of T antigen as a consequence of a reduction in the amount of viral mRNA. This reduction in the accumulation of SV40 mRNA is most probably due to a direct reduction of the rate of transcription, or an enhanced degradation of SV40 mRNA in the nucleus (82). Most probably, the observed inhibition of SV40 early mRNA accumulation is not a consequence of impaired virus absorption, penetration and uncoating on the one hand; or a secondary consequence of directs effect on viral translation on the other. However, it has been reported that interferon treatment does not affect the production of SV40 mRNA, if "naked" SV40 DNA is used for infection instead of the virus (83). Also, SV40 mRNA, produced in vitro and microinjected into monkey cells, translates into T antigen, and pretreatment of the cells with interferon inhibits T antigen formation, indicating a direct inhibition of viral protein synthesis in such cells (84). Kingsman et al. (85) used a temperature-sensitive mutant of SV40 at the nonpermissive temperature in the presence of arabinosylcytosine to create a situation in which only early functions of SV40 are expressed in a permissive host. They found that interferon pretreatment inhibits the synthesis of large T and small t antigens under such conditions. It seems safe to conclude, therefore, that interferon-pretreatment does have an effect on the early gene-expression of SV40. Whether the effects are at the level of transcription or translation is not settled, although the present evidence favors an effect at the RNA synthesis level.

Yakobson et al. (81, 86) made an extensive investigation on the effects of interferon treatment on SV40 replication, treating the cells with interferon after SV40 infection had been established. They found that if BSC-1 cells are treated with interferon even 24 hours after SV40 infection, the yield of progeny SV40 is reduced by over 90%. The rate of DNA synthesis is slowly reduced, and is at about a 20% level 24 hours after interferon treatment. By 24 hours after SV40 infection, SV40 DNA replication and late protein synthesis in these cells have started, and they already contain SV40 T antigen. Interferon treatment at this stage does not inhibit transcription of viral RNA from the early and late part of the genome. Even as late as 30–40 hours after interferon addition, there is no decrease in the rate of uridine incorporation into nuclear or cytoplasmic viral RNA under these conditions. Processing of newly synthesized viral RNA, including polyadenylylation and splicing, are normal in the treated cells. This normal synthesis and processing of viral RNA goes on even when viral DNA synthesis is strongly inhibited. There is no massive breakdown of newly synthesized viral RNA although an increased rate of turnover has not been ruled out totally. However, viral protein synthesis is severely affected by interferon treatment at 24 hours after infection. Syntheses of VP-1, large T antigen, and small t antigen are all inhibited. The inhibition increases with increasing length of time after interferon treatment. These results strongly suggest that there is a direct block in viral RNA translation in such cells. At 20 hours after interferon treatment, viral RNAs are no longer associated with polysomes, but are found in smaller ribonucleoprotein particles. However, the overall pattern of polysomes with host mRNAs is unchanged.

When cell-free protein-synthesizing systems are made from these SV40-infected cells, an inhibition of protein synthesis is observed in the extracts from interferon-treated cells as compared to extracts from control cells. This inhibition is due to dominant inhibitors present in the interferon-treated cells. However, as is the case with other cell–virus systems, the selective inhibition of viral mRNA translation observed in whole cells treated with interferon cannot be demonstrated in the cell-free extracts. The exact molecular basis for the absence of SV40 mRNA translation in interferon-treated cells is not clear. Apparently the mRNAs are not broken down, and are physically available for translation. The only known modification in their structures is an alteration in the pattern of nucleotide methylation. According to unpublished data quoted in a recent review (4), SV40 mRNAs in the interferon-treated cells are overmethylated both in the "caps" and internally. The increase in internal methylation is larger than the increase in cap methylation. The biological significance of this overmethylation is not clear. SV40 mRNAs extracted from interferon-treated cells can still be translated *in vitro* into VP-1 and VP-3 capsid proteins, according to unpublished data of Revel *et al.* Thus it seems that there has been no irreversible damage of these mRNAs that would interfere with their ability to be translated. The observed overmethylation of SV40 mRNAs in interferon-treated monkey cells is in direct contrast to the undermethylation of reoviral mRNA cap structures, observed in interferon-treated mouse cells, and undermethylation of vaccinia viral mRNAs, observed in interferon-treated chick cells (see Section VI,C).

When SV40 infects nonpermissive hosts, such as mouse cells, no productive infection ensues, but the cells are transformed, presumably by integration of SV40 genes, into the chromosomal DNA. T antigen is expressed in such cells, though no late functions of SV40 are expressed. Infectious SV40 can be recovered from such transformed cells by fusion with permissive cells, suggesting that the whole SV40 genome is present. The T antigen synthesis in such transformed cells is insensitive to interferon treatment (87). However, the transformation of the same nonpermissive mouse cells by SV40 is inhibited by pretreatment of the cells with interferon; presumably this inhibits T antigen synthesis from SV40 genes still not integrated into the cellular genome. An acquired resistance to inhibition of SV40 T antigen synthesis caused by interferon treatment also occurs in adenovirus-SV40 hybrids. The synthesis of adenovirus T antigen is, in general, 100-fold less sensitive to interferon treatment than SV40 T antigen synthesis in lytic infection. Some of the adeno–SV40 hybrid viruses express both adeno T antigen and SV40 T antigen. Surprisingly, SV40 T antigen production in cells infected with these hybrids displays a resistance to interferon treatment similar to the expression of adenoviral T antigen (88). As in the case of SV40-transformed cells, the synthesis of SV40 T antigen acquires the sensitivity to interferon of the genome into which SV40 DNA has been integrated.

C. RNA Tumor Viruses

Studies on the effects of interferon on the replication of retroviruses have revealed yet another mode of its antiviral action (2). Retroviruses contain single-stranded RNA as their genome. They also carry, in the virions, the reverse transcriptase that copies the RNA into the corresponding double-stranded DNA, which is eventually integrated into the host genome. Once the proviral DNA is integrated into the host genome, the retroviral gene expression follows the usual path of cellular gene expression. Viral RNA and proteins are synthesized, and virus particles are assembled on cell membranes and continuously excreted from the cells without any apparent damage to the cell functions. Some of the retroviruses transform cells *in vitro*, whereas most of them cause some kind of neoplasia in animals. Various investigators have studied the effects of interferon treatment on the establishment of the infection by retroviruses up to the proviral integration stage, on the production of retroviruses by cells that have retroviral DNA already integrated into the genome, and on the process of transformation by transforming retroviruses. These studies reveal that interferon treatment inhibits retrovirus production by impairing a late stage of viral morphogenesis. The assembly or maturation of these viruses is impaired in interferon-treated cells. There is some evidence that, in addition to this late block, there is an early step of virus infection that is also sensitive to interferon under certain conditions. High doses of interferon can irreversibly block an early step of MSV/MLV infection process and thereby prevent both cell transformation and virus production (89). This block is beyond the viral adsorption, penetration, and uncoating stages and is probably at the level of synthesis and integration of proviral DNA (89a).

The most intriguing results have come from studying the effects of interferon on cells chronically infected with a retrovirus. Some of these cell lines continuously produce viruses without any external stimulus, whereas virus production can be induced in others by treatment with certain chemicals or hormones. Since the retroviral genomes are already integrated into the cellular DNA in these cells, one would expect that interferon would fail to exert any inhibitory action on the synthesis of these viruses. In the strictest terms, interferon does not inhibit the expression of these integrated proviral genomes. What interferon does inhibit, however, is the later process of virus assembly, maturation, and release from the plasma membrane.

Most of these studies have been done with murine leukemia virus-infected cells. Depending on the cell–virus combination, either of the two general phenomena is observed when these cells are treated with interferon. In some systems, there is a drastic inhibition of virus production in the culture medium as measured by quantitating the virus either by metabolic labeling or by measuring virus-associated reverse-transcriptase activity. In these interferon-treated cells, increased numbers of virus-like particles accumlate on the cell surface, indicating some interferon-induced aberration in virus assembly and release. In the other type of situation, there is not much inhibition of virus particle production by the interferon-treated cells. However, most of these virus particles are noninfectious. Thus, in this latter case, virus-like particles containing all the viral proteins and RNA are released, but, owing to some unknown defect in assembly, they are noninfectious (90–92). Many of the cell–virus systems respond to interferon in an intermediate fashion; i.e., fewer virus particles are produced, and even among the released particles there are many nonin fectious virions. The molecular basis for the inability of these viruses to infect cells successfully is unknown. Uncleaved glycoprotein precursors (93), gag polyprotein processing intermediates (93a), and an abnormal complex of viral p30 protein and viral reverse transcriptase (94) appear to be present in these noninfectious virions. It has also been observed that these virions package a low amount of $(2'\text{-}5')A_n$ synthetase (94a).

These studies have been extended to another interesting murine retrovirus, viz., murine mammary tumor virus (95). This is a type B virus, whereas the leukemia viruses are type C viruses. The morphology, the pathway of morphogenesis, and the biology of MuMTV are considerably different from those of type C viruses. MuMTV is produced by tissue culture cell lines established from mammary tumor cells. MuMTV proviral genome is integrated into the genome of these cells. However, these cells do not produce MuMTV unless glucocorticoid hormones are included in the culture medium. The hormone presumably triggers enhanced viral RNA transcription and thereby augments virus production. The effects of the hormone are reversible and disappear when the hormone is removed. Inclusion of interferon in the culture medium inhibits extracellular virus production from the hormone-stimulated cells by about 80%. That this effect is due to interferon itself was confirmed by the use of pure interferon. Although the interferon-treated cells produced fewer extracellular virus particles, the intracellular levels of viral RNA, as measured by hybridization analysis, and of the proteins, as measured by radioimmunoassays, were not lowered in the interferon-treated cells. Thus any gross inhibition of viral RNA or protein synthesis is eliminated as the primary cause of less virus production. Electron microscopy revealed an increased number of virus particles on the cell surface of the interferon-treated cells. These results suggest that for type B particles, the effects of interferon are similar to the effects on type C particle production (95).

Since it has been established, through the use of pure interferon, that the antiretroviral activities and the regular antiviral activities of interferons are caused by the same molecules (95), the question arises whether they are mediated through the same biochemical changes induced by interferon treatment of the host cells. It appears that interferon treatment causes a multitude of changes in the enzyme systems present in a cell. Some of these, through a mechanism not yet fully understood, could preferentially inhibit transcription and translation of viral RNA and proteins whereas cellular functions remain relatively unaffected. Most of the nontumor viruses are probably inhibited through these pathways. But the expression of the integrated RNA tumor viral genome escapes these inhibitory effects. It is possible that they are recognized as cellular gene functions by the interferon-induced enzyme systems. But in spite of unabated synthesis of retroviral RNA and proteins in the interferon-treated cells, the virus particles are not assembled and released properly. What causes these defects is completely unknown. One can speculate that interferon causes alterations in cellular membrane topology that hinder virus budding, or that the functioning of various cellular or virally coded enzymes needed for proper processing and maturation of the viral proteins is impaired in these cells. The finding that VSV, an enveloped virus that buds through the plasma membrane like retroviruses, is also affected in a similar way by interferon treatment (77) indicates that the production of noninfectious defective virus particles is not restricted to retroviruses. It would be interesting to test whether interferon treatment causes the production of such noninfectious particles even for nonenveloped viruses that do not bud through the plasma membrane.

VI. Studies with Extracts of Interferon-Treated Cells: Activities Independent of Double-Stranded RNA

A. Inhibition of Translation

Inhibition of viral RNA translation as the molecular basis of interferon action was first suggested in 1966 and 1967 (96–98). Kerr (99) reported the existence of an inhibitor of EMC RNA translation associated with the ribosomes from interferon-treated cells. Friedman et al. noted that, in extracts from interferon-treated L cells, EMC RNA translation is strongly inhibited only if the cells are also infected with vaccinia virus (100). The translation products are shorter in this case. The same investigators reported later that the inhibition of translation observed in the interferon-treated cell extracts is mainly at the level of initiation, although some inhibition at the level of peptide chain elongation was also observed (101). With hindsight, these observations could possibly be explained by the fact that vaccinia virus infection produces some dsRNA that, when added to an extract of interferon-treated cells caused inhibition of peptide chain initiation and elongation (discussed in detail in Section VII). A curious observation (102) was that the addition of fMet-tRNA^{fMet} to such an extract relieved the initiation block, probably by bypassing the requirement of some initiation factor. It is interesting to note the report of Ohtsuki et al. (103) that there is a 50–70% inhibition of the formation of the Met-tRNA^{fMet}-GTP-(eIF-2) initiation complex if a ribosomal wash from interferon-treated L cells is used as a source of the initiation factor (103).

In extracts of interferon-treated but uninfected L cells, translation of both mengo RNA and globin mRNA are inhibited (104). The inhibitors are associated with ribosomes. The inhibition is both at the level of initiation and of elongation (105). Very similar observations have been made in interferon-treated EAT cells incubated in advance to reduce the amount of endogenous translation: the translation of both cellular and viral mRNAs was inhibited if the cells were treated with interferon (106). The inhibitors were dominant and bound to ribosomes. There is also an inhibition of translation of globin mRNA in extracts from interferon-treated mouse erythroleukemic cells (107). The inhibition of translation in such cell extracts is reversed by the addition of tRNA (108, 109). There is only one report of a selective inhibition of translation of a viral RNA but not of a cellular RNA (110). This reflects the *in vivo* situation, in which such selectivity is observed. Unfortunately, the significance of this finding is in doubt since the viral mRNA used was possibly contaminated with dsRNA, which has a profound inhibitory effect on translation in extracts of interferon-treated cells.

B. tRNA Effects

As discussed earlier, translation of exogenously added viral or cellular mRNAs in interferon-treated cell extracts is strongly inhibited. The major block is at the level of peptide chain elongation. It was observed that addition of mammalian tRNAs to the interferon-treated cell extracts can restore its capacity to translate exogenous mRNAs. tRNA could be added either at the beginning of translational incubation or at a point where translation had been completely stopped (108, 109). tRNAs from different organisms have different specific activity in terms of their ability to restore translation.

The dependence of translation, in extracts of interferon-treated cells, on added exogenous tRNA could be attributed to a rapid loss of the amino-acid accepting activity of some endogenous tRNAs upon incubation. The loss of aminoacylation activity of leucine, lysine, and serine tRNAs, but not of others, is much faster in extracts of interferon-treated cells than in extracts of control cells (111). This loss is due not to inactivation of the aminoacyl-tRNA synthetases, but to the unavailability of chargeable tRNAs. This is shown by the fact that added purified aminoacyl-tRNA synthetases do not restore aminoacylation, but addition of exogenous tRNA does. The tRNA isolated from incubated extracts of interferon-treated cells accepts much less leucine, using purified synthetase, than the same amount of tRNA isolated from unincubated extracts of similarly treated cells. The structural change in the tRNA molecules responsible for this loss of amino acid acceptance activity was not identified.

In extracts of interferon-treated L cells, certain minor species of leucine tRNAs are necessary to restore mengo RNA translation, and a different minor species of leucine tRNA is required to restore globin synthesis (112). Most surprisingly, the major species of leucine tRNA, which recognizes the same codon (CUG) as the minor species, does not restore globin translation. The basis for this discrimination is not known. Translation of poly(U,C) is also restored by a specific yeast leucine tRNA species in extracts of interferon-treated L cells (113). In extracts of interferon-treated Friend cells, lysine tRNA restores EMC RNA translation (114).

The biological significance of the tRNA inactivation phenomenon in extracts of interferon-treated cells is not clear. The cell extracts used for testing translational capacity are routinely prepared by incubating the cell lysate and removing small molecules by dialysis or gel filtration prior to their use for translating added mRNA. The functional lability of the leucine tRNA appears only in gel-filtered or dialyzed cell extracts. Thus it seems that certain artificial manipulations are necessary to trigger the action of the inhibitory agent. The slight inhibition of exogenous EMC RNA translation in nonincubated, non-gel-filtered extracts of interferon-treated cells is not reversed by added tRNA (111). In line with these observations, tRNAs isolated from control and interferon cells are equally rich in those species of tRNA that restore translation in lysates of interferon-treated cells (111, 115). Moreover, chromatographic analysis of leucine tRNAs, aminoacylated *in vivo,* from control and interferon-treated cells showed no differences in isoacceptor distribution (115).

The agent responsible for inactivating certain tRNA species in interferon-treated cell extracts could be identical (4, 116) to (2'-5') A_n-phosphodiesterase,[3] which preferentially cleaves 2'-5' phosphodiester bonds and the level of which in cells is enhanced by interferon treatment (for more about this enzyme, see Sections VII,A and C). This enzyme can remove the 3'-terminal adenosine of tRNAs as 5'-AMP and may also remove the adjoining cytidine residues. Incubation of tRNAs with this enzyme would therefore decrease the amino-acid accepting activity of the tRNAs, which, however, can be

---

[3] (2'-5')A_n is an abbreviation for oligoadenylate(s) linked from 2' to 5' instead of 3' to 5'; the latter are customarily represented by oligo(A), poly(A), or A_n. Another abbreviation for (2'-5')oligoadenylate is Iso(A). The natural, active oligomers have a triphosphate group at the 5' end; a more correct abbreviation is thus $pppA(2'-5'A)_n$. The pppA is omitted for brevity. [Ed.]

completely restored by the CCA-end-repair enzyme, tRNA adenylyl-transferase (EC 2.7.7.25), plus ATP and CTP. When added to extracts of normal (control) cells, $(2'-5')$ A_n-phosphodiesterase inhibits translation of exogenous mRNAs; this can be alleviated by adding exogenous tRNA, thus mimicking the situation in interferon-treated cell extracts. It is conceivable that this enzyme is really responsible for inactivation of tRNAs in extracts of interferon-treated cells. The necessary gel-filtration step may remove some low-molecular-weight inhibitors of this enzyme and trigger its action. In such an extract, at least in principle, a balance would be struck between the action of this enzyme and the CCA-terminus repair enzyme. An additional interesting regulation comes from the fact that this enzyme can act on a tRNA only if the 3' OH of its terminal A is not esterified. Therefore, although the enzyme is nonspecific in regard to different species of tRNA, the species that is present mostly in unacylated form will have the greatest chance of being attacked. All these factors may explain why certain minor species of tRNA are preferentially inactivated in extracts of interferon-treated cells. Whether all these processes are operative in the cell, however, is still not known.

C. Impairment of mRNA Methylation

Most eukaryotic cellular and viral mRNAs have "cap" structures[4] at their 5' termini. The extent of methylation of the cap on an mRNA influences the efficiency of translation of the mRNA under certain conditions as well as the stability of the mRNA (117).

The extent of methylation in vitro of capped but unmethylated reoviral RNA in cell extracts prepared from interferon-treated mouse ascites cells is less than the extent of methylation in extracts of control cells (118). The impairment is due to the presence of an inhibitor of cap methylation in the extracts of interferon-treated cells. The impairment is not due to depletion of S-adenosylmethionine, the methyl donor, nor to accumulation of S-adenosylhomocysteine, a competitive inhibitor of methylation. The methylating enzyme is not inactivated irreversibly, and the nonmethylated viral RNA can be recovered from the extracts of the interferon-treated cells and further methylated in extracts of untreated cells. The above observations indicate that the inhibitor and the methylase probably compete for the same sites on the mRNA, and the extent of methylation reflects the state of balance reached between these molecules. The inhibitor is a macromolecule and is very labile at 37°. The inhibition is not alleviated by the addition

---

[4] See symposium on mRNA in Vol. 19 of this series. [Ed.]

of noncapped EMCV RNA, rRNA, tRNA, poly(U), m^7GTP, or $m^7GpppGm$, indicating that the inhibitor specifically recognizes capped mRNA. The inhibitor also inhibits the reovirion-associated cap methylase, which is responsible for methylating reo-mRNAs under physiological conditions. Double-stranded RNA apparently has no effect on the methylation.

Similar results have been observed in extracts of interferon-treated HeLa cells (120). The failure of certain workers (121, 122) to observe any inhibition of cap methylation in extracts of interferon-treated cells could be superficially attributed to the methods of preparation of the cell extracts. Gel filtration and prior incubation of the cell extracts could have inactivated the inhibitor, which is unusually labile (119). It should be emphasized that although this inhibitor has been characterized solely by its ability to impair cap methylation, it is possible that this effect is only one aspect of the interaction between it and mRNA. Thus it is conceivable that the same agent may also interfere directly with the process of attachment of mRNA to ribosomes, which takes place at or near the cap structure on the mRNA molecule. Such inhibition of ribosome attachment would result in impaired translation. Similarly, those factors that confer greater stability upon methylated capped mRNAs may be prevented by the inhibitor from interacting with the caps on the mRNAs, thereby increasing the lability of the mRNAs.

The observed inhibition of cap methylation in extracts of interferon-treated cells inspired the search for such inhibitors in interferon-treated, virus-infected cells. A unified picture is yet to emerge from these studies. Reovirus mRNAs synthesized in interferon-treated L cells contain about 50% less "cap-2" termini than viral mRNA of control cells (123). (In "cap-2" structures, the first three nucleosides from the 5' terminus are methylated; in "cap-1," only the first two are methylated, and in "cap-0," only the first nucleoside is methylated.)[4] The conversion of cap-1 to cap-2 termini, i.e., addition of the third methyl group, is carried out by a cellular methylase in vivo.

Similar results were obtained in interferon-treated chick fibroblasts (124); there was more than a 50% decrease in the methylation of cap-0 to cap-1 in the mRNAs from uninfected cells, and in both cellular and viral mRNAs from vaccinia virus-infected cells. In interferon-treated VSV-infected HeLa cells, all VSV mRNA molecules are capped, but about 60% of the nonpolysomal VSV mRNAs are unmethylated in the 5'-terminal guanosine (124a).

Monkey cells infected with SV40 and then treated with interferon contain more internally methylated (m^6A) SV40 mRNAs (4). Thus, by

calculation, about 25–30% of the RNA chains are internally methylated in control cells whereas almost all are methylated in interferon-
treated cells. Moreover, the cap structures of SV40 mRNAs isolated
from interferon-treated cells are also overmethylated. Methylation of
cellular mRNAs both in caps and internally is also increased in the
treated monkey cells.

Although the results from the reo, vaccinia, and VSV systems on the
one hand, and the SV40 system on the other, cannot be easily recon-
ciled at this time, it is clear that there is a noticeable effect on viral
mRNA cap methylation in interferon-treated cells. However, whether
these effects are partly or wholly responsible for the observed inhibition of viral RNA translation in such cells, or whether these effects are
merely a consequence of inhibition of translation caused by some other
agents, remains to be examined.

VII. Studies with Extracts from Interferon-Treated Cells: Activities Dependent upon Double-Stranded RNA

A. Inhibition of Translation: Two Independent Pathways

Addition of dsRNA to extracts of interferon-treated cell strongly
inhibits protein synthesis (125). A similar inhibition is also observed in
reticulocyte lysate (36), a commonly used protein-synthesizing system, although reticulocytes have not knowingly been treated with interferon. The observations that protein synthesis is strongly inhibited
in extracts of interferon-treated, vaccinia virus-infected cells (100),
and that interferon-treated cells are more sensitive to the cytotoxic
effects of dsRNA than control cells (28), led to the discovery, in 1974,
that protein synthesis in extracts of interferon-treated L cells is inhibited by the addition of dsRNA (125). These observations led to the idea
that dsRNA, in addition to being an inducer of interferon synthesis,
may also play a vital role in the mechanism of interferon action. The
implicit assumption, supported by some experimental evidence, was
that dsRNA is produced during the replicative cycle of most animal
viruses and could act as the trigger for initiating inhibition of translation in the interferon-treated cells.

Two other important observations contributed significantly to the
present understanding of the above mechanism. Namely, it was observed independently in several laboratories that addition of dsRNA to
extracts of interferon-treated cells causes enhanced phosphorylation of

several proteins (*121, 126–128*). One of these is a subunit of initiation factor eIF-2,[5] which is nonfunctional in its phosphorylated form. Thus, inhibition of translation was traced to enhanced protein phosphorylation. The other noteworthy observation was that addition of dsRNA and ATP enhances a single-strand RNA-specific endonuclease activity much more in extracts of interferon-treated cells than in the control extracts (*129*). These observations led to the elucidation of the "nuclease pathway" of translational inhibition in interferon-treated cells. Since then, a great deal of information has been gathered on the mechanism by which dsRNA inhibits mRNA translation in extracts of interferon-treated cell or in reticulocyte lysates. The present understanding is schematically depicted in Fig. 1. Similar models have been proposed by several workers, and there is general agreement on at least the main features of this model.

Double-stranded RNA inhibits mRNA translation in extracts of interferon-treated cells using two independent pathways. In the protein kinase pathway, dsRNA activates an inactive protein kinase in the presence of ATP. The activated protein kinase utilizes ATP to phosphorylate the smallest subunit of the peptide chain initiation factor eIF-2, which thus becomes inactive in protein synthesis. However, a phosphoprotein phosphatase can remove the phosphate and regenerate the unphosphorylated eIF-2. The protein kinase pathway leads to inhibition of protein synthesis at the level of peptide chain initiation. In the nuclease pathway, dsRNA interacts with an enzyme, $(2'-5')A_n$-synthetase, that converts ATP into $pppA(2'-5')A_n$, where $n = 1$ to 14.[6] This structure has been established unequivocally by chemical and enzymic analyses, and by chemical synthesis (*130, 131*). $(2'-5')A_n$ can activate an inactive endonuclease that then can cleave single-stranded RNAs (*132–134*). It can also be hydrolyzed to ATP and AMP by another enzyme, $(2'-5')A_n$ phosphodiesterase.

The nuclease pathway leads to degradation of mRNAs and causes irreversible translational inhibition. In the following sections, I present the evidence supporting the existence of these pathways, the observations leading to their elucidation, the characteristics of the different components, and the requirements for the individual reactions.

[5] See article by Jagus, Anderson, and Safer in Vol. 25 of this series. The nomenclature is set out in *FEBS Lett.* **76**, 1 (1977). [Ed.]

[6] In these compounds [collectively called $(2'-5')A_n$], the phosphodiester bonds are $2'-5'$ instead of the usual $3'-5'$ bonds. They are the first examples of natural oligonucleotides with $2'-5'$ linkages. See also footnote 3.

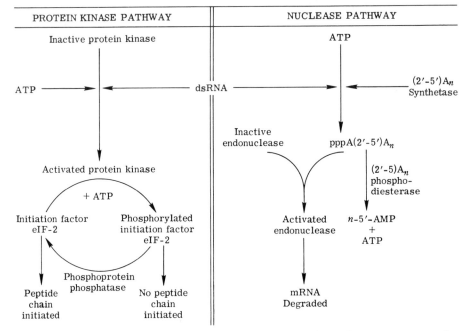

FIG. 1. Double-stranded-RNA-dependent translational regulation in extracts of interferon-treated cells.

B. The Protein Kinase Pathway

The discovery of the dsRNA-dependent protein-kinase pathway operating in extracts made from interferon-treated cells was inspired by several related observations: first, the knowledge that many enzymes from a variety of metabolic pathways are activated or inactivated by phosphorylation (135); second, the findings that dsRNA inhibits protein synthesis in the presence of ATP in extracts from interferon-treated cells (125); third, the observation that dsRNA and ATP are needed for the activation of an endonuclease in such extracts (136); and fourth, the discovery that heme-regulated translational inhibition in reticulocyte lysates involves protein phosphorylation (137). All these led to the same basic observation in several laboratories, namely, that dsRNA enhances the phosphorylation of several specific proteins in extracts of interferon-treated cells. The phosphorylation of these proteins does not occur, or occurs only to a much lesser extent, in extracts from untreated (control) cells even in the presence of dsRNA.

When extracts from control or interferon-treated cells are incubated with ATP in the presence or the absence of dsRNA, many proteins are phosphorylated (126–128). However, at least two, P_1 and P_2, are phosphorylated only in the presence of dsRNA, and even then only very slightly in extracts of control cells. Thus phosphorylation of P_1 and P_2 is dependent both on a prior interferon treatment of the cells as well as inclusion of dsRNA in the reaction mixture. As isolated from mouse cell extracts, P_1 has a molecular weight around 67,000 and P_2 one of about 37,000. In human cell extracts, P_1 is slightly larger (68,000) (120). The molecular weights assigned to P_1 and P_2 are approximate, and different values are used by different laboratories. In addition to P_1 and P_2, the dsRNA-dependent protein kinase present in extracts of interferon-treated cells can phosphorylate some added substrates, e.g., histones (127). Whether histones are physiological substrates for the dsRNA-activated protein kinase is not known. The action of the protein kinase is antagonized by the presence of a phosphoprotein phosphatase that dephosphorylates phosphorylated P_1 and P_2.

Protein Kinase. The dsRNA-dependent protein kinase has been purified several thousandfold from interferon-treated EAT cells (138). The level of this enzyme is increased about 5- to 10-fold upon interferon treatment of the cells. The purified kinase preparation is free of any dsRNA-independent phosphorylating activity. P_1 protein copurifies with the enzymic activity, and could be the enzyme itself. The most highly purified kinase preparation has P_1 as its major component, although there is still another minor protein present (as tested by labeling with ^{125}I) (6). If P_1 turns out to be the kinase itself, then obviously it becomes phosphorylated in a dsRNA-dependent fashion. It is not clear whether autophosphorylation is necessary for the enzyme to be able to phosphorylate other substrates.

The P_2 protein that can be phosphorylated by the dsRNA-dependent kinase has been identified as the smallest (α) subunit of the peptide chain initiation factor eIF-2 (132). This protein is phosphorylated also by the dsRNA-dependent protein kinase present in the reticulocyte lysates, and the same sites on the protein are phosphorylated by the two kinases (139).

Either viral dsRNA (reoviral genomic RNA) or synthetic dsRNA, e.g., poly(I) · poly(C), can activate the kinase purified from interferon-treated cells. Neither single- nor double-stranded DNA or RNA · DNA hybrids can substitute for dsRNA (138). Single-stranded RNAs, e.g., poly(I) or poly(C), are also incapable of activating the kinase, although it has been reported that reoviral mRNA can stimulate the kinase (139). It is possible that there are long double-stranded loops within the mRNA molecules that are sufficient to activate the kinase activity. GTP cannot replace ATP in this phosphorylation reaction. Moreover, a low concentration of cAMP (10^{-9} to 10^{-7} M) does not affect the phosphorylation of histone H_1 by the kinase, but at higher concentrations, cAMP is inhibitory. cGMP at 10^{-4} M does not affect the process. KCl strongly inhibits the kinase reaction. The half-maximal initial rate of histone phosphorylation is obtained at dsRNA (reoviral) concentrations of 25 ng/ml. Both serine and threonine residues are phosphorylated by this kinase.

It has been suggested (138) that the functioning of the kinase might be divided into two phases. In the first phase, the protein kinase is activated in the presence of dsRNA and ATP. In the second phase, the activated kinase phosphorylates its substrate. The evidence for this notion is indirect. It was observed that, if the partially purified protein kinase is incubated with dsRNA and ATP before the histone is added, the phosphorylation of the latter starts immediately and continues at a constant rate. On the other hand, if the prior incubation is omitted, histone phosphorylation starts after a distinct lag period and proceeds at a slower rate. The latter pattern is seen also if the reaction mixture is first incubated without either dsRNA or ATP. Histones probably interfere with the activation of the kinase, presumably by binding to dsRNA.

The two-step mechanism of action of the kinase is also supported by these findings. The kinase is stimulated by low amounts of dsRNA (≤ 0.4 μg/ml), but is not stimulated, or is stimulated less, by high amounts of dsRNA (20 μg/ml) (140). However, if the kinase is first activated at low concentrations of dsRNA and ATP, it becomes resistant to inhibition by high concentrations of dsRNA. It was also observed (140) that the rate of phosphorylation of eIF-2 is fivefold higher if the kinase is first activated. The ATP analog, AMP-P[NH]P, whose β-γ phosphate bond cannot be hydrolyzed, cannot replace ATP in the activation phase.

What actually constitutes the "activation" of the kinase is not known. It is quite possible that the process is autophosphorylation of the enzyme in the presence of dsRNA, but no experimental evidence has been put forward to support this contention. However, if P_1 is the kinase, the fact that phosphorylation of it is dsRNA-dependent is consistent with the above line of thinking. Another possible role of ATP could be to effect a conformational change in the enzyme. The activated enzyme seems to have a higher thermal stability (4).

The presence of dsRNA may not be necessary during the action phase of the activated kinase. If the kinase is first activated in the presence of dsRNA and ATP, and the reaction mixture is then incubated with RNase III (an enzyme, EC 3.1.26.3, that cleaves dsRNA into short fragments), the kinase can still phosphorylate histone at a normal rate. However, it is possible that the enzyme, having a strong affinity for dsRNA, protects a part of it from the attack of RNase III, and thus a bound fragment of dsRNA is needed for the action of the kinase.

Phosphorylation of P_1 is increased *in vivo* when dsRNA is added to interferon-treated intact cells (but not in control cells) (*141*). This indicates that the dsRNA-dependent protein kinase is functional under physiological conditions. However, enhanced phosphorylation of P_2 with the addition of dsRNA to intact interferon-treated cells is yet to be shown.

The partially purified protein kinase isolated from interferon-treated cells strongly inhibits protein synthesis in extracts of untreated cells or in rabbit reticulocyte lysates, which also contain a dsRNA-dependent kinase (*132, 140*). However, the latter kinase is not activated at high dsRNA concentrations (20 μg/ml). The kinase purified from the interferon-treated cells was therefore activated with ATP at low dsRNA concentrations and then added to the reticulocyte lysate in the presence of high dsRNA. The activated kinase inhibited endogenous protein synthesis after a lag of about 5 minutes. The inhibition was at the peptide chain-initiation level and was totally overcome by added eIF-2. Under the same conditions, the α subunit of eIF-2 (equivalent to P_2) present in the lysate is strongly phosphorylated.

Why phosphorylated eIF-2 is nonfunctional is not clear. Evidence from several laboratories indicates that phosphorylated eIF-2 fails to interact with other ancillary factors needed for initiation complex formation (*142, 143*). The partially purified protein kinase preparation does not generate $(2'-5')A_n$, the nuclease activator, even in the presence of ATP and dsRNA. Similarly, $(2'-5')A_n$ cannot substitute for dsRNA in activating the protein kinase (*132*). These results demonstrate that dsRNA-induced inhibition of protein synthesis in extracts of interferon-treated cells is mediated through two distinct pathways that share no other common elements except for ATP and dsRNA.

Phosphoprotein Phosphatase. Crude extracts from interferon-treated cells contain a phosphoprotein phosphatase that can dephosphorylate P_1 and P_2 (*140*). It stimulates mRNA translation in extracts of interferon-treated cells supplemented with dsRNA (*4*). It dephosphorylates P_1 and P_2 in crude ribosomes, or P_2 in purified eIF-2. It may dephosphorylate a couple of other phosphoproteins, but most phosphoproteins present in L-cell ribosomal extracts are not sensitive to this specific protein phosphatase. Interferon treatment probably does not increase or decrease the level of this phosphatase in L cells. Some observations (*144*) suggest that its action might be strongly inhibited by certain dsRNA, e.g., poly(I)·poly(C), and not inhibited by others, e.g., poly(I)·poly(br^5C). The extent of inhibition also depends on other components present in the reaction mixture.

C. Endonuclease Pathway

The discovery of this pathway of inhibition of protein synthesis in extracts from interferon-treated cells can be traced to the serendipitous observation (129) that single-stranded reoviral RNA is degraded much faster in extracts of interferon-treated cells than in control extracts, but only when the mRNA is contaminated with dsRNA. The elucidation of the pathway was also greatly facilitated by the discovery of (2'-5')A_n, the potent inhibitor of protein synthesis that is synthesized in extracts from interferon-treated cells in the presence of dsRNA.

Reo mRNAs, when prepared *in vitro* and contaminated with reo genomic dsRNA, are degraded much faster in extracts made from interferon-treated cells than in extracts made from untreated cells (129). This differential effect is eliminated when reo mRNA is purified free of dsRNA, and reappears when dsRNA is added to the reaction mixture. The enhanced degradation is due to the presence of an endonuclease system in the extracts from interferon-treated cells. The activation of this latent system requires dsRNA. These experiments were carried out under the conditions of *in vitro* protein synthesis, i.e., in the presence of all amino acids, ATP, GTP, energy source, etc. However, only ATP is needed in addition to dsRNA to activate the endonuclease system (136). The enhanced degradation of mRNA in response to the addition of dsRNA and ATP to extracts from interferon-treated cells can be divided functionally into two phases: activation and action. In the first phase, dsRNA and ATP are needed, but the mRNA is not. In this phase, the system becomes "activated," by a mechanism at first not clear. In the second phase, neither dsRNA nor ATP is needed; in this phase, the activated endonuclease cleaves the mRNA. The endonuclease system has been separated into two complementary fractions (145). The first fraction responds to dsRNA and ATP and synthesizes a heat-stable, low-molecular-weight substance that in turn activates the second fraction into the active endoribonuclease. Thus there is a low-molecular-weight nuclease activator molecule that transmits the action of dsRNA to the nuclease. The nuclease activator turned out to be identical to the low-molecular-weight inhibitor of protein synthesis, (2'-5')A_n, discovered earlier (127, 130). Activation of the nuclease is most probably the only mechanism by which (2'-5')A_n inhibits protein synthesis.

(2'-5')A_n-*Synthetase*. This enzyme (also called 2'-5'-oligo(A)-polymerase or oligoisoadenylate synthetase E)[3] synthesizes a series of (2'-5')-linked oligoadenylates from ATP in the presence of dsRNA.

The level of this enzyme is elevated 10- to 100-fold upon interferon treatment of various cells in tissue-culture. The induction of this enzyme by interferon has also been demonstrated in whole animals (146). Elevated levels of $(2'-5')A_n$-synthetase activity in tissue homogenates and serum from mice either treated with interferon or the interferon-inducer poly(I)·poly(C) or infected with EMC virus have been detected (146).

The enzyme has been purified to apparent homogeneity from interferon-treated mouse EAT[1] cells (147) and human HeLa cells (147a). The apparent molecular weight of the mouse enzyme is 105,000 from gel electrophoresis in dodecyl sulfate, and about 85,000 from its sedimentation velocity through a glycerol gradient. It has also been partially purified from interferon-treated mouse L cells (148) and chicken cells (149), with apparent molecular weights of about 60,000 and 55,000 respectively. The reason for the apparent discrepancies in the estimated molecular weights of the enzyme purified from different sources is not clear. In the presence of dsRNA, the purified enzyme catalyzes the synthesis from ATP of $(2'-5')$-linked oligoadenylates with $5'$-terminal triphosphate residues. The size of the oligoadenylates extends from dimer to hexadecamer, but the dimer, trimer, and tetramer predominate. The stoichiometry of the reaction catalyzed by this enzyme was shown to be as follows:

$$nATP \rightarrow pppA(2'-5')A_{n-1} + (n-1) PP_i$$

Pyrophosphate is not cleaved by the enzyme. The extent of conversion of ATP to $(2'-5')A_n$ is very high (97% or more). The extent of the reverse reaction, i.e., the incorporation of [^{32}P]pyrophosphate into ATP in the presence of unlabeled $(2'-5')A_n$, dsRNA, and enzyme is below 0.3%, if any. The rate of $(2'-5')A_n$ synthesis in the absence of dsRNA is less than 4% of that in the presence of dsRNA. Although the affinity of the enzyme for dsRNA is extremely high, that for ATP is remarkably low. Even 5 mM ATP does not saturate the enzyme; the rate of reaction increases by about 10% if the concentration of ATP is increased to 10 mM. Kinetic studies reveal that the proportion of the longer products increases with increasing time of incubation, indicating successive addition of ATP to enzyme-bound oligomers. In fact, added dimer $(A2'-5'A)$ can be used as a primer and extended by this enzyme to oligomers. The enzyme can also add AMP residues in $2'-5'$ linkage, using NAD, ADP-ribose[7] and Ap_4A $(3'-5')$ as the primers. The plot of the reaction rate versus enzyme concentration is sigmoidal, indicating some cooperativity (150).

[7] See article by Mandel et al. in this volume.

The $(2'-5')A_n$-synthetase polymerizes ATP only in the presence of dsRNA. Single-stranded RNA, single- or double-stranded DNA, or DNA·RNA hybrids cannot substitute for dsRNA (151, 152). Replicative forms of viral RNAs, and mRNAs to which oligo(U) is hybridized to produce a double-stranded region with the poly(A) "tail" of mRNA, can activate this enzyme (153). The optimal concentration of dsRNA needed for the activation of the enzyme increases with the concentration of the pure enzyme. As tested at 0.4, 2, and 10 μg/ml enzyme concentrations, close to maximal $(2'-5')A_n$ synthesis can be obtained if reoviral dsRNA or poly(I)·poly(C) are used at about half the concentration (in w/v) of the enzyme (150). Synthetic dsRNAs shorter than 30 base-pairs cannot activate the synthetase, whereas dsRNA longer than 65–80 base-pairs causes maximal activation. The partially double-stranded polymers poly(I)·poly(G,C), with an average of one mismatch for every 8 nucleotides, do not activate the enzyme, whereas those with an average of one mismatch for every 45 nucleotides do activate it (154, 155). The physicochemical mechanism by which dsRNA activates this enzyme remains to be understood. In the near future, one can expect to see extensive investigations on this system to understand the nature of this novel nucleic acid–protein interaction.

$(2'-5')A_n$ *Phosphodiesterase.* Because of its $2'-5'$ phosphodiester linkage, $(2'-5')A_n$ is resistant to most cellular nucleases. However an enzyme activity that degrades $(2'-5')A_n$ has been detected in L cells (116), mouse reticulocytes (156), and Hela cells (155). The level of this phosphodiesterase in L cells is elevated four- to fivefold by interferon treatments, and it preferentially cleaves $2'-5'$ bonds over $3'-5'$ bonds, yielding ATP and AMP from $(2'-5')A_n$. It is not specific for any given sequence, and splits many dinucleoside monophosphates. For C-A and U-U, the rate of cleavage of $2'-5'$ form is 30 times greater than the $3'-5'$ form. For U-A the ratio is 3. The enzyme is very active with A-C and splits both $2'-5'$ and $3'-5'$ bonds equally well.

With respect to tRNAs, this phosphodiesterase attacks from the $2'$ (or $3'$) end. The $3'$-terminal phosphodiester bond of tRNAs are susceptible, but a $3'$ phosphate blocks the action of this enzyme. Esterification of the $5'$ end of the substrate does not inhibit the action.

By degrading $(2'-5')A_n$, the phosphodiesterase may regulate the activity of the $(2'-5')A_n$-dependent endonuclease and thereby regulate the extent of inhibition of protein synthesis in extracts made from interferon-treated cells. Moreover, it may also play a role in the pathways of dsRNA-independent inhibition of protein synthesis by removing the CCA terminus of tRNAs. It is a strong inhibitor of tRNA aminoacylation and of translation (4, 116). Its action is reversed by addition of tRNA (see Section VI,B). The evidence for the belief that the enzyme degrading $(2'-5')A_n$ and that removing the CCA termini of tRNAs are the same is the following: the activities copurify; both are heat inactivated at 55° for 10 minutes; and tRNA inactivation is prevented by adding 2'-5' A-A or U-U.

Endonuclease. The endoribonuclease (also called RNase L or RNase F), that is activated by $(2'-5')A_n$[3] has not yet been purified to homogeneity. However, it has been partially purified from interferon-treated EAT (157) and L (156) cells. However, interferon treatment of these cells causes only a slight elevation (about twofold) of the level of this enzyme. The partially purified EAT enzyme preparation is low in $(2'-5')A_n$-independent nuclease activity. It cleaves RNA only in the presence of divalent cations, but it is not known whether the cations are required for its activation or for its catalytic function.

The endoribonuclease is activated by nanomolar concentrations of $(2'-5')A_n$, $n > 2$ (i.e., trimers or larger are effective). The dimer has no activity. At least two 5'-terminal phosphates and two free 3'-OH groups on the trimer are needed for activation of the nuclease (157a). The activation of the nuclease by $(2'-5')A_n$ is reversible. Upon removal of the activator by gel filtration, the enzyme reverts to its latent form, from which it can be reactivated by the addition of fresh $(2'-5')A_n$. The activation does not seem to result in a large change of size of the enzyme. Thus binding or release of a protein, or multimerization of the enzyme, is probably not the mechanism of its activation. However, the activation may require the binding of the activator to the nuclease. Partially purified preparations of the nuclease retain the activator on nitrocellulose filters. The agent doing this comigrates with the nuclease in both ion-exchange chromatography and gel filtration. Moreover, N-ethylmaleimide treatment of a partially purified nuclease preparation abolishes both its activation by $(2'-5')A_n$ and its ability to retain this activator on nitrocellulose filters (157).

The activated endonuclease cleaves a large variety of single-stranded RNAs at widely different rates, but it does not cleave dsRNA. It does not cleave viral mRNAs per se any faster than cellular mRNAs. Ribosomal RNAs are cleaved both in the naked form as well as in intact ribosomes. Discrete RNA-cleavage products are obtained when intact ribosomes are incubated with the nuclease (157b). The susceptibility of particular RNA to the action of this enzyme is probably affected by its length and secondary structure (151, 158). Cleavage occurs primarily at the 3' side of UA, UG, and UU sequences to yield UpNp-terminated products. However, some cleavage after CA and AC sequences is also observed (158a,b). Such limited specificity of the nuclease precludes its preferential action on viral mRNAs on the basis of some specific primary sequences being present in these RNAs.

The $(2'-5')A_n$-dependent nuclease[3] is present even in cells not treated with interferon. For this reason, addition of the activator causes inhibition of protein synthesis in extracts from control L cells or in rabbit reticulocyte lysates. Among the various enzyme components of the endonuclease pathway, only the level of $(2'-5')A_n$-synthetase seems to be greatly elevated by interferon treatment. The levels of the nuclease and the phosphodiesterase are elevated only slightly by interferon treatment. The interferon system therefore utilizes preexisting cellular components for its action.

The activated nuclease may have a much broader role in cellular regulation; it may not be restricted solely to the interferon system. Similarly, the level of the $(2'-5')A_n$-synthetase may be elevated by biological stimuli other than interferons. The amounts of $(2'-5')A_n$-synthetase activity in various cells and tissues vary over a 1000-fold range, and even in the same tissue, the amount varies tremendously depending on the growth and hormonal status of the organism (159). A high level of the enzyme is present in lymphocytes from normal mouse spleen, although the brain and the liver of the same animal do not contain detectable amounts of enzyme (159a). The level of the enzyme increases in Daudi and Raji human lymphoblastoid cell lines upon treatment with hydrocortisone or dexamethasone (159b).

VIII. Relevance of Activities Dependent upon Double-Stranded RNA to the Antiviral Action of Interferon

A. Do the Double-Stranded RNA-Dependent Pathways Operate in Vivo?

Although the details of inhibition of protein synthesis through the endonuclease pathway and the protein kinase pathway have been elucidated to a great extent in the cell-free systems, it has been difficult to demonstrate that they are operative in vivo. I discuss here the experimental evidence relevant to this question.

"Preactivated" kinase may be present in extracts prepared from interferon-treated mouse L cells infected with EMC virus (160). If it can be convincingly demonstrated that the activation occurred in whole cells rather than in the cell lysate, it would be strong evidence that the kinase is indeed active in such cells. ^{32}P-labeling of a 65,000-dalton protein (P_1) is greatly enhanced in interferon-treated cells in vivo by addition of dsRNA to the cell culture medium (141). Thus exogenously added dsRNA does activate the kinase *in vivo*. However, there is no enhanced phosphorylation of P_1 in interferon-treated cells infected with mengovirus or vesicular stomatitis virus (*141*).

When deliberately introduced into intact cells, $(2'-5')A_n$ causes inhibition of protein synthesis, presumably by transient activation of the nuclease. Since cells are not permeable to $(2'-5')A_n$ as such, it was introduced by making cells permeable and then "resealing" them (*161*) or by using the calcium-phosphate-precipitation technique of introduction of nucleic acids (*162*). Introduced immediately after virus infection, $(2'-5')A_n$ also inhibited virus growth (*163*). The nonphosphorylated core of $(2'-5')A_n$ can also inhibit DNA synthesis and cell growth (*167*). Both $(2'-5')A_n$ and its core have been detected in interferon-treated EMC virus-infected cells (*164, 164a*). There is some evidence that the endonuclease is active in such cells. Ribosomal RNAs isolated from these cells are cleaved into the same discrete products as are obtained by incubating intact ribosome with the endonuclease *in vitro* (*157b*).

The $(2'-5')A_n$ system might have a wider biological role, including effects on cell growth, differentiation, and regulation of gene expression, in addition to its role in the interferon system. Some of these actions may even not be mediated through the nuclease. For example, $(2'-5')A_n$-synthetase can add AMP in a $2'-5'$ linkage to an important metabolic intermediate, NAD, and $2'$-adenylylated NAD is unable to function as a redox coenzyme, thus affecting cellular metabolism (*165*). Introduced into intact cells, $(2'-5')A_n$ inhibits DNA synthesis and cell growth in human lymphoblastoid cells (*160, 166*). It also inhibits DNA synthesis in lymphocytes stimulated by mitogens (*167*). The $3'-5'$ isomers show none of these activities. It is not known whether the inhibitions of cell growth and of DNA synthesis are mediated through inhibition of protein synthesis.

If the nuclease pathway is operative *in vivo* in interferon-treated, virus-infected cells, one would expect to observe a faster turnover rate of viral RNA in such cells than in infected cells not so treated, and such has been observed (*6*) in a reovirus-infected L-cell system. In control and interferon-treated L cells infected with reovirus, cellular RNA synthesis was inhibited with actinomycin D and newly synthesized RNA was pulse-labeled with [^{3}H]uridine for 25 minutes. The label was "chased" with unlabeled uridine and cytidine, and RNA was extracted after several time intervals. Single-stranded (ss) and double-stranded (ds) RNAs were separated, and the amount of label in reoviral ssRNA was measured by liquid hybridization with reoviral genomic dsRNA followed by degradation of nonhybridized ssRNA

with RNase under proper conditions. The label in viral ssRNA decreased with time, because of conversion of ssRNA to dsRNA and
degradation of the ssRNA. The label from reo ssRNA disappeared
faster in interferon-treated cells than in control cells, and little of the
label appeared in dsRNA in interferon-treated cells. Therefore, reoviral ssRNA must turn over faster in interferon-treated cells. Calculations
of the actual rate yielded an average half-life of 12.3 hours in control
cells and 5.3 hours in interferon-treated cells. These results therefore
demonstrate that in reovirus-infected interferon-treated cells, viral
ssRNAs decays about 2.5 times more rapidly than in control cells. It is
not known whether cellular ssRNAs also turn over faster in the
interferon-treated cells. The above results are consistent with, but by
no means proof of, an active endonuclease system in the interferon-
treated virus-infected cells.

Another interesting observation is that subviral particles isolated
from reovirus-infected interferon-treated cells transcribe and methyl-
ate reo mRNAs *in vitro* at the same rate as subviral particles isolated
from control cells (72). However, the accumulated RNA of subviral
particles isolated from treated cells was mostly of a smaller size,
whereas the RNAs synthesized by subviral particles isolated from control cells were mostly full-size. This was probably due to the action of
an endoribonuclease activity associated only with the subviral particles isolated from the treated cells. However, it has not been established whether the dsRNA-dependent endonuclease system is operative here.

Another ill-understood effect of interferon on cellular metabolism
is that trisomy 21 human fibroblasts respond to human interferon with
a marked reduction in the level of cytoplasmic ribosomal RNA (168).

B. Why Would Interferon Action Be Affected by dsRNA?

The interferon system appears to use dsRNA as a modulator at both
the induction and the action phases. If the dsRNA-activated enzyme
systems induced in interferon-treated cells contribute toward the
mechanism of antiviral action of interferons, and if dsRNA really is one
of the physiological inducers of interferon synthesis, then one can ra-
tionalize that, in effect, dsRNA serves as the physiological signal elicited by active virus replication. It has been demonstrated for some
viruses that dsRNA strands (or at least complementary RNA strands)
are generated as side products or as intermediates in their replication
cycles. This line of thinking has led to the general consensus of a
two-staged operation of the interferon system, at least insofar as its antiviral action in multicellular organisms is concerned. Low levels of

virus infection induces interferon synthesis in some cells, possibly through the use of dsRNA as a signal. The newly synthesized interferons are secreted and circulated in the system so that other cells are exposed to interferons. In these cells, exposed to interferons prior to virus infection, the dsRNA-dependent enzyme systems are all present, owing to the newly induced synthesis of some of its components. However, the pathways are still inoperative because no dsRNA is available in these (uninfected) cells. Therefore, these latent enzymes do not interfere with cellular metabolism; they only keep the cells fully equipped to deal with any subsequent viral infection. If those interferon-treated cells are now infected with viruses, dsRNA may be produced during virus multiplication and cause the triggering of the dsRNA-dependent pathways of inhibition of protein synthesis. The overall inhibition of protein synthesis may lead to a halt of the virus replication, and the infected cells may eventually survive, or even be killed because of the gross inhibition of protein synthesis. Either way, the spread of the virus infection is blocked by impairing the amplification of the number of infectious virus particles.

There is some experimental evidence that dsRNA may not have to be in a "naked" form to activate the $(2'-5')A_n$-synthetase and protein kinase. Reovirions, reovirus cores (prepared by treating reovirions with chrymotrypsin, which removes the outer protein coat of the virions), or reo subviral particles (isolated from reovirus-infected cells), all activate the endonuclease system and the protein kinase system (6). Reovirions that have gone through repeated cycles of isopycnic banding in CsCl gradients can still activate the nuclease system. However, dsRNA in this form is only 4% as efficient, on a weight basis, as naked dsRNA in its ability to activate the nuclease system. Moreover, reovirions treated with RNase III (dsRNA-cleaving enzyme) no longer activate the nuclease system in spite of the fact that, under these conditions, little dsRNA inside the virions is degraded. This suggests that dsRNA exposed on the surface of the virions is responsible for the activation of the enzyme system. Whether these dsRNAs come from nonspecific superficial binding of dsRNA, or are tips of genomic RNAs protruding from the protein coat, is not known.

In vitro, the dsRNA-dependent pathways of inhibition of protein synthesis do not discriminate between cellular mRNAs and viral mRNAs per se. On the other hand, at least in some cell–virus systems (e.g., L cells infected with reovirus), it has been definitely established that, in cells that have been treated with interferon before virus infection, there is a preferential inhibition of viral protein synthesis as compared to cellular protein synthesis (73). If this is indeed caused by the two dsRNA-dependent pathways of inhibition of protein synthesis, it is not at all clear how the selectivity is exerted *in vivo*.

It has been suggested that the dsRNA-dependent enzyme system is finely tuned and is active within a subcellular microenvironment. For example, if viral dsRNA is the signal for turning on the nuclease system, the nuclease may attack ssRNAs only in close physical proximity to the dsRNA, thereby causing more damage to viral RNA rather than cellular RNAs. The dissipation of the nuclease activity to a point farther from the dsRNA could be prevented by a rapid destruction of $(2'-5')A_n$ by the phosphodiesterase. Thus one can imagine formation of restricted centers of nuclease activity around a source of dsRNA.

Some experimental data support this hypothesis. Single-stranded portions of mRNAs, artificially made partially double-stranded, are preferentially degraded in extracts of interferon-treated cells (153). One model substrate used was EMC viral RNA, which is known to contain a long poly(C) stretch near its 5' end. Poly(I) was annealed to this poly(C) stretch to make the viral RNA partially double stranded. When this RNA was incubated in an extract from interferon-treated cells, it was degraded faster than another completely single-stranded viral RNA included in the same reaction mixture. These results indicated that localized activation of the $(2'-5')A_n$-dependent endonuclease was taking place. When a more natural RNA with partial double-stranded structure, namely the "replicative intermediate" isolated from EMCV-infected cells, was incubated with extracts from interferon-treated cells, its single-stranded RNA portion was "shaved off," leaving behind a double-stranded RNA core. If this phenomenon does occur in interferon-treated whole cells infected with EMCV, it might account for the decreased accumulation of viral mRNA in such cells.

IX. Induction of New Proteins in Cells Treated with Interferons

The attempts to define the "antiviral state" in molecular terms have been confined mostly to a search for new enzymic activities appearing in interferon-treated cells. But several laboratories have started to search for new (induced) proteins synthesized in the cell upon interferon treatment without any preconceived notions about the functions of such proteins. Since 1979, a number of papers reported the detection of "new" proteins in interferon-treated mouse, chicken, or human cells.

TABLE II

PROTEINS INDUCED BY TREATMENT OF CELLS WITH INTERFERON

Cells	Molecular weight	Remarks	Reference
Mouse Krebs ascites	48,000	Ribosome-associated	110
Mouse EAT	14,500	In vitro translated	169
Mouse EAT and L	67,000 80,000 120,000	Bind to dsRNA	170
Mouse embryo fibroblast and JLSV5	63,000		171
Human FS4 and GM254 fibroblasts	80,000 120,000	Bind to dsRNA	170
	56,000 67,000 88,000	Do not bind to dsRNA	174
Human FS4 fibroblasts	56,000 67,000 80,000 120,000	Induced by γ-interferon	173a
Human fibroblasts	44,000 to 80,000	Four proteins induced	172
Human HeLa	50,000 53,000	Translated in vitro	173
Chick embryo fibroblasts	56,000	Binds to dsRNA, coelutes with $(2'\text{-}5')A_n$ synthethase	149

The basic design of these experiments was to label treated and untreated cells with radiolabeled amino acids, lyse the cells, and analyze the labeled proteins before or after some fractionation step. The appearance of any new protein in the treated cells was usually shown to parallel the appearance of an antiviral state by one or more criteria, e.g., the kinetics, the susceptibility to actinomycin D, the dependence on interferon concentration, and the species specificity for interferon.

In two cases, in vitro translation of mRNA isolated from interferon-treated and untreated cells shows that the mRNA levels of the newly induced proteins are higher in the treated cells. Table II lists all the interferon-induced protein reported so far.

The synthesis of these proteins in interferon-treated cells is tightly regulated. The proteins are not continuously synthesized even if the cells are in constant contact with interferon. Their rates of synthesis peak within a few hours of commencement of interferon-treatment and then decline sharply with time. Moreover, the kinetics of synthesis of the different induced proteins are different (*174*). When inhibitors of RNA synthesis are added together with interferon, the proteins are not synthesized, showing the need for new RNA synthesis. However, if the inhibitors are added 4–8 hours after the interferon-treatment has begun, "superinduction" of these proteins occurs. More of the induced protein are synthesized as compared to the cells treated with interferon only. The same is true for $(2'-5')A_n$ synthetase activity and the antiviral state (*174a*).

X. Future Directions

Although much progress has been made in interferon research within the last few years, we are still far from understanding the mechanism of interferon actions in molecular terms. Biochemical studies, no matter how elegant, cannot by themselves establish cause-and-effect relationships. Traditionally, molecular biologists have used genetic mutants for this purpose. Some attempts have been made in this direction for studying the mechanisms of action of interferons, but success has been limited. No viral mutant resistant to interferon action has yet been isolated, although isolation of a mutant that is relatively more sensitive to interferon has been reported (*175*). Isolation of the proper mutants would greatly facilitate the understanding of the mechanism of action of interferons. An interferon-resistant mouse cell line has been established and well characterized (*176*). However, the lesion in this variant cell line is apparently at the level of interaction of interferons with cell surface receptors. Therefore, although this cell line would be extremely useful in interferon-receptor studies, it is not of much use for understanding the later events of interferon action. One attempt to isolate mouse cell mutants constitutively in the antiviral state yielded semiconstitutive producers of a low level of interferons (*177, 178*). More efforts in this direction are definitely desirable.

What is especially needed is to establish whether the variety of biochemical changes observed in interferon-treated cells is essential for the antiviral state, and, if so, what is their relative importance? Some recent studies provide a useful system for answering this kind of question (*179*). It has been observed that embryonal carcinoma cells do not become resistant to Semliki Forest virus or VSV upon treatment with interferon (*180, 181*). These cells do not lack interferon receptors, as interferon-treatment causes an elevation of their $(2'-5')A_n$-synthetase activity. But, surprisingly, their dsRNA-dependent protein kinase activity is not elevated (*181*). Then it was found that, although interferon treatment did not block the multiplication of Sindbis, flu, and wild-type VSV in these embryonal carcinoma cells, multiplication of EMC, mengo, and two temperature-sensitive mutants of VSV was completely blocked. It thus appears that interferon induces a partial antiviral state in these cells. It remains to be seen whether there is a direct correlation between the induction of a partial antiviral state and the induction of only a part of the dsRNA-dependent enzyme systems in these cells.

There are other examples of the establishment of partial antiviral states. In a clone of Moloney MuLV-infected Swiss/3T3 cells, EMC replication is insensitive to interferon but MuLV replication is not (182). Similarly, EMC replication is insensitive to interferon in NIH/3T3 cells, but replication of VSV, mengovirus, and MuLV is sensitive (182, 183). Moreover, $(2'-5')A_n$ synthetase is induced in the latter cells by interferon treatment, but the protein kinase is not induced (183). Differential sensitivity of different viruses in the same cells could be determined by the genetic makeup of the cells (184). The nature of the interferon may also determine the degree of sensitivity of different viruses. Vaccinia and reo viruses are more sensitive to γ interferon as compared to α interferon, whereas VSV and EMC are equally sensitive to both (173a).

In two cases, the association between the antiviral state and the induction of dsRNA-dependent enzymes seems to be uncoupled. A human carcinoma cell line, HEC-1, is totally insensitive to both antiviral and anticellular actions of interferons (185, 186). However, both interferon-treated and untreated cells have high levels of $(2'-5')A_n$ synthetase and dsRNA-dependent protein kinase activities (185). Conversely, in a human embryonic lung fibroblast line, interferon treatment causes the development of antiviral state, but no $(2'-5')A_n$-synthetase or dsRNA-dependent protein kinase can be detected in these cells before or after interferon treatment (186).

The development of the new technologies of gene cloning and introduction of macromolecules into living cells has opened up new ways of solving the same problems without resorting to isolation of cell mutants. For example, one can adopt the following approach if one wants to ask the specific question: Is an elevated level of $(2'-5')A_n$-synthetase enough to render a cell resistant to virus infection? Instead of elevating the level of $(2'-5')A_n$-synthetase in a cell by treating it with interferon (which also causes numerous other changes), one should try to elevate its level by the physical introduction of the protein, its mRNA, or its gene from an extracellular source. Since the protein has been purified, and the mRNA can be isolated and assayed by translation in frog oocytes (187), it is fairly straightforward (with the modern technology of recombinant DNA), to isolate the gene coding for this protein. Cells can then be transfected with this isolated DNA. The recipient cells in which this exogenous DNA is expressed can be selected and tested for the antiviral state.

The biggest hiatus in the present state of knowledge of interferon actions is that little is known about what happens immediately after a cell comes into contact with interferons. It is fairly obvious now that eventually the expression of some specific cellular genes is augmented by interferon action. But how interferons bring this about is anyone's guess. Any explanation must take into account two basic facts: only a few molecules of interferon are needed per cell, and a multitude of changes in cell metabolism is caused. This is typically true for many hormones, and one can foresee very similar questions being asked for interferon action. Does interferon act only on the cell surface, or is it internalized? Is there a "second messenger" that amplifies the primary signal of interferon? What is the nature of interferon receptors, and are they membrane-bound or cytoplasmic? Do they travel to the nucleus? What portion of an interferon molecule is essential for its biological actions? Can interferon action be divided into immediate effects and long-term effects, the immediate effects being those on cell membrane and cell surface, not needing any modulation of gene expression?

The discovery of the dsRNA-dependent enzyme activities have implications beyond the interferon system. These are the first examples of enzymes activated by interaction with dsRNA. Understanding the physicochemical basis of this interaction will be worthwhile. How an enzyme is activated by interaction with another protein or nucleic acid is a central question of molecular biology. The fact that dsRNA can activate the protein kinase and the $(2'-5')A_n$-synthetase, whereas ssRNA cannot, gives added interest to the problem. Since these enzymes exist in cells of such diverse origin, is dsRNA a ubiquitous biological molecule? Or is dsRNA mimicking the action of some other yet unidentified natural molecule? Is the use of $(2'-5')A_n$ restricted to the interferon system only, or is it synthesized in response to other biological signals too? How does it activate the nuclease, and does it have any functions other than activating the nuclease? Considering the present pace of interferon research, I am sure that we will know the answer to some of these questions in the not-so-distant future.

Acknowledgments

I am indebted to Peter Lengyel for a critical reading of the manuscript. I wish to thank Sohan L. Gupta for valuable discussion and Wanda Zablocki and Alicia Bralove for secretarial help. I am supported by grants from the National Cancer Institute.

REFERENCES

1. A. Isaacs and J. Lindenmann, *Proc. R. Soc. London Ser. B* **B147**, 258 (1957).
2. R. M. Friedman, *Bacteriol. Rev.* **41**, 543 (1977).
3. C. Baglioni, *Cell* **17**, 255 (1979).
4. M. Revel, in "Interferon" (I. Gresser, ed.), Vol. 1, p. 101. Academic Press, New York, 1979.
5. B. R. G. Williams and I. M. Kerr, *Trends Biochem. Sci.* (*Pers. Ed.*) **5**, 138 (1980).
6. P. Lengyel, R. Desrosiers, R. Broeze, E. Slattery, H. Taira, J. Dougherty, H. Samanta, J. Pichon, P. Farrell, L. Ratner, and G. Sen, in "Microbiology—1980" (D. Schlessinger, ed.), p. 106, Am. Soc. Microbiol. Press, Washington, D.C., 1980.
7. N. B. Finter, ed. "Interferons and Interferon Inducers." North-Holland, Amsterdam, 1973.
8. W. E. Stewart II, "The Interferon System." Springer-Verlag, Vienna and New York, 1979.
9. E. A. Havell, T. G. Hayes, and J. Vilček, *Virology* **89**, 330 (1978).
10. J. S. Youngner, *Tex. Rep. Biol. Med.* **35**, 17 (1977).
11. D. Slate and F. H. Ruddle, *Pharmacol. Ther.* **4**, 221 (1979).
12. A. Meager, H. E. Graves, J. R. Walker, D. C. Burke, D. M. Swallow, and A. Westerveld, *J. Gen. Virol.* **45**, 309 (1979).
13. N. Mantei, M. Schwarzstein, M. Streuli, S. Panem, S. Nagata, and C. Weissmann, *Gene* **10**, 1 (1980).
14. A. Adams, B. Lindin, H. Strander, and K. Cantell, *J. Gen. Virol.* **28**, 219 (1975).
15. P. Marcus and M. J. Sekellik, *Nature* **266**, 815 (1977).
16. R. R. Wagner, *Nature* **204**, 49 (1964).
17. D. C. Burke and G. Veomett, *PNAS* **74**, 3391 (1977).
18. S. L. Abreu and F. C. Bancroft, *BBRC* **82**, 1300 (1978).
19. E. De Maeyer and J. De Maeyer-Guignard, in "Comprehensive Virology" (H. Frankel-Conrat and R. R. Wagner, eds.), Vol. 15, p. 205. Plenum, New York, 1979.
20. W. E. Stewart II, L. B. Grosser, and R. Z. Lockart, *J. Virol.* **7**, 792 (1971).
21. H. M. Frankfort, E. A. Havell, C. M. Croce, and J. Vilček, *Virology* **89**, 45 (1978).
22. J. S. Youngner and J. V. Hallum, *Virology* **37**, 473 (1969).
23. J. De Maeyer-Guignard, A. Cachard, and E. De Maeyer, *Virology* **102**, 222 (1980).
23a. P. B. Sehgal and S. L. Gupta, *PNAS* **77**, 3489 (1980).
24. J. J. Greene, C. W. Dieffenbach, L. C. Yang, and P. O. P. Ts'o, *Bchem* **19**, 2485 (1980).
25. J. Vilček, E. A. Havell, and M. Kohase, *J. Infect. Dis.* **133**, A22 (1976).
26. R. L. Cavalieri, E. A. Havell, J. Vilček, and S. Pestka, *PNAS* **74**, 4415 (1977).
27. P. B. Sehgal, D. S. Lyles, and I. Tamm, *Virology* **89**, 186 (1978).
28. W. E. Stewart II, E. De Clercq, A. Billiau, J. Desmyter, and P. De Somer, *PNAS* **69**, 1851 (1972).
29. W. A. Carter, and E. De Clercq, *Science* **186**, 1172 (1974).
30. W. Jelinek, and L. Leinwand, *Cell* **15**, 205 (1978).
31. D. Baltimore, *JMB* **32**, 359 (1968).
31a. T. W. Nilsen, D. Wood, and C. Baglioni, *Virology* **109**, 82 (1981).
32. C. Colby, and P. H. Duesberg, *Nature* **222**, 940 (1969).
33. J. J. Lucas and H. S. Ginsberg, *BBRC* **49**, 39 (1972).
34. B. Cordell-Stewart and M. W. Taylor, *J. Virol.* **11**, 232 (1973).
35. W. E. Stewart II, E. De Clercq, and P. De Somer, *J. Gen. Virol.* **18**, 237 (1973).
36. E. Ehrenfeld and T. Hunt, *PNAS* **68**, 1075 (1971).

37. S. Ochoa and C. de Haro, *ARB* **48**, 549 (1979).
38. J. Content, B. Lebleu, and E. De Clercq, *Bchem* **17**, 88 (1978).
39. P. Torrence and R. M. Friedman, *JBC* **254**, 1259 (1979).
40. M. Kawakita, B. Cabrer, H. Taira, M. Rebello, E. Slattery, H. Weideli, and P. Lengyel, *JBC* **253**, 598 (1978).
41. J. De Maeyer-Guignard, M. G. Tovey, I. Gresser, and E. De Maeyer, *Nature* **271**, 622 (1978).
42. M. Rubinstein, S. Rubinstein, P. C. Familletti, M. S. Gross, R. S. Miller, A. A. Waldman, and S. Pestka, *Science* **202**, 1289 (1978).
43. E. Knight, Jr., *PNAS* **73**, 520 (1976).
44. K. C. Zoon, M. E. Smith, P. J. Bridgen, D. Zur Nedden, and C. B. Anfinsen, *PNAS* **76**, 5601 (1979).
45. H. Taira, R. J. Broeze, B. M. Jayaram, P. Lengyel, M. W. Hunkapiller, and L. E. Hood, *Science* **207**, 528 (1980).
46. E. Knight, Jr., M. W. Hunkapiller, B. D. Korant, R. W. F. Hardy, and L. E. Hood, *Science* **207**, 525 (1980).
47. K. C. Zoon, M. E. Smith, P. J. Bridgen, C. B. Anfinsen, M. W. Hunkapiller, and L. E. Hood, *Science* **207**, 527 (1980).
48. M. Streuli, S. Nagata, and C. Weissmann, *Science* **209**, 1343 (1980).
49. R. Derynck, J. Content, E. De Clercq, G. Volckaert, J. Tavernier, R. Deuof, and W. Fiers, *Nature* **285**, 542 (1980).
50. T. Taniguchi, S. Ohno, Y. Fujii-Kuriyama, and M. Muramatsu, *Gene* **10**, 11 (1980).
51. D. V. Goeddel, D. Leung, T. J. Dull, M. Gross, R. M. Lawn, R. McCandliss, P. Seeburg, A. Ullrich, E. Yelverton, and P. W. Gray, *Nature* **290**, 20 (1981).
52. M. Houghton, M. A. W. Eaton, A. G. Stewart, J. C. Smith, S. M. Doel, G. H. Catlin, H. M. Lewis, T. P. Patel, J. S. Emtage, N. H. Carey, and A. G. Porter, *NARes* **8**, 2885 (1980).
53. T. Taniguchi, N. Mantei, M. Schwarzstein, S. Nagata, M. Muramatsu, and C. Weissmann, *Nature* **285**, 547 (1980).
53a. P. B. Sehgal and A. D. Sagar, *Nature* **288**, 95 (1980).
53b. D. Owerbach, W. J. Rutter, T. B. Shows, P. Gray, D. Goeddel, and R. M. Lawn, *PNAS* **78**, 3123 (1981).
53c. R. M. Lawn, J. Adelman, T. J. Dull, M. Gross, D. V. Goeddel, and A. Ullrich, *Science* **212**, 1159 (1981).
53d. S. Nagata, N. Mantei, and C. Weissmann, *Nature* **287**, 40 (1980).
53e. M. G. Masucci, R. Szigeti, E. Klein, G. Klein, J. Gruest, L. Montagnier, H. Taira, A. Hall, S. Nagata, and C. Weissmann, *Science* **209**, 1431, 1980.
53f. D. V. Goeddel, E. Yelverton, A. Ullrich, H. L. Heyneker, G. Miozzari, W. Holmes, P. H. Seeberg, T. J. Dull, L. May, N. Stebbing, R. Crea, S. Maeda, R. McCandliss, A. Sloma, J. M. Tabor, M. Gross, P. C. Familletti, and S. Pestka, *Nature* **287**, 411 (1980).
53g. M. Streuli, A. Hall, W. Boll, W. E. Stewart II, S. Nagata, and C. Weissmann, *PNAS* **78**, 2848 (1981).
54. L. M. Pfeffer, E. Wang, and I. Tamm, *J. Cell Biol.* **85**, 9 (1980).
54a. P. Lindahl-Magnusson, P. Leary, and I. Gresser, *Nature NB* **237**, 120 (1972).
54b. S. L. Lin, P. O. P. Ts'o, and M. D. Hollenberg, *BBRC* **96**, 168 (1980).
54c. S. Keay and S. E. Grossberg, *PNAS* **77**, 4099 (1980).
54d. P. B. Fisher, R. A. Mufson, and I. B. Weinstein, *BBRC* **100**, 823 (1981).
54e. K. Chandrabose, P. Cuatrecasas, and R. Pottathil, *BBRC* **98**, 661 (1981).
55. B. R. Bloom, *Nature* **284**, 593 (1980).

56. I. Gresser and M. G. Tovey, *BBA* **516**, 231 (1978).
57. V. E. Vengris, B. D. Stollar, and P. M. Pitha, *Virology* **65**, 410 (1975).
58. F. Besancon and H. Ankel, *Nature* **252**, 478 (1974).
59. C. Chany, *Biomedicine* **25**, 148 (1976).
60. F. Dianzani and S. Baron, *Nature* **257**, 682 (1975).
61. J. Taylor, *BBRC* **14**, 447 (1964).
62. F. Dianzani, C. E. Buckler, and S. Baron, *PSEBM* **130**, 519 (1969).
63. K. L. Radke, C. Colby, J. R. Kates, H. M. Krider, and D. M. Prescott, *J. Virol.* **13**, 623 (1974).
64. Y. H. Tan, *in* "Interferons and Their Actions" (W. E. Stewart II, ed.), p. 73. CRC Press, Boca Raton, Florida, 1977.
65. D. L. Slate, L. Shulman, J. Lawrence, M. Revel, and F. H. Ruddle, *J. Virol.* **25**, 319 (1978).
66. M. Revel, O. Bash, and F. H. Ruddle, *Nature* **269**, 139 (1976).
67. P.-F. Lin, D. L. Slate, F. C. Lawyer, and F. H. Ruddle, *Science* **209**, 287 (1980).
68. J. E. Blalock and S. Baron, *Nature* **269**, 422 (1977).
69. J. E. Blalock and S. Baron, *J. Gen. Virol.* **42**, 363 (1979).
70. W. K. Joklik, *in* "Comprehensive Virology" (H. Fraenkel-Conrat and R. Wagner, eds.), Vol. 2, p. 231. Plenum, New York, 1974.
71. M. E. Wiebe and W. K. Joklik, *Virology* **66**, 229 (1975).
72. R. L. Galster and P. Lengyel, *NARes* **3**, 581 (1976).
73. S. L. Gupta, W. D. Grazidei III, H. Weideli, M. L. Sopori, and P. Lengyel, *Virology* **57**, 49 (1974).
74. A. K. Banerjee, G. Abraham, and R. J. Colonno, *J. Gen. Virol.* **34**, 1 (1977).
75. P. I. Marcus and M. J. Sekellick, *J. Gen. Virol.* **38**, 391 (1978).
76. H. R. Thacore, *J. Gen. Virol.* **41**, 421 (1978).
77. R. K. Maheshwari, A. E. Demsey, S. B. Mohanty, and R. M. Friedman, *PNAS* **77**, 2284 (1980).
78. B. Moss, *in* "Comprehensive Virology" (H. Fraenkel-Conrat and R. R. Wagner, eds.), Vol. 3, p. 405. Plenum, New York (1974).
79. D. H. Metz, *Cell* **6**, 429, (1975).
80. N. P. Salzman, and G. Khoury *in* "Comprehensive Virology" (H. Fraenkel-Conrat and R. R. Wagner, eds.), Vol. 3, p. 63, Plenum, New York (1974).
81. E. Yakobson, C. Prives, J. R. Hartman, E. Winocour, and M. Revel, *Cell* **12**, 73 (1977).
82. D. H. Metz, M. J. Levin, and M. N. Oxman, *J. Gen. Virol.* **32**, 227 (1976).
83. K. Yamamoto, N. Yamaguchi, and K. Oda, *Virology* **68**, 58 (1975).
84. A. Graessman, M. Graessman, H. Hoffman, J. Niebel, G. Brandner, and N. Mueller, *FEBS Lett.* **39**, 249 (1974).
85. S. M. Kingsman and C. E. Samuel, *Virology* **101**, 458 (1980).
86. E. Yakobson, M. Revel, and E. Winocour, *Virology* **80**, 225 (1977).
87. M. N. Oxman, S. Baron, P. H. Black, K. K. Takemoto, K. Habel, and W. P. Rowe, *Virology* **32**, 122 (1967).
88. M. N. Oxman, M. J. Levin, and A. M. Lewis, Jr., *J. Virol.* **13**, 322 (1974).
89. A. G. Morris and D. C. Burke, *J. Gen. Virol.* **43**, 173 (1979).
89a. R. I. Avery, J. D. Norton, J. S. Jones, D. C. Burke, and A. G. Morris, *Nature* **288**, 93 (1980).
90. R. M. Friedman, E. H. Chang, J. M. Ramseur, and M. W. Meyers, *J. Virol.* **16**, 569 (1975).
91. P. A. Pitha, W. P. Rowe, and M. N. Oxman, *Virology* **70**, 324 (1976).

92. A. Billiau, H. Hermans, P. T. Allen, J. De Maeyer-Guignard, and P. De Somer, *Virology* **73**, 537 (1976).
93. E. J. Chang, and R. M. Friedman, *BBRC* **77**, 392 (1977).
93a. P. M. Pitha, B. Fernie, F. Moldarelli, T. Haltman, and N. A. Wivel, *J. Gen. Virol.* **46**, 97 (1980).
94. A. D. Bandyopadhyay, E. H. Chang, C. C. Levy, and R. M. Friedman, *BBRC* **87**, 983 (1979).
94a. D. Wallach and M. Revel, *Nature* **287**, 68 (1980).
95. G. C. Sen and N. H. Sarkar, *Virology* **102**, 431 (1980).
96. P. I. Marcus and J. M. Salb, *Virology* **30**, 502 (1966).
97. W. K. Joklik and T. C. Merigan, *PNAS* **56**, 558 (1966).
98. W. A. Carter and H. B. Levy, *Science* **155**, 1254 (1967).
99. I. M. Kerr, *J. Virol.* **7**, 448 (1971).
100. R. M. Friedman, D. H. Metz, R. M. Esteban, D. R. Tovell, L. A. Ball, and I. M. Kerr, *J. Virol.* **10**, 1184 (1972).
101. I. M. Kerr, R. M. Friedman, R. M. Esteban, R. E. Brown, L. A. Ball, D. H. Metz, D. Risby, D. R. Tovell, and J. A. Sonnabend, *Adv. Biosci.* **11**, 109 (1973).
102. I. M. Kerr, R. M. Friedman, R. E. Brown, L. A. Ball, and J. C. Brown, *J. Virol.* **13**, 9 (1974).
103. K. Ohtsuki, F. Dianzani, and S. Baron, *Nature* **269**, 536 (1977).
104. E. Falcoff, R. Falcoff, B. Lebleu, and M. Revel, *J. Virol.* **12**, 421 (1973).
105. J. Content, B. Lebleu, U. Nudel, A. Zilberstein, H. Berissi, and M. Revel, *EJB* **54**, 1 (1975).
106. S. L. Gupta, M. Sopori, and P. Lengyel, *BBRC* **54**, 777 (1973).
107. G. Hiller, I. Winkler, G. Viehauser, C. Jungwirth, G. Bodo, S. Dube, and W. Ostertag, *Virology* **69**, 360 (1975).
108. J. Content, B. Lebleu, A. Zilberstein, H. Berissi, and M. Revel, *FEBS Lett.* **41**, 125 (1974).
109. S. L. Gupta, M. L. Sopori, and P. Lengyel, *BBRC* **57**, 763 (1974).
110. C. E. Samuel and W. K. Joklik, *Virology* **58**, 476 (1974).
111. G. C. Sen, S. L. Gupta, G. E. Brown, B. Lebleu, M. A. Rebello, and P. Lengyel, *J. Virol.* **17**, 191 (1976).
112. A. Zilberstein, B. Dudock, H. Berissi, and M. Revel, *JMB* **108**, 43 (1976).
113. R. Falcoff, B. Lebleu, J. Sanceau, J. Weissenbach, G. Dirheimer, J. P. Ebel, and E. Falcoff, *BBRC* **68**, 1323 (1976).
114. V. Mayr, H. P. Bermayer, G. Weindinger, C. Jungwirth, H. J. Gross, and G. Bodo, *EJB* **76**, 541 (1977).
115. C. Colby, E. E. Penhoet, and C. E. Samuel, *Virology* **74**, 262 (1976).
116. A. Schmidt, Y. Chernajovsky, L. Shulman, P. Federman, H. Berissi, and M. Revel, *PNAS* **76**, 4788 (1979).
117. A. J. Shatkin, *Cell* **7**, 305 (1977).
118. G. C. Sen, B. Lebleu, G. E. Brown, M. A. Rebello, H. Furuichi, M. Morgan, A. J. Shatkin, and P. Lengyel, *BBRC* **65**, 427 (1975).
119. G. C. Sen, S. Shaila, B. Lebleu, G. E. Brown, R. C. Desrosiers, and P. Lengyel, *J. Virol.* **21**, 69 (1977).
120. S. Shaila, B. Lebleu, G. E. Brown, G. C. Sen, and P. Lengyel, *J. Gen. Virol.* **37**, 535 (1977).
121. C. E. Samuel, D. A. Farris, D. A. Eppstein, *Virology* **83**, 56 (1977).
122. L. A. Ball and C. N. White, *Virology* **84**, 496 (1978).
123. R. C. Desrosiers and P. Lengyel, *BBA* **562**, 471 (1979).

124. H. Kroath, H. G. Janda, G. Hiller, E. Kuhn, C. Jungwirth, H. J. Gross, and G. Bodo, *Virology* **92**, 572 (1979).
124a. F. de Ferra and C. Baglioni, *Virology* **112**, 426 (1981).
125. I. M. Kerr, R. E. Brown, and L. A. Ball, *Nature* **250**, 57 (1974).
126. B. Lebleu, G. C. Sen, S. Shaila, B. Cabrer, and P. Lengyel, *PNAS* **73**, 3107 (1976).
127. W. K. Roberts, A. Hovanessian, R. E. Brown, M. J. Clemens, and I. M. Kerr, *Nature* **264**, 477 (1976).
128. A. Zilberstein, P. Federman, L. Shulman, and M. Revel, *FEBS Lett.* **68**, 119 (1976).
129. G. E. Brown, B. Lebleu, M. Kawakita, S. Shaila, G. C. Sen, and P. Lengyel, *BBRC* **69**, 114 (1976).
130. I. M. Kerr and R. E. Brown, *PNAS* **75**, 256 (1978).
131. E. M. Martin, N. J. M. Birdsall, R. E. Brown, and I. M. Kerr, *EJB* **95**, 295 (1979).
132. P. J. Farrell, G. C. Sen, M. F. Dubois, L. Ratner, E. Slattery, and P. Lengyel, *PNAS* **75**, 5893 (1978).
133. M. J. Clemens and B. R. G. Williams, *Cell* **13**, 565 (1978).
134. C. Baglioni, M. A. Minks, and P. A. Maroney, *Nature* **273**, 684 (1978).
135. C. S. Rubin and O. M. Rosen, *ARB* **44**, 831 (1975).
136. G. C. Sen, B. Lebleu, G. E. Brown, M. Kawakita, E. Slattery, and P. Lengyel, *Nature* **264**, 370 (1976).
137. P. J. Farrell, K. Balkow, T. Hunt, and R. J. Jackson, *Cell* **11**, 187 (1977).
138. G. C. Sen, H. Taira, and P. Lengyel, *JBC* **253**, 5915 (1978).
139. C. E. Samuel, *PNAS* **76**, 600 (1979).
140. A. Kimchi, A. Zilberstein, A. Schmidt, L. Shulman, and M. Revel, *JBC* **254**, 9846 (1979).
141. S. L. Gupta, *J. Virol.* **29**, 301 (1979).
142. A. Das, R. O. Ralston, M. Grace, R. Roy, P. Ghosh-Dastidar, H. K. Das, B. Yaghmai, S. Palmieri, and N. K. Gupta, *PNAS* **76**, 5076 (1979).
143. C. de Haro, A. Datta, and S. Ochoa, *PNAS* **75**, 243 (1978).
144. D. A. Epstein, P. F. Torrence, and R. M. Friedman, *PNAS* **77**, 107 (1980).
145. L. Ratner, R. C. Wiegand, P. J. Farrell, G. C. Sen, B. Cabrer, and P. Lengyel, *BBRC* **81**, 947 (1978).
146. I. Krishnan and C. Baglioni, *Nature* **285**, 485 (1980).
147. J. P. Dougherty, H. Samanta, P. J. Farrell, and P. Lengyel, *JBC* **255**, 3813 (1980).
147a. K. Yang, H. Samanta, J. Dougherty, P. Jayaram, R. Broeze, and P. Lengyel, *JBC* **256**, 9324 (1981).
148. A. Zilberstein, A. Kimchi, A. Schmidt, and M. Revel, *PNAS* **75**, 4734 (1978).
149. L. A. Ball, *Virology* **94**, 282 (1979).
150. H. Samanta, J. P. Dougherty, and P. Lengyel, *JBC* **255**, 9807 (1980).
151. L. Ratner, G. C. Sen, G. E. Brown, B. Lebleu, M. Kawakita, B. Cabrer, E. Slattery, and P. Lengyel, *EJB* **79**, 565 (1977).
152. M. A. Minks, S. Benvin, P. A. Maroney, and C. Baglioni, *JBC* **254**, 5058 (1979).
153. T. W. Nilsen and C. Baglioni, *PNAS* **76**, 2600 (1979).
154. M. A. Minks, D. K. West, S. Benvin, and C. Baglioni, *JBC* **254**, 10180 (1979).
155. M. A. Minks, S. Benvin, P. A. Maroney, and C. Baglioni, *NARes* **6**, 767 (1979).
156. A. Schmidt, A. Zilberstein, L. Shulman, P. Federman, H. Berissi, and M. Revel, *FEBS Lett.* **95**, 257 (1978).
157. E. Slattery, N. Ghosh, H. Samanta, and P. Lengyel, *PNAS* **76**, 4778 (1979).
157a. C. Baglioni, S. B. D'Alessandro, T. W. Nilsen, J. A. J. den Hartog, R. Crea, and J. H. Van Boom, *JBC* **256**, 3253 (1981).

157b. D. H. Wreschner, T. C. James, R. H. Silverman, and I. M. Kerr, *NARes* **9**, 1571 (1981).

158. D. A. Eppstein and C. E. Samuel, *Virology* **89**, 240 (1978).

158a. D. H. Wreschner, J. W. McCauley, J. J. Skehel, and I. M. Kerr, *Nature* **289**, 414 (1981).

158b. G. Floyd-Smith, E. Slattery, and P. Lengyel, *Science* **212**, 1030 (1981).

159. G. R. Stark, W. J. Dower, R. T. Schimke, R. E. Brown, and I. M. Kerr, *Nature* **278**, 471 (1979).

159a. N. Shimizu and Y. Sokawa, *JBC* **254**, 12034 (1979).

159b. I. Krishnan and C. Baglioni, *PNAS* **77**, 6506 (1980).

160. R. R. Golgher, B. R. G. Williams, C. S. Gilbert, R. E. Brown, and I. M. Kerr, *Ann. N.Y. Acad Sci.* **350**, 448 (1980).

161. B. R. G. Williams and I. M. Kerr, *Nature* **276**, 88 (1978).

162. A. G. Hovanessian, J. Wood, E. Meurs, and L. Montagnier, *PNAS* **76**, 3261 (1979).

163. B. R. G. Williams, R. R. Golgher, and I. M. Kerr, *FEBS Lett.* **105**, 47 (1979).

164. B. R. G. Williams, R. R. Golgher, R. E. Brown, C. S. Gilbert, and I. M. Kerr, *Nature* **282**, 582 (1979).

164a. M. Knight, P. J. Cayley, R. H. Silverman, D. H. Wreschner, C. S. Gilbert, R. E. Brown, and I. M. Kerr, *Nature* **288**, 189 (1980).

165. L. A. Ball and C. N. White, *in* "Regulation of Macromolecular Synthesis" (G. Koch and D. Richter, eds.), Academic Press, New York, in press.

166. A. G. Hovanessian and J. Wood, *Virology* **101**, 81 (1980).

167. A. Kimchi, H. Shure, and M. Revel, *Nature* **282**, 849 (1979).

168. L. E. Maroun, *BBA* **517**, 109 (1978).

169. P. J. Farrell, R. J. Broeze, and P. Lengyel, *Nature* **279**, 523 (1979).

170. S. L. Gupta, B. Y. Rubin, and S. L. Holmes, *PNAS* **76**, 4817 (1979).

171. M. De Ley, A. Billiau, and P. De Somer, *BBRC* **89**, 701 (1979).

172. E. Knight, Jr. and B. D. Korant, *PNAS* **76**, 1824 (1979).

173. P. J. Farrell, R. J. Broeze, and P. Lengyel, *Ann. N. Y. Acad. Sci.* **350**, 615 (1980).

173a. B. Y. Rubin and S. L. Gupta, *PNAS* **77**, 5928 (1980).

174. B. Y. Rubin and S. L. Gupta, *J. Virol.* **34**, 446 (1980).

174a. S. L. Gupta, B. Y. Rubin, and S. L. Holmes, *Virology* **111**, 331 (1981).

175. E. H. Simon, S. Kung, T. T. Koh, and P. Brandman, *Virology* **69**, 727 (1976).

176. I. Gresser, M. T. Bandu, and D. Brouty-Boyé, *J. Natl. Cancer Inst.* **52**, 533 (1974).

177. A. P. Jarvis and C. Colby, *Cell* **14**, 355 (1978).

178. A. P. Jarvis, C. White, A. Ball, S. L. Gupta, L. Ratner, G. C. Sen, and C. Colby, *Cell* **14**, 879 (1978).

179. T. W. Nilsen, D. L. Wood, and C. Baglioni, *Nature* **286**, 178 (1980).

180. D. C. Burke, C. F. Graham, and J. M. Lehman, *Cell* **13**, 243 (1978).

181. J. N. Wood and A. G. Hovanessian, *Nature* **282**, 74 (1979).

182. C. W. Czarniecki, T. Sreevalsan, R. M. Friedman, and A. Panet, *J. Virol.* **37**, 827 (1981).

183. A. G. Hovanessian, E. Meurs, and L. Montagnier, *J. Interferon Res.* **1**, 179 (1981).

184. O. Haller, H. Arnheiter, J. Lindenmann, and I. Gresser, *Nature* **283**, 660 (1980).

185. M. Verhaegen, M. Divizia, P. Vandenbussche, T. Kuwata, and J. Content *PNAS* **77**, 4479 (1980).

186. E. Meurs, A. G. Hovanessian, and L. Montagnier, *J. Interferon Res.* **1**, 219 (1981).

187. L. Shulman and M. Revel, *Nature* **288**, 98 (1980).

RNA-Helix-Destabilizing Proteins

JOHN O. THOMAS AND
WLODZIMIERZ SZER

Department of Biochemistry
New York University School of
Medicine
New York, New York

I. Introduction

In 1963, Felsenfeld *et al.* found that pancreatic ribonuclease destabilizes the native conformation of DNA by binding preferentially to single strands (*1*). Although this was purely a model investigation, the authors pointed out that some "as yet undetected proteins" might have the ability to "destabilize helical structure" and, in this sense, ribonuclease "may be a prototype of protein-DNA interactions which have a regulatory role in biological systems." This prediction was proved correct with the isolation of coliphage T4 gene 32 protein in 1970 (*2*), and the subsequent isolation of many other DNA-helix-destabilizing proteins from both prokaryotic and eukaryotic cells (reviewed in *3–7*).[1,2] The "melting activity" of helix-destabilizing proteins, which can be demonstrated *in vitro*, is related to their role in facilitating the formation of, and transiently stabilizing, single-stranded DNA whenever the need for this conformation arises during replication recombination, repair, and transcription.

[1] See also Wells *et al.* in Vol. 24 of this series.
[2] See also Gassen in Vol. 24 of this series.

Progress in Nucleic Acid Research
and Molecular Biology, Vol. 27

Under physiological conditions, "single-stranded" RNA contains many internal double-stranded regions (at least 65% of the nucleotides of coliphage MS2 RNA are base-paired (8)). Some of these "hairpin" loops arise as a consequence of evolutionary design. They play key roles in transcription, translation, and RNA processing, and to a large extent, particularly in tRNA and in rRNA, define the ultimate three-dimensional structure of the RNA molecule. Other double-stranded regions arise as a consequence of random base–base interactions and have no apparent function. During the past few years, it has become increasingly apparent that cells contain a number of proteins that interact with RNA and induce conformational changes that alter and remove, perhaps transiently, these secondary structural features. In spite of their potential importance in controlling the function of RNA, our knowledge of these proteins is fragmentary; we are only beginning to acquire a list of the RNA-helix-destabilizing proteins, and our understanding of the mechanisms of their involvement in cellular processes is just beginning to emerge.

Knowledge gained from the extensive studies of phage T4 gene-32 protein,[1] the prototype helix-destabilizing protein, often serves as a point of reference for investigations of other helix-destabilizing proteins (9–11). Gene-32 protein binds to single-stranded polynucleotides selectively and cooperatively (i.e., with a preference for contiguous vs noncontiguous binding) but without significant sequence specificity. Binding is sensitive to increased ionic strength, pointing to electrostatic interactions between the phosphate backbone and basic amino acids. Some aromatic amino acids also appear to be involved in the binding, but the molecular details of the interactions are not clear. Owing primarily to a kinetic block, gene-32 protein does not disrupt natural DNA. In prokaryotic DNA replication systems (e.g., T4 and *E. coli*), ATP-requiring helicases first unwind the DNA, then helix-destabilizing proteins bind to the unwound strands and maintain the single-stranded conformation until replication of that particular region has occurred (5). In denatured DNA, the single-stranded regions that are interspersed with double-stranded hairpin structures provide nucleation sites for the initiation of gene-32 protein binding with subsequent melting of the helices. It has been shown that gene-32 protein regulates its own expression by binding to, and preventing the translation of, gene-32 mRNA (12, 13). This autogenous repression occurs *in vivo* after all available single-stranded DNA regions (replication forks and single-stranded sequences involved in repair and recombination) have been saturated with the protein. A number of other helix-destabilizing proteins that have been described since 1970 bind tightly to both single-stranded DNA and RNA with little preference for either. In some cases, their *in vivo* role in DNA or RNA metabolism has not been determined (7, 14).

The first review on RNA-helix-destabilizing proteins has appeared (14). In this essay, after outlining some aspects of RNA metabolism where the need for helix-destabilizing proteins appears to be evident, we focus our attention on ribosomal protein S1 from *E. coli* and protein HD40 from the brine shrimp *Artemia salina*, a major component of heterogeneous nuclear ribonucleoprotein (hnRNP) particles. In both cases, the *in vitro* unwinding activity of these proteins can be correlated with their respective functions.

II. Survey of RNA-Helix-Destabilizing Proteins

The secondary structure of mRNA is disrupted by the binding and movement of the ribosomes during the initiation and elongation steps of protein synthesis. Several proteins of the translational apparatus with demonstrated *in vitro* helix-destabilizing activity have been implicated in the melting process.

Initiation factor eIF-3[3] from rabbit reticulocytes significantly decreases the T_m of globin mRNA (15), prevents the formation of the intramolecular poly(U) helices and, as revealed by electron microscopy, disrupts the secondary structure of ϕX174 DNA (16). eIF-3 is a multisubunit protein (9–11 subunits, $M_r \sim 700,000$, ref. 17) that promotes the ribosomal binding and translation of mRNA. Translation of the synthetic messenger $AUG(U)_n$, in contrast to that of globin mRNA, does not require eIF-3. The double-stranded complex of $AUG(U)_n$ and A_n is not translated either with or without eIF-3, but when the $AUG(U)_n$ messenger is complexed with a random 9 : 1 copolymer of (A,U), efficient translation is totally dependent on the presence of eIF-3. These results suggest that the melting activity of eIF-3 makes translation possible by disrupting A · U hairpin helices of the $AUG(U)_n + (U,A_9)$ model message during elongation (15). Since eIF-3 dissociates from the initiation complex before the onset of elongation, it has been proposed that an essential component, such as a ribosomal protein, copurifies with the multisubunit eIF-3 (which is isolated from the high-salt ribosomal wash) and reconstitutes the washed ribosomes upon readdition of eIF-3 (15). Some support for this argument comes from the observation that the maximum rate of protein synthesis is

---

[3] The nomenclature used is set out in the essay, Initiation Mechanisms of Protein Synthesis, by Grunberg-Manago and Gros, in Vol. 20 of this series.

160   JOHN O. THOMAS AND WLODZIMIERZ SZER

attained when the molar ratio of eIF-3 to ribosomes approaches one, an unexpectedly large ratio of the initiation factor to ribosomes. The putative helix-destabilizing component of eIF-3 has not yet been identified.

Escherichia coli initiation factor IF-3, a basic protein with a molecular weight of 21,000, promotes the binding of mRNA to 30 S ribosomal subunits and, independently, facilitates the dissociation of 70 S ribosomes into subunits (*18, 19*). Purified IF-3 binds to single-stranded polynucleotides with a stoichiometry of 14 ± 1 nucleotides per protein (*20*). The binding of IF-3 reduces the circular dichroism of a number of synthetic polyribonucleotides, indicative of protein-induced changes in their secondary structures, but no analogous effect in CD is observed with natural nucleic acids (*20*). Binding experiments employing oligonucleotides suggest that IF-3 may have multiple binding sites. It is not known whether the helix-destabilizing activity of IF-3 is related to its function in protein synthesis.

Ribosomal protein S1 from *E. coli* and an analogous protein from *Caulobacter crescentus* destabilize the helices of a variety of synthetic and natural ribo- and deoxyribopolynucleotides (*21–23*). S1 is required for the ribosomal binding of natural mRNA (*24, 25*), and its unwinding activity appears to be central to its function on the ribosomes (*26–28*). The properties of protein S1 from *E. coli*, and its role in protein synthesis, are discussed in more detail in Section III.

In eukaryotic cells, newly transcribed heterogeneous nuclear RNA (hnRNA) associates with a distinct group of generally well-conserved proteins (*29–33*) to form the core of heterogeneous nuclear ribonucleoprotein particles (hnRNP, for review see *32–36*). A major protein component of hnRNP from the brine shrimp *Artemia salina* is a helix destabilizer (*37–40*). The properties of this protein, provisionally termed HD40,[4] the similarities between HD40 and the proteins found in hnRNP from other eukaryotes, and the potential role of HD40 in hnRNP are discussed in Section IV.

A helix-destabilizing protein from calf thymus termed UP1 (M_r 21,000 ± 2000) has been shown by spectrophotometry, circular dichroism, and electron microscopy to distort the conformation of single-stranded polynucleotides with no obvious selectivity toward ribo- or deoxyribopolymers (*41–44*). The length of the polynucleotide chain covered by the protein is 7 ± 1 nucleotides. The protein stimulates the homologous DNA polymerase α *in vitro*, whereas T4 gene-32 protein does not (*43*). While this may reflect the *in vivo* function of UP1, it is surprising that the protein is isolated from the postnuclear

[4] A systematic nomenclature of helix-destabilizing proteins has not been devised.

supernatant and appears to be absent from sucrose-purified nuclei (45).

Another *in vitro* effect of UP1 is a dramatic acceleration of the renaturation of tRNA and 5 S RNA (46). At low ionic strength, these RNAs assume inactive conformations. At increased salt and Mg^{2+} concentrations, they renature slowly with a half-time of about 11 hours at 25°. Renaturation consists of the elimination of the "incorrect" features of secondary structure, i.e., of a melting step characterized by a relatively high activation energy barrier, and the subsequent folding of the RNA into its native state. Addition of a stoichiometric amount of UP1 to the inactive conformer at low ionic strength permits nearly instantaneous renaturation of the RNA when the ionic environment is restored to physiological conditions (0.01 M Mg^{2+}, 0.1 M salt). The RNA in the RNA · UP1 complex formed at low ionic strength is nearly devoid of any base–base interactions. At increased ionic strength, the complex dissociates and the active RNA conformer is formed (45, 46). These experiments represent a good demonstration of a potential function for an RNA-helix-destabilizing protein, but their relevance to physiological processes has not been established.

III. Ribosomal Protein S1 from *Escherichia coli*[2]

Tal *et al.* were the first to show in 1972 that ribosomal protein S1 can bind RNA independently of ribosomes, and they suggested that this protein may function as part of the mRNA binding site on the ribosomes (47). Indeed, ribosomes lacking S1 are unable to initiate protein synthesis with natural mRNA (25, 48). On the other hand, the presence of S1 has no effect on the trinucleotide AUG-dependent ribosomal binding of fMet-tRNA (26, 49). Polysomes formed both *in vitro* and *in vivo* contain close to one copy of S1 per ribosome, indicating that S1 is not an initiation factor and suggesting that its role is not limited to the initiation step (50, 51). In addition to its role in protein synthesis, S1 is the only ribosomal protein known to function outside the ribosome; upon infection of *E. coli* with phage Qβ, it becomes the α subunit of Qβ replicase (52). These are the two well-documented functions of S1 (reviewed in 53). The protein was also found to be identical with interference factor i, an inhibitor of protein synthesis (54–56). This inhibition is observed *in vitro* when the molar ratio of S1 to ribosomes is greater than one. It probably reflects the binding of S1 to the messenger, and it is relieved by an excess of messenger. Since S1 is present in the cell in amounts approximately equimolar to ribosomes, the physiological significance of factor i activity is not clear.

The association of protein S1 with the ribosomes is the weakest of all ribosomal proteins. S1 bound to 30 S subunits is freely exchangeable with S1 that is free in solution (57). It can be washed off the ribosomes nearly selectively with high- or low-salt buffers (58–60). With a molecular weight of 68,000, S1 is more than twice the size of the next largest ribosomal protein (S2, $M_r \sim 29,000$). The presence of a high-molecular-weight S1-type protein on the small subunit appears to be a feature of many prokaryotic (26, 61), but not eukaryotic (62), ribosomes. S1 is an acidic protein (pI $\sim$ 4.8) that contains a large proportion of hydrophobic amino acids (63–66). It exists as a monomer in solution at neutral pH and moderate ionic strength. Investigations on the physical properties and the structure of S1 (26, 57, 67–71) reveal a highly extended conformation with the largest diameter between 200 Å and 250 Å, i.e., equal to, or even greater than the largest diameter of the ribosome. It contains about 13–17% α-helix and roughly 40% β structure (57, 72). The protein appears to be organized into a segmentally flexible V-shaped structure containing two stable domains connected by a flexible "hinge" (70, 73–75). It is possible that part of the S1 molecule, e.g., one of its domains, may be extended away from the ribosome. The center of gravity of S1 bound to the 30 S subunit is quite far from that of the particle ($\sim$75 Å), and 30 S subunits selectively deprived of S1 sediment somewhat faster than normal 30 S subunits despite an 8–9% decrease in mass (24, 57, 76–78). An N-terminal fragment ($M_r \sim 24,000$), obtained by cyanogen bromide cleavage, contains at least part of the ribosomal binding site of S1 (79).

A. Nucleic Acid Binding and Helix-Destabilizing Properties of Protein S1

Earlier studies showed that S1 forms complexes with single-stranded polynucleotides as demonstrated by nitrocellulose filter binding assays and RNA-cellulose chromatography. Binding is relatively nonspecific, but the protein has a particular affinity for polymers of pyrimidine nucleotides and pyrimidine-rich sequences of natural RNAs (27, 47, 58, 59, 80–89).

Examination of the interaction of S1 with a number of polynucleotides by optical methods (UV hyperchromicity and CD ellipticity) reveals a dramatic disruption of their secondary structure similar to that resulting from thermal denaturation, i.e., an increase in UV absorbance and a decrease in the CD ellipticity (21, 22, 68). Synthetic polynucleotides serve as convenient model compounds for these studies, as their secondary structural features have been well defined (90–92). In solution, poly(rU) forms an intramolecular double-helical hairpin structure in the presence of Mg^{2+} or polyamines. With an equimolar amount of spermine, the melting temperature (T_m) of this structure is 28°C and the helix-coil transition is highly cooperative (92). The X-ray diffraction pattern of ordered poly(U) suggests a similarity to the A form of DNA (93). This structure is completely unfolded at 0–10° by a stoichiometric amount of S1 (one S1 per about 10 nucleotides) as revealed by the CD and UV spectra (21, 22, 68). Alternatively, the random-coil poly(U) complexed with S1 will not form the ordered state upon subsequent addition of spermine. Poly(C) and poly(A) form single-stranded stacked helices that undergo noncooperative helix-coil transitions over wide temperature ranges (90). Titration of poly(A) with S1 in 5 mM TrisCl (pH 7.4) in 10 mM NaCl at 18°C induces a hyperchromic effect in UV accompanied by a small red shift. When fully titrated at a molar ratio of S1 to adenylic acid residues approaching 1 : 10, the spectrum at 18°C is similar to that obtained by thermal melting to about 50–55°C (22). At a much higher ionic strength (10 mM cacodylate at pH 7.0 in 100 mM NaCl with 10 mM Mg^{2+}), the CD spectrum of poly(A) is unaltered by S1 (21).

Poly(C) is either nearly completely disordered (measured by UV in 10 mM NaCl as above) or partially disordered (measured by CD in 100 mM NaCl as above) by S1. The double-helical structure formed by poly(C) at acid pH (94) is also perturbed by S1 (21). The results of the optical studies cited above are measures of polynucleotide backbone distortion (CD) and base unstacking (UV). For a polymer such as poly(U), hydrogen bonding is required to stabilize the secondary structure in which the bases are stacked (91). In the absence of spermine, hydrogen-bonded hairpins are not formed and the polynucleotide exists as an unstacked random coil at room temperature. By binding to the single-stranded random coil form of poly(U) with much higher affinity than to the double-stranded hairpin structure, the hairpin structure and, as a consequence, the base-stacking of poly(U) is disrupted. A somewhat different situation exists with respect to poly(A) and poly(C), which form single-stranded helices with no hydrogen bonding. S1 binds to these polymers and, depending on the polymer and on the ionic strength, produces nearly complete or partial unstacking, as judged by comparing the S1-induced spectra with those obtained by heating.

A large portion of the secondary structure of natural single-stranded RNAs and DNAs, which consists of intramolecular hairpin loops and single-stranded stacked regions, is lost upon complexing with S1 (22, 23, 68). The addition of S1 to coliphage MS2 RNA at 20°C to a molar ratio of approximately one protein per 10 nucleotide res-

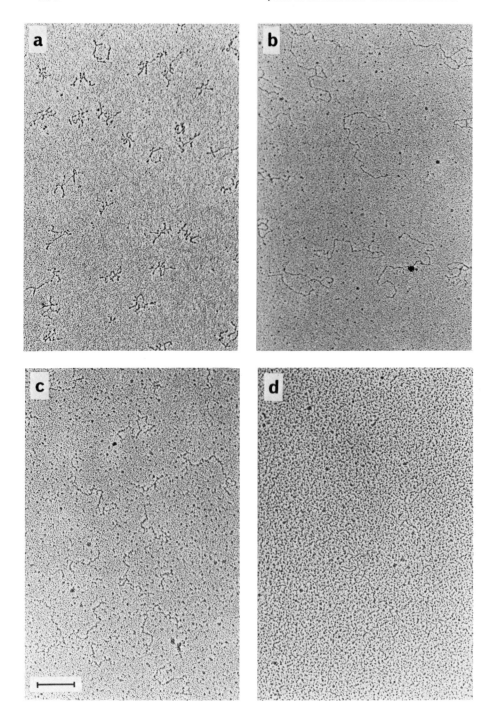

idues results in the "melting" of approximately 75% of the secondary structure as shown by an increased hyperchromicity. The extent of the increase depends on the salt concentration of the solution, there being a greater loss of secondary structure in 10 mM than in 100 mM NaCl. In either case though, the extent of polynucleotide unwinding corresponds to that produced by heating the solution to 53–54°C in the absence of the protein. Little or no unwinding occurs in the presence of 10 mM Mg^{2+}, which increases the T_m of the RNA to about 73°C in the absence of protein (22). Analogous behavior is seen with E. coli ribosomal RNA (16 S and 23 S), tRNA, and single-stranded (heat-denatured) DNA. With all polynucleotides examined, the ability of S1 to function as a helix-destabilizer is reversed either partially or completely by high salt and Mg^{2+}. This behavior is also seen with the DNA-helix-destabilizing proteins.

The unwinding of natural nucleic acids by helix-destabilizing proteins can be visualized by electron microscopy. As S1 is added to either coliphage MS2 RNA or to single-stranded ϕX174 DNA, the polynucleotides progress from compact forms, in which a great deal of secondary structure can be seen, to extended protein-rich complexes (23, 68). The ability of S1 to unwind MS2 RNA is shown in Fig. 1. The contour length of the collapsed naked RNA is about 0.2 μm (Fig. 1a). If the RNA is denatured by heating to 70°C in 1% formaldehyde prior to mounting, it appears as a thin filament with a length of 1.2 μm (Fig. 1b), which represents an internucleotide spacing in the denatured molecule of about 0.34 nm (MS2 RNA contains 3569 nucleotides (8)). The addition of S1 to a molar ratio of one S1 per 20 nucleotides results in a lengthening of the RNA from 0.2 to 0.6 μm, and a loss of a considerable amount of the secondary structure present in the free RNA (Fig. 1c). The samples used for the experiments of Fig. 1 were mounted by the high resolution "anthrabis method" (23, 95) in which the conventionally used cytochrome c is replaced by the cationic dye anthrabis, 1,4-bis[3-(benzyldimethylammonio)propylamino]-9,10-anthraquinone

---

FIG. 1. The unwinding of MS2 RNA by S1 can be visualized by electron microscopy. Under the conditions used for mounting the samples, MS2 RNA alone (a) contains a considerable amount of secondary structure, which is eliminated by heating it to 70°C in 1% formaldehyde (b). In the presence of S1 at a molar ratio of one S1 per 20 nucleotides (c), a considerable amount of the secondary structure of the RNA is unwound and the contour length is increased to 0.6 μm (it is 1.2 μm in panel b). When S1 is added at a ratio of one S1 per 10 nucleotides, the RNA is completely saturated and the field is obscured by the presence of excess S1 (d). The S1 concentration is 2 μg/ml in panels c and d. The samples are mounted using anthrabis in 10 mM Tris, pH 8.5, 1 mM EDTA, 30% formamide (23). The bar represents 0.2 μm.

dichloride. This technique is extremely sensitive to the presence of unbound protein (as little as 0.2 μg of free protein per milliliter is easily detectable) and can be used to determine the approximate end point of titration. As seen from Fig. 1d, at an S1 : nucleotide molar ratio of 1 : 10, there is so much unbound protein on the grid that the MS2 RNA-S1 complex is nearly obscured. From a series of titrations, the stoichiometry of the complex was estimated to be one S1 per 10–15 nucleotides, in agreement with the values determined by optical methods. At low S1 : nucleotide ratios (less than 1 : 30 nucleotides), the observed length increase is about 4 nm per S1 bound. This represents the minimal size of the average length of the RNA occupied by one molecule of S1 and corresponds to an internucleotide spacing of about 0.33 nm, if a 1 : 12 stoichiometry is assumed. This correlates well with the internucleotide spacing of the fully denatured RNA of Fig. 1b. However, at S1 : nucleotide ratios greater than 1 : 30, the increase in the length of the RNA levels off while binding continues. This was interpreted as representing a low-affinity binding of S1 to double-stranded regions of the RNA (23). In contrast to the RNA seen in Fig. 1a, no obvious structures, such as loops, can be seen in Fig. 1c. Consequently, the remaining regions of stable secondary structure to which S1 binds are not large (a loop containing about 100 base-pairs should be detectable). It is also clear that interactions between distant regions of the RNA molecule are abolished by S1.

In general, while S1 will disrupt, or prevent the formation of, relatively unstable ordered regions of polynucleotides, lowering their T_m by as much as 30–35°C (i.e., from about 50–55°C to 18–20°C, see above), it will allow more stable structures to form. S1 does not unwind double-stranded structures, such as native DNA and the homopolymer duplexes poly(A) · poly(U), poly(I) · poly(C), and poly(dA) · poly(dT), even at very low salt concentrations where the thermodynamics of unwinding is favorable ($T_m < 50$°C) (21, 22). This is typical for a number of helix-destablizing proteins and has been explained as a kinetic effect: opening a sufficiently large region of the helix to permit the association of the protein with the single strands is prohibitively slow. The formation of duplex structures, however, can be inhibited by S1. For instance, at 10–25 mM NaCl, the poly(A) · poly(U) duplex is not formed at 18°C if either of the homopolymers is mixed with S1 (one protein per about 10 nucleotide residues) prior to the addition of the complementary strand. In 100 mM NaCl, the duplex is formed in the presence of S1, but at a much slower rate than in its absence. At a salt concentration of 50 mM NaCl ($T_m = 46$–47°, ref. 96), about 50% of the duplex is formed, showing, in agreement with the results discussed above, that S1 effectively lowers the T_m of nucleic acids by about 30°C. The formation of the homopolymer pair poly(I) · poly(C) is similarly affected by S1. The deoxyhomopolymer pair poly(dA) · poly(dT) does form in 16 mM NaCl at 20°C but at a much slower rate than in the absence of S1, the $t_{1/2}$ being increased from 11 to about 90 min. The poly(dA-dT) (alternating sequence) copolymer is not affected by S1 under conditions where it is unfolded by DNA-helix-destabilizing proteins (22, 68).

The intrinsic tryptophan fluorescence of S1 is quenched by the binding of oligo- and polynucleotides (26, 88, 97–99). The results of a number of studies in which titrations were monitored by fluorescence has led to the postulate that there may be two separate, but not totally independent, polynucleotide binding sites on S1 (88, 97–99). Site I (occluded site size $n \simeq 5$ nucleotides) binds ribo- and deoxyribonucleotides with approximately equal affinity in a noncooperative fashion. Although binding constants at this site are highly salt-dependent (two basic residues at site I interact with polynucleotide phosphates), a major portion of the free energy of interaction appears to be nonelectrostatic. Site II ($n \simeq 10$) binds ribopolymers only, shows some cooperativity with respect to poly(C) (cooperativity parameter $\omega = 33$) but not with poly(A), and its association with RNA appears to be nonelectrostatic. The intrinsic binding constant of site II is about three times greater for poly(C) than for poly(A) and, when taken together with the cooperativity factor of 33 for poly(C), gives a total preference of about two orders of magnitude for poly(C) over poly(A). Although the cooperativity factor for poly(U) has not been determined, these results are consistent with the preferential binding of polypyrimidines by S1. The combined size of sites I and II is about 15 nucleotides. This agrees with the site size of 12–15 nucleotides for the binding of ribopolymers as determined by CD and UV titrations, filter binding, equilibrium dialysis, and electron microscopy (22, 23, 87). However, some binding experiments seem inconsistent with the two-site model. Several oligoribonucleotides with chain lengths greater than five nucleotides bind to S1 with a 1:1 stoichiometry (27, 87, 100). Also, a prediction of the model is that S1 should act as an RNA–RNA or a DNA–RNA cross-linker. Such cross-links have not been observed by electron microscopy or by sedimentation velocity. When mixtures of S1, coliphage ϕX174 DNA (single-stranded) and poly(U) are sedimented through a sucrose gradient, no S1 · DNA · poly(U) complex is detected under a variety of conditions, even though S1 forms poly(U) · S1 and DNA · S1 complexes (23). It should, however, be borne in mind that the electron microscopy and sedimentation experiments employed two distinct polynucleotides. These conditions are different from the fluorescence titration experiments on which the two-site model is based, as these employed a deoxyoligomer (to saturate site I) followed by a ribopolymer or two different oligomers. The two-site model is attractive from the point of view of S1 function, and it seems that further investigations are required, e.g., additional experiments capable of determining the simultaneous presence of two distinct nucleic acid molecules bound to S1.

The apparent binding constants for polyribopyrimidines are in the 10^7 M^{-1} range as determined by fluorescence titrations and filter binding (87, 88, 100) while that for poly(A) is about one order of magnitude lower. The association constants of a series of U_n and A_n (determined by equilibrium dialysis for $n < 15$) were shown to fall off considerably as the chain lengths fall below 12–14. For example, in the U_n series for n = $\overline{80}$, 12, 7, and 5, the binding constants are 4, 0.9, 0.023, and 0.0049×10^7 M^{-1}, respectively (87). An analogous relationship between the chain lengths and binding constants is observed in the A_n series, except that, for identical chain lengths, the constants are roughly one-tenth those in the U_n series (87). The apparent binding constants for poly(dA) and poly(dC) are roughly the same, within the 10^6 M^{-1} range, while binding to double-stranded DNA, as determined by sedimentation velocity (98, 99), is about 1000-fold weaker.

B. Modifications of S1

Several investigations employed chemically modified or truncated derivatives of S1 to gain insight into the relationship between the nucleic acid binding and helix-destabilizing properties of S1 and its role in translation. S1 contains two cysteine residues located at 57 and 67% of the polypeptide chain length from the amino terminus. The sulfhydryl group of the cysteine residue farthest from the amino terminus reacts more readily with N-ethylmaleimide (101). This modification (MalNet : S1 molar ratio of about 1) completely abolishes the ability of the resulting protein to disrupt the secondary structure of poly(U), poly(C), poly(A), coliphage MS2 RNA, and ϕX174 DNA (26). The modified protein does, however, bind to these polymers, although with decreased affinity. It is also easily incorporated into 30 S subunits deficient in S1, but the 30 S subunits containing the maleimide-modified protein, unlike their S1-containing counterparts, are unable to bind MS2 RNA and cannot form a polypeptide chain initiation complex with MS2 RNA as messenger (26, 77). They retain activity in the binding of fMet-tRNA in response to the AUG trinucleotide codon and can bind Phe-tRNA in response to poly(U), as do 30 S subunits deficient in S1. Since the only activity of the 30 S subunits that is adversely affected by the substitution of MalNEt-S1 for S1 is the binding of natural mRNA, these results were interpreted to mean that the helix-destabilizing properties observed with the isolated protein are associated with the messenger-binding function of S1 when it is part of the ribosome. In another study (74), S1 was modified by MalNEt and by two fluorescent cysteine-specific reagents, 5-{2-[(iodoacetyl)amino]-ethyl}amino-1-naphthalenesulfonic acid (an asymmetrically substituted ethylenediamine) and iodoacetylaminofluorescein. Since derivatization with MalNEt prevents the reaction with the diamine, the same sulfhydryl group(s) is (are) probably modified by both reagents. The modified proteins produced with either reagent can bind to 30 S ribosomal subunits lacking S1, and the reconstituted subunits retain nearly full activity in the poly(U)-directed synthesis of polyphenylalanine. However, the reconstituted subunits differ in their ability to form initiation complexes with coliphage R17 RNA. Whereas S1 modified by either MalNEt or the fluorescein derivative is nearly inactive, in agreement with the previous study, the 30 S subunit containing the diamine modified S1 retains $\sim$ 88% activity in the R17 RNA-dependent binding of fMet-tRNA. These results were interpreted to mean that the modification of the sulfhydryl group does not in itself lead to reduced activity (at least in this assay). Rather, the presence of a large group, such as fluorescein or a maleimide ring, attached directly to the sulfur leads to steric problems. In the ethylenediamine derivative, the naphthol group is extended from the sulfhydryl by the ethylene diamine linker and has greater steric freedom (74). The nucleic acid binding and helix-destabilizing properties of the two fluorescent derivatives have not been reported.

Two truncated derivatives of S1 have been investigated. A mutant S1 (ml-S1) obtained from E. coli AF410 lacks about 140 amino acids from the carboxy terminus (102). This is a "silent" mutation, and the mutant protein can replace wild-type S1 in in vitro protein synthesis directed by synthetic and natural messengers. It is also nearly as effective as S1 in binding to and unwinding polynucleotides (103). So far, only one qualitative effect of the shortened carboxy terminus has been observed. S1 is present as a single copy per native 30 S subunit and, in polysomes, as a single copy per 70 S monomer. A 30 S species containing two copies of S1 can be prepared (77) in vitro, but there are no indications so far that this species has any physiological role. The ml-S1, however, is unable to form 30 S subunits containing more than one copy of the mutant protein. Since both wild-type and mutant S1 influence the electrophoretic mobility of 30 S subunits, species containing none, one, or two copies of the protein can easily be resolved (77, 103).

Another truncated derivative of S1 is a fragment with a molecular weight of about 48,000; it lacks the amino terminal region of the protein. This fragment (S1-F1) is produced *in vitro* by limited tryptic digestion (73). It contains the two cysteine residues of S1 and an intact carboxy terminus. S1-F1 binds to S1 depleted 30 S subunits, albeit with a low affinity. The reconstituted ribosomes are unable to support protein synthesis using either poly(U) or coliphage f2 RNA as messengers. Filter binding assays show that S1-F1 retains some nucleic acid binding capacity; it binds poly(U) and heat-denatured DNA, although less efficiently than wild-type S1 and ml-S1, but does not bind MS2 RNA. Although it binds to these polymers, an examination of the helix-destabilizing properties of S1-F1 by optical methods and by electron microscopy shows that it does not unwind them (103). It appears that the polynucleotide binding site(s) of S1-F1 is(are) altered but not entirely abolished, and that the amino terminal part of the molecule, in contrast to the carboxy terminal part, provides an essential component of the binding and unwinding site. Again, as in the case of MalNEt-S1, alterations in the nucleic acid binding and unwinding domains of S1 render the molecule biologically inactive.

C. S1-RNA Interactions and Protein Synthesis

Two general proposals have been advanced for the role of S1 in the translation of natural mRNA. In one, emphasis is placed on the interaction of S1 with the message. The helix-destabilizing activity of S1 is used to disrupt the secondary structure of the incoming mRNA, a mechanism that assumes an analogous function for the protein in initiation and in elongation (49, 104). In the second proposal, S1 interacts with the 3' end of 16 S RNA, disrupts its intramolecular secondary structure, and facilitates transient intermolecular rRNA · mRNA base-pairing during initiation (82).

It is generally accepted that, during initiation, correct message binding is determined, in part, by base-pairing between a conserved purine-rich sequence on the 5' side of the initiator codon and a pyrimidine-rich sequence, the "Shine–Dalgarno" sequence, at the 3' end of 16 S RNA (28, 105–107). The Shine–Dalgarno sequence has been shown to possess a substantial but variable amount of homology with a region on the 5' side of the initiation codon of a variety of *E. coli* mRNAs (28). Evidence for mRNA · rRNA pairing during initiation comes from the finding that the colicin E3 fragment (produced by the action of colicin E3 on *E. coli* ribosomes and comprising the 3'-

terminal 49 nucleotides of 16 S RNA) can be isolated as a complex with an mRNA initiator region from 70 S initiation complexes disassembled by detergent treatment (*106*). Also, an octanucleotide complementary to the Shine–Dalgarno sequence binds to ribosomes and, by doing so, prevents the formation of an mRNA · ribosome complex (*108*).

There is some evidence that S1 may be related both spatially and functionally to the 3' end of 16 S RNA. S1 can be cross-linked to the 3' end of 16 S RNA, to initiation factors, and to several ribosomal proteins that form the "16 S RNA 3' end cluster" comprising the messenger binding site (*109–112*). In vitro, S1 interacts strongly with the isolated 3'-terminal colicin E3 fragment, forms a 1 : 1 complex, and disrupts the secondary structure of the polypyrimidine tract of the fragment (*27, 82*). Although the formation of such a complex is consistent with a physiological role for an S1 · 16 S RNA complex, it might merely reflect the fact that S1 has an affinity for single-stranded regions, particularly those that are rich in pyrimidines. The essential question is whether the 3' terminus of 16 S RNA in native 30 S subunits interacts functionally with the protein. Despite the results of the cross-linking experiments, the answer to this question appears to be negative. Contrary to some early data, it has been shown that colicin-treated ribosomes lacking the 49 nucleotide sequence at the 3' end of 16 S RNA can bind a single copy of S1 strongly, and that the colicin fragment can be removed from the ribosomes independently of the removal of S1 (*77*). Furthermore, MalNEt-S1, which is unable to disrupt the secondary structure of polynucleotides (see preceding section), binds to S1-depleted ribosomes with nearly normal affinity (*26, 77*). These results appear to confirm that S1 binding to 30 S subunits involves a considerable contribution from protein–protein interactions. Indeed, a substantial decrease in S1 binding affinity has been demonstrated for 30 S particles reconstituted without protein S9. Several other ribosomal proteins also contribute to the binding affinity (*113*).

It should be noted that although the free energy of the S1 · 30 S binding includes a contribution from protein–RNA interactions, a portion of the 16 S RNA other than the 3' end may be involved (*77, 114*). In summary, it seems unlikely that the helix-destabilizing activity of S1 is used to expose the 3' terminus of 16 S RNA for base-pairing with mRNA; in fact, a recent investigation suggests that protein S21, another member of the "16 S 3'-end cluster," may function in this capacity (*115*).

In view of these observations, and since the experiments discussed in the preceding section argue strongly that the unwinding activity is essential to the function of S1 on the ribosomes, the first model (the unfolding of the incoming mRNA by S1), while not supported by rigorous evidence, appears to gain credence. This proposal was originally based on the observation that ribosomal binding and translation of formaldehyde-unfolded MS2 RNA is independent of S1 (49) although it still requires fMet-tRNA for initiation. In another investigation, the S1-dependence of initiation complex formation with three coliphage R17 RNA cistron initiation regions (the coat, replicase, and A protein cistrons) was examined. The requirement for S1 is inversely correlated with the degree of complementarity between a particular initiation region and the Shine–Dalgarno sequence (28, 116). This suggests that S1 favors the formation of intermolecular base-pairs, and again it may be related to an unwinding effect on mRNA.

The exact molecular mechanism of S1 function is complex, perhaps more complex than envisioned by the two working models discussed, and has not yet been established. Further progress is likely to depend on a more detailed understanding of the properties of the protein and its functional domains and on a more precise description of the contribution of other ribosomal proteins and initiation factors to the messenger binding site on the ribosomes.

IV. Protein HD40 from hnRNP of *Artemia salina*

HD40 is an RNA helix-destabilizing protein identified as a major component of the heterogeneous ribonucleoprotein (hnRNP) particles in the brine shrimp *Artemia salina* (40). In eukaryotes, newly synthesized heterogeneous nuclear RNA (hnRNP) associates with proteins as it is being transcribed, forming hnRNP particles (for a review, see 32–36). There is considerable interest in the structure and function of these particles, as they are believed to be involved in processing the primary transcripts destined to become cytoplasmic mRNA, and in the degradation of the others. As shown by electron microscopy of newly transcribed hnRNA, the nascent RNA chains are folded into nucleoprotein complexes that resemble strings of beads (117–120). Several investigators have made the interesting observation that the RNA packaged into hnRNP complexes has less secondary structure than hnRNA that is free in solution. This was shown by CD spectra (121–123), and it is also supported by ethidium bromide binding studies (124). Consequently, one might expect that the hnRNP proteins function to unwind the residual secondary structure of hnRNA (or to keep it from forming) and then fold the extended unstacked RNA chain into the compact hnRNP structure. In fact, HD40 has a number of properties compatible with such a structural role in hnRNP (37–40).

The hnRNP particles can be isolated by incubating nuclei with isotonic buffers at pH 8.0. This brings about the fragmentation of the hnRNP "beads-on-a-string" structure, presumably as a result of the cleavage of nuclease-sensitive regions between the beads. The resulting fragments of RNA are released from the nuclei in the form of globular nucleoprotein complexes that sediment at about 30–40 S (29, 30, 125, 126). Alternatively, larger hnRNP complexes that sediment at 75–200 S can be isolated from sonically disrupted nuclei (127–129). Visualization of the 30 S particles by electron microscopy reveals a somewhat heterogeneous population of roughly globular particles with a diameter of about 20 nm (29, 30, 125–130). These particles contain most of the pulse-labeled hnRNA, a fraction of which is homologous to cytoplasmic mRNA (131–136). Estimates of the length of RNA present in a single 30 S particle vary from 300 to 1000 nucleotides, and the total protein mass is estimated at about 800,000 (36, 125, 131, 138). The reported protein to RNA mass ratios vary from 4 to 9, depending on the method of isolation and the cell type.

The monomeric 30 S particles obtained by the pH 8.0 extraction procedure have a smaller number of associated proteins than the particles obtained by the sonication procedure (36, 128, 130, 133, 137). Also, nonspecific binding of proteins to the RNA during isolation cannot be rigorously excluded. These and other factors have led to considerable differences in the literature with respect to the number and molecular weight distribution of individual hnRNP proteins (34–36, 125, 133). Most of the protein mass of purified 30 S hnRNP however, is accounted for by a relatively conserved class of basic proteins (pI's around 7.5–9) in the 30,000–40,000 molecular weight range. In all the organisms examined so far, the proteins within this class have similar amino acid compositions that are quite characteristic. They have a high content of glycine (about 20%), but little or no cysteine, and contain the unusual amino acid dimethylarginine (29–32, 37, 126, 139, 140). In rat brain, mouse ascites cells, and A. salina, the amino-terminal amino acid of all the glycine-rich proteins is blocked (31, 32, 40). In 30 S particles from higher eukaryotes (e.g., mammals and birds), the number of polypeptides within this class ranges from 4 to 12 as identified by two-dimensional gel electrophoresis (29, 36, 130, 133, 141). Based on the similarities in their peptide maps (31), it seems likely that these proteins arise from posttranslational modifications of a smaller number of common precursors. It has been suggested that the glycine-rich proteins form the core of hnRNP particles and may function as an RNA-binding structural component of hnRNP (32–36).

Tentative models (35, 36) postulate that the globular 30 S particle containing the glycine-rich proteins is, essentially, the repeating structural unit of hnRNP; it serves to condense the long RNA chain and to protect it from digestion. Globular particles are probably separated by less protein-rich filamentous spacers that appear to contain some double-stranded regions of hnRNA and a different set of proteins (32, 142–145). A slower sedimenting (about 15 S) particle with the post-transcriptionally added 3′ poly(A) segment contains again a different distinct set of proteins (36, 126, 146). It is assumed that in addition to the structural proteins, hnRNP are associated, perhaps transiently, with enzymes and recognition elements (e.g., small nuclear RNP) required for the processing of the primary transcripts (147, 148). It has been pointed out by a number of investigators (35, 36) that this simple model, at least at the gross-structural level, bears some relationship to the organization of histones and DNA into nucleosomes, the glycine-rich proteins playing a role somewhat similar to that of histones. On the other hand, possible heterogeneity of the 30 S particles (130) and the fact that they may not be regularly spaced along the nascent RNA chain (117–120, 149) imply less uniformity and suggest that any analogy to chromatin structure should be, at present, treated with caution. Much more information about the particles, and the properties and function of individual hnRNP proteins is required before more-detailed models can be proposed.

A. Physical Properties

1. Protein HD40 (M_r = 40,000) has been purified in milligram quantities to better than 95% homogeneity as judged by electrophoresis in dodecyl sulfate on polyacrylamide gels. The six-step purification procedure involves affinity chromatography on single-stranded DNA-agarose or RNA-cellulose columns (37). The protein is isolated on a preparative scale from extracts in which the nuclei have been largely broken. It is a prominent constituent of cellular proteins, as the number of copies of HD40 in such extracts is estimated to be nearly twice the number of 80 S ribosomes. The protein is monomeric in solution at neutral pH and moderate ionic strength (50–500 mM NaCl) and has a relatively low content of α-helix (14–17%). It has a molecular weight of 40,000 and a sedimentation coefficient of 2.4 S in 0.1 M NaCl (37). The amino-acid composition of HD40 is remarkably similar to that of core hnRNP proteins: it contains a high proportion of glycine (19.5%), cysteine is absent, and over a third of all the arginine residues contain two methyl substituents (37). Curiously, the DNA-helix-destabilizing protein of E. coli (M_r ~ 19,500) has a similar content of glycine and lacks cysteine but has no dimethylarginine (150).

HD40 can be separated into at least three isoelectric species with pI's from 7.6 to 8.2. Peptide maps produced by cleavage of the individual species with several endopeptidases indicate that the three polypeptide species represent posttranslational modifications of a common precursor. The amino termini of all the species are blocked (40).

B. Nucleic Acid Binding and Helix-Destabilizing Properties

Filter binding experiments show that HD40 binds strongly to natural and synthetic single-stranded RNA and DNA, but not to native DNA or duplex RNA. Although the binding of HD40 to polynucleotide templates is largely nonspecific, competition experiments using labeled coliphage MS2 RNA and unlabeled nucleic acids indicate a preference for natural RNA over single-stranded DNA. The most effective competitors of MS2 RNA binding are uracil- and thymine-containing ribo- and deoxyribohomopolymers, which, under the conditions of the assay, exist as nearly completely unstacked random coils. The binding of HD40 gives a number of single-stranded RNA and DNA substrates considerable protection from digestion by snake venom phosphodiesterase, pancreatic ribonuclease, and deoxyribonuclease, but has little or no effect on the action of micrococcal nuclease. HD40 is an inhibitor of in vitro protein synthesis directed by poly(U) and by A. salina poly(A)-containing RNA (RNA-A_n), but the inhibition is largely relieved by an excess of the messenger, indicating that it may be due to mRNA binding by HD40 (37). This is similar to the behavior of protein S1 (56, 83).

The binding of HD40 to single-stranded nucleic acids brings about changes in their conformation analogous to the effect of other helix-destabilizing proteins. The double helical hairpin structure that poly(U) forms in the presence of spermine ($T_m = 28°C$) is disrupted by HD40 at 5–10°C. As measured by either CD or UV spectroscopy, the poly(U) · HD40 complex is completely saturated at a stoichiometry of about one HD40 per 12 nucleotides. When completely saturated, the ellipticity and hypochromicity of the poly(U) is the same as the thermally denatured form (38). HD40 binds to the single-stranded stacked helices of poly(rA), poly(rC), poly(dA), and poly(dC) causing unstacking as indicated by the CD and UV spectra. When fully titrated, at a stoichiometry of about one HD40 per 12 nucleotides, poly(rC) is unstacked to an extent nearly equivalent to its fully denatured form, and poly(rA) is unstacked to about 75% of its fully denatured form (equivalent to thermal denaturation at 60–65°C). Estimates for the intrinsic binding constants of about 0.05×10^6 M^{-1} for poly(rA) and 0.1×10^6 M^{-1} for poly(rC) can be made from the titration curves. A small degree of cooperativity (ω = 20–40) is also indicated by the data. HD40 has a much greater affinity for poly(rU) (as judged from filter binding as well as optical titrations), and binds too tightly to permit an estimation of its binding constant from the available data (38).

HD40 binds to, and unwinds, a considerable amount of the secondary structure in natural single-stranded RNA and DNA. Titrating MS2 RNA or ϕX174 viral (single-stranded) DNA with HD40 to its end point, which occurs at about one HD40 per 10–15 nucleotides, results in changes in the CD and UV spectra corresponding to those obtained by heating the polynucleotides to about 55°C. Addition of Mg^{2+} to the solution stabilizes the secondary structure such that, at 30 mM Mg^{2+}, no changes in the spectra are produced by HD40 (36, 38). Sucrose gradient centrifugation of MS2 RNA and ϕX174 DNA partially saturated with HD40 fails to reveal any bimodal distribution of the nucleic acid, indicating that, in agreement with results from optical methods, the interaction is not highly cooperative (38). This is similar to the behavior of S1 but is in sharp contrast to the behavior of phage T4 gene-32 protein ($\omega \simeq 10^3$) and the E. coli helix-destabilizing protein. With both of these proteins, two bands are observed at subsaturating protein levels: one containing nucleic acid essentially free of protein and the other containing a nearly saturated protein · nucleic acid complex.

As is the case with most helix-destabilizing proteins, HD40 does not unwind duplex structures [native DNA; the homopolymer pairs $(rA)_n \cdot (rU)_n$; $(rI)_n \cdot (rC)_n$; $(dA)_n \cdot (dT)_n$] or multistranded structures (e.g., $rA_n \cdot 2rU_n$) even at very low ionic strength. It does, however, influence the rate and extent of their formation. In 39 mM NaCl or less, the formation of the $U_n \cdot A_n$ helix is prevented, but raising the salt concentration to 143 mM enables the formation of the double helix, although at a slower rate than in the absence of HD40. In 78 mM NaCl, about 50% of the helix is formed at 20°, which corresponds to an effective reduction in the T_m of about 33°C (38).

The most interesting feature of the HD40–nucleic acid interaction is the fact that HD40 functions not only as a helix-destabilizing protein, but also has the capacity to compact the extended nucleic acid chain into a higher-order structure. When the titration of nucleic acids with HD40 is monitored by sedimentation velocity, it is observed that the sedimentation coefficients of the HD40–nucleic acid complexes do not level off at a protein to nucleotide molar ratio of 1 : 12 which, according to the stoichiometry determined by spectral titrations, should fully saturate the templates. As HD40 is added in excess of 1 : 12, faster sedimenting species are found, indicating that protein continues to bind to the complex (38). This behavior has not been observed with other helix-destabilizing proteins and appears to be unique to HD40 (see below). For example, sedimentation coefficients of complexes of ribosomal protein S1 and polynucleotide reach limiting values when the protein : nucleotide ratio exceeds that at which maximal spectral changes occur, and free protein is found at the top of the gradients (23). When the titration of MS2 RNA or ϕX174 viral DNA is monitored by electron microscopy (38, 40), it is seen that, like S1, HD40 causes a loss in the secondary structure of the nucleic acid (compare Fig. 2a and d with Fig. 2b and e), in accord with the results of optical studies. When HD40 is added in excess of the 1 : 12 stoichiometry, the binding of HD40 continues, resulting not in further unwinding of the polynucleotide, but in a compacting of the nucleoprotein complex into structures that resemble beads on a string. The "beads" are about 20 nm in diameter in platinum–palladium shadowed-preparations. While the unwinding of RNA, DNA, or polynucleotides that occurs at HD40 : nucleotide ratios less than 1 : 12 shows little cooperativity, in accord with sedimentation studies, the transition from the extended filamentous RNA · HD40 complex to the complex with a "beads-on-a-string" structure appears to be much more cooperative as indicated by the fact that, in complexes formed at a stoichiometry of about 1 : 6, both highly folded and open complexes can be seen in the same field (38, 40). At protein : nucleotide molar ratios exceeding 1 : 3, aggregates of the nucleoprotein complexes form, as seen in Fig. 2g, without an appreciable increase in the size of the individual beads. The contour length of the "beads-on-a-string" structure is about 50–70% shorter than the fully unfolded structure seen at a 1 : 12 stoichiometry (Fig. 2b, c). This observation suggests that the beads function to compact the RNA without an increase in secondary structure, perhaps as a coiled RNA · protein complex.

Electron microscopic images of native 30 S hnRNP particles from A. salina (Fig. 3a), which contain HD40 as their major protein component (see Section IV, C), and the complexes reconstituted from HD40 and hnRNA fragments (Fig. 3b) imply an overall structural similarity. Both native and reconstituted particles are somewhat heterogeneous in size, but the major population consists, in either case, of roughly globular particles with a diameter of about 15 nm. In the reconstituted complexes, there are also structures containing several globular particles along the RNA chain. These are presumably formed from larger hnRNA fragments isolated from the nuclei. In shadowed preparations (Fig. 2) mounted with the high-resolution anthrabis method (40, 95), the globular structures appear larger than in the negatively stained

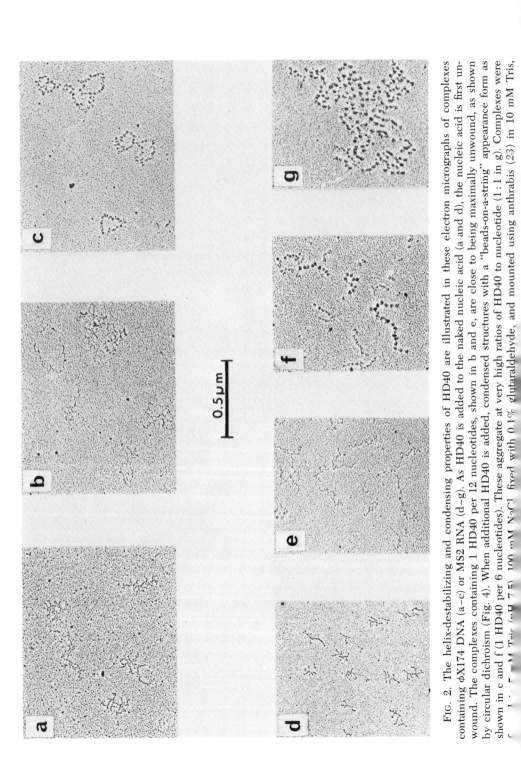

FIG. 2. The helix-destabilizing and condensing properties of HD40 are illustrated in these electron micrographs of complexes containing φX174 DNA (a–c) or MS2 RNA (d–g). As HD40 is added to the naked nucleic acid (a and d), the nucleic acid is first unwound. The complexes containing 1 HD40 per 12 nucleotides, shown in b and e, are close to being maximally unwound, as shown by circular dichroism (Fig. 4). When additional HD40 is added, condensed structures with a "beads-on-a-string" appearance form as shown in c and f (1 HD40 per 6 nucleotides). These aggregate at very high ratios of HD40 to nucleotide (1:1 in g). Complexes were ⎡⎡⎡ ⎡⎡ M Tris (pH 7.5), 100 mM NaCl, fixed with 0.1% glutaraldehyde, and mounted using anthrabis (23) in 10 mM Tris,

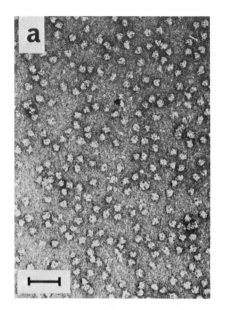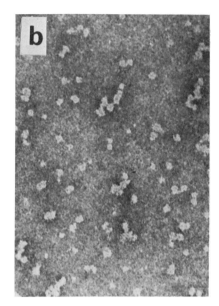

FIG. 3. The 30 S hnRNP particles from *Artemia salina* (a) have an overall structural similarity to HD40 · hnRNA complexes formed at an HD40:nucleotide molar ratio of 1 : 6 (b). The hnRNA used for reconstituting the complexes shown in (b) was obtained by phenol extraction of a pH 8.0 nuclear extract and, on the average, is longer than the RNA in the 30 S hnRNP particles. Multiple "beads" can be seen on these larger RNAs. The samples were contrasted with uranyl acetate. The bar represents 50 nm (*40*).

structures (Fig. 3), presumably due to shadowing. Circular dichroism spectra show that the RNA in the *A. salina* 30 S hnRNP particles is unfolded and unstacked to a considerable extent as compared to free hnRNA in solution, and the RNA in the reconstituted HD40 · hnRNA complexes is unwound to a similar degree (Fig. 4) (*40*).

C. Intracellular Location of Protein HD40

Antibodies to HD40 were formed in rabbits to facilitate the identification of the protein in subcellular fractions, during the early developmental process of *A. salina*. This organism provides a useful source of components for investigations of macromolecular synthesis and a convenient system for developmental studies (*152*). The encysted cryptobiotic gastrulae, which are stable and metabolically inactive, quickly resume development upon immersion in aerated salt solutions, as shown by the formation of polysomes in the cytoplasm and RNA synthesis in the nucleus. Development proceeds in the absence of cell division until the prenauplius stage. Comparative investigations of the properties of HD40 isolated on a preparative scale from extracts of

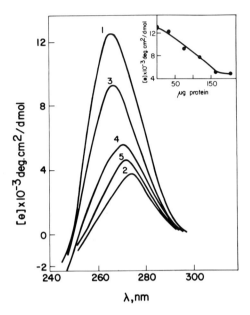

FIG. 4. As shown by circular dichroism, most of the secondary structure of hnRNP is unwound when it complexes with HD40 (curves 3 and 4 which represent HD40:nucleotide molar ratios of 1 : 22 and 1 : 10, respectively, and inset) or in 30 S nuclear RNP particles (curve 5). Curves 1 and 2 are spectra of hnRNA at 23°C and 80°C, respectively. Samples contained 42 nmol of nucleotide (spectra 1–4) or 32 nmol of nucleotide (spectrum 5) (*40*).

either dormant or developed cysts provide no evidence for any detectable modifications during development. Nor is there any significant change in the overall amount of the protein as development proceeds (*37, 40*). Analysis of total nuclear proteins by crossed immunoelectrophoresis [dodecyl sulfate/polyacrylamide followed by immunoelectrophoresis in the second dimension (*39*)] shows that nuclei of dormant cysts contain only a trace of HD40, but after development a significant amount of the protein is present in the nucleus, along with small amounts of antigenically related proteins in the 25,000–35,000 molecular weight range (*39, 40*). The 30 S particles obtained from pH 8.0 extracts of developed *A. salina* nuclei contain RNA and protein in a mass ratio of about 1 : 6, but not DNA. HD40 was identified by crossed immunoelectrophoresis as their major protein component (35–60% of total protein). Presumably, the protein appears in the nucleus concomitant with the resumption of transcriptional activity during development. In the lower eukaryote *Physarum polycephalum*, a glycine-rich protein analogous to hnRNP proteins disappears from the quiescent nuclei of spores and cysts (153).

Attempts at locating HD40 in the cytoplasm of undeveloped cysts indicate that part of it may exist as a free protein and another, larger part, sediments as a broad 10–30 S peak that coincides with the sedimentation of the translationally inactive stored poly(A)-containing mRNP (mRNP-A$_n$). Chromatography on oligo(dT)-cellulose columns, a method commonly employed for the purification of these particles, yields a poly(U)-hybridizable RNA species complexed with HD40 and several other proteins (39). However, free HD40 also binds, as expected, to oligo(dT)-cellulose and elutes under conditions similar to those required for the release of RNP-A$_n$. It seems that the present methods for isolating mRNPs are not sufficiently specific to permit the identification of protein that copurifies with cytoplasmic RNA-A$_n$ as a component of mRNP. In the case of HD40, the association may be an artifact of isolation related to the affinity of the protein to RNA. Even in developed cysts, a significant amount of HD40 is found in the postnuclear supernatant. It remains to be established whether this is due to nuclear lysis and leakage [cf. early findings on the cytoplasmic location of eukaryotic DNA polymerase α (154)], or whether HD40 is indeed involved in cytoplasmic metabolism of RNA. Immunofluorescent determination of the intracellular distribution of glycine-rich core hnRNP proteins in mouse and chicken cells shows that the antigenic sites are restricted to the nuclei in interphase cells (36, 155).

Ribosomes and ribosomal subunits from A. salina, after purification through the standard high-salt wash procedure, contain no antigens that cross-react with HD40 (39).

D. Concluding Remarks

With the exception of HD40, little is known about the nucleic acid binding properties of the glycine-rich core hnRNP proteins. While comparative investigations of analogous proteins from other eukaryotes are needed, HD40 may prove to be a good model for in vitro studies on the structure and function of hnRNP; its physical properties appear to be representative of the glycine-rich core proteins, and it can be purified in relatively large amounts. HD40 · RNA complexes are similar to native 30 S hnRNP in terms of gross structure, RNA conformation, and resistance to nucleases. All the properties of HD40 so far described imply that it may have a structure forming function in the in vivo assembly of hnRNP. Investigations on the RNA · protein and protein · protein interactions giving rise to the in

vitro self-assembly of globular complexes containing a largely unstacked RNA component are now possible. HD40 may also be useful
in conjunction with attempts at reconstructing *in vitro* systems for the
processing and splicing of primary transcripts.

In *A. salina*, a primitive crustacean, HD40 is by far the most abundant core hnRNP protein [cf. a somewhat similar situation in
Physarum polycephalum (140)]. In higher eukaryotes, where there are
at least several core proteins differing in their affinity for RNA, the
structure–function problem may be much more complex. In this respect, the precise role of the individual isoelectric species of HD40
(40) in the formation of the globular complex is of particular interest, as
is the nature of the posttranslational modifications of the protein.

In contrast to helix-destabilizing proteins participating in dynamic
processes that appear to exercise a transient effect on the conformation
of the nucleic acid (e.g., eIF-3 and S1 on mRNA and/or rRNA in translation), HD40 is a component of an isolatable nucleoprotein in which
the single-stranded RNA is maintained in an unfolded state owing to
its interaction with the protein. The conformation of the RNA in
hnRNP differs from that in other ribonucleoprotein complexes (e.g.,
ribosomes and RNA coliphages) in which single-stranded RNA molecules exist in an ordered, compact state. A somewhat analogous situation has been described in the literature with respect to the conformation of some viruses containing single-stranded nucleic acids. For example, as the RNA of the tobacco mosaic virus is assembled into virions, it is forced into a moderately extended single-stranded conformation as a result of its interaction with coat proteins (156). In the
Pseudomonas aeruginosa PF1 virions, base–base interactions in the
single-stranded DNA are completely abolished and replaced by
base–tyrosine stacking, the tyrosine residues coming from the major
coat protein of the phage (157, 158). And, in the host cell, coliphage-fd
DNA forms a complex with fd gene-V protein (a precursor complex in
the assembly process of the fd virions) in which the fd circular DNA is
unstacked (7, 159, 160).

It is apparent from a review of the current literature that the function of hnRNP proteins is largely unknown, and the structure of
hnRNP particles is poorly understood. *In vitro* investigations involving purified individual hnRNP proteins and mRNA precursors along
with the development of specific methods for the isolation of native
hnRNP appear to be essential in a field that involves a crucial step in
gene expression and in which important findings have yet to be made.

ACKNOWLEDGMENTS

The studies in our laboratory described in this article are the results of collaboration with Drs. Miloslav Boublik, José Hermoso, Annie Kolb, Steven Leffler (then a graduate student), Douglas Marvil, Leszek Nowak, Raziuddin and Andrzej Sobota. The work was supported by grants from the U. S. Public Health Service and from the American Cancer Society, Inc.

REFERENCES

1. G. Felsenfeld, G. Sandeen, and P. H. von Hippel, *PNAS* **50**, 644 (1963).
2. B. M. Alberts and L. Frey, *Nature* **227**, 113 (1970).
3. J. J. Champoux, *ARB* **47**, 449 (1978).
4. J. E. Coleman and J. L. Oakley, *CRC Crit. Rev. Biochem.* **7**, 247 (1980).
5. A. Kornberg, "DNA Replication." Freeman, San Francisco, California, 1980.
6. P. H. von Hippel, D. E. Jensen, R. C. Kelly, and J. D. McGhee, *in* "Nucleic Acid-Protein Recognition" (H. J. Vogel, ed.), p. 65. Academic Press, New York, 1977.
7. S. C. Kowalczykowski, D. G. Bear, and P. H. von Hippel, *in* "The Enzymes" (P. D. Boyer, ed.), 3rd ed., Vol. 14, p. 373. Academic Press, New York, 1981.
8. W. Fiers, R. Contreras, F. Duerinck, G. Haegeman, D. Iserantant, J. Merregaert, W. Min Jou, F. Molemans, A. Raeymaekers, A. Van den Berghe, G. Volckaert, and M. Ysebaert, *Nature* **260**, 500 (1976).
9. S. C. Kowalczykowski, N. Lonberg, J. W. Newport, and P. H. von Hippel, *JMB* **145**, 75 (1981).
10. J. W. Newport, N. Lonberg, S. C. Kowalczykowski, and P. H. von Hippel, *JMB* **145**, 105 (1981).
11. N. Lonberg, S. C. Kowalczykowski, L. S. Paul, and P. H. von Hippel, *JMB* **145**, 123 (1981).
12. G. Lemaire, L. Gold, and M. Yarus, *JMB* **126**, 73 (1978).
13. H. M. Krisch and G. B. Selzer, *JMB* **148**, 199 (1981).
14. R. L. Karpel, *in* "Gene Amplification and Analysis" (J. G. Chirikjian and T. S. Papas, eds.), p. 509. Elsevier-North Holland, Amsterdam, 1981.
15. J. Ilan and J. Ilan, *PNAS* **74**, 2325 (1977).
16. W. Szer, J. O. Thomas, C. Freienstein, and A. Kolb, *in* "Translation of Synthetic and Natural Polynucleotides" (A. Legocki, ed.), p. 70. Elsevier-North Holland, Amsterdam, 1977.
17. J. W. B. Hershey, *in* "Cell Biology" (L. Goldstein and D. M. Prescott, eds.), Vol. 4, p. 1. Academic Press, New York, 1980.
18. M. Grunberg-Manago and F. Gros, *This Series* **20**, 209 (1977).
19. M. Revel, *in* "Molecular Mechanisms of Protein Biosynthesis" (H. Weissbach and S. Pestka, eds.), p. 245. Academic Press, New York, 1977.
20. T. Schleich, E. Wickstrom, K. Twombly, B. Schmidt, and R. W. Tyson, *Bchem* **19**, 4486 (1980).
21. D. G. Bear, R. Ng, D. Van Derveer, N. P. Johnson, G. Thomas, T. Schleich, and H. F. Noller, *PNAS* **73**, 1824 (1976).
22. W. Szer, J. M. Hermoso, and M. Boublik, *BBRC* **70**, 957 (1976).
23. J. O. Thomas, A. Kolb, and W. Szer, *JMB* **123**, 163 (1978).
24. W. Szer, J. M. Hermoso, and S. Leffler, *PNAS* **72**, 2325 (1975).

25. G. Van Dieijen, C. J. van der Leken, P. H. van Knippenberg, and J. van Duin, *JMB* **93**, 351 (1975).
26. A. Kolb, J. M. Hermoso, J. O. Thomas, and W. Szer, *PNAS* **74**, 2379 (1977).
27. R. C. Yuan, J. A. Steitz, P. B. Moore, and D. M. Crothers, *NARes* **7**, 2399 (1979).
28. J. A. Steitz, *in* "Biological Regulation and Development" (R. F. Goldberger, ed.), Vol. 1, p. 349. Plenum, New York, 1979.
29. J. Karn, G. Vidali, C. L. Boffa, and V. G. Allfrey, *JBC* **252**, 7307 (1977).
30. A. L. Beyer, M. E. Christensen, B. W. Walker, and W. M. LeStourgeon, *Cell* **11**, 127 (1977).
31. L. P. Fuchs, C. Judes, and M. Jacob, *Bchem* **19**, 1087 (1980).
32. P. B. Billings and T. E. Martin, *Methods Cell Biol.* **17**, 349 (1978).
33. V. M. Kish and T. Pedersen, *Methods Cell Biol.* **17**, 377 (1978).
34. A. A. Preobrazhensky and A. S. Spirin, *This Series* **21**, 1 (1978).
35. W. J. Van Venrooij and D. B. Janssen, *Mol. Biol. Rep.* **4**, 3 (1978).
36. T. E. Martin, J. M. Pullman, and M. D. McMullen, *in* "Cell Biology" (L. Goldstein and D. M. Prescott, eds.), Vol. 4, p. 137. Academic Press, New York, 1980.
37. D. K. Marvil, L. Nowak, and W. Szer, *JBC* **252**, 6466 (1980).
38. L. Nowak, D. K. Marvil, J. O. Thomas, M. Boublik, and W. Szer, *JBC* **255**, 6473 (1980).
39. W. Szer, J. O. Thomas, L. Nowak, D. K. Marvil, and A. Sobota, *in* "Biological Implications of Protein–Nucleic Acid Interactions" (J. Augustyniak, ed.), p. 603. Elsevier-North Holland, Amsterdam, 1980.
40. J. O. Thomas, Raziuddin, A. Sobota, and W. Szer, *PNAS* **78**, 2888 (1981).
41. G. Herrick and B. Alberts, *JBC* **251**, 2124 (1976).
42. G. Herrick and B. Alberts, *JBC* **251**, 2133 (1976).
43. G. Herrick, H. Delius, and B. Alberts, *JBC* **251**, 2142 (1976).
44. R. L. Karpel and A. C. Burchard, *Bchem* **19**, 4674 (1980).
45. R. L. Karpel, N. S. Miller, and J. R. Fresco, *in* "Molecular Mechanisms in the Control of Gene Expression" (D. P. Nierlich, W. J. Rutter, and C. F. Fox, eds.), p. 411. Academic Press, New York, 1976.
46. R. L. Karpel, D. G. Swistel, N. S. Miller, M. E. Geroch, C. Lu, and J. R. Fresco, *Brookhaven Symp. Biol.* **26**, 165 (1974).
47. M. Tal, M. Aviram, A. Kanarek, and A. Weiss, *BBA* **281**, 381 (1972).
48. W. Szer and S. Leffler, *PNAS* **71**, 3611 (1974).
49. G. van Dieijen, P. H. van Knippenberg, and J. van Duin, *EJB* **64**, 511 (1976).
50. P. H. van Knippenberg, P. J. J. Hoorykaas, and J. van Duin, *FEBS Lett.* **41**, 323 (1974).
51. J. van Duin and P. H. van Knippenberg, *JMB* **84**, 185 (1974).
52. R. I. Kamen, *in* "RNA Phages" (N. D. Zinder, ed.), p. 203. Cold Spring Harbor Laboratory, Cold Spring Harbor, New York, 1975.
53. H. G. Gassen, *This Series* **24**, 57 (1980).
54. H. Inouye, Y. Pollack, and J. Petre, *EJB* **45**, 109 (1974).
55. A. J. Wahba, M. J. Miller, A. Niveleau, T. A. Landers, G. C. Carmichael, K. Weber, D. Hawley, and L. I. Slobin, *JBC* **249**, 3314 (1974).
56. J. H. Hermoso and W. Szer, *PNAS* **71**, 4708 (1974).
57. M. Laughrea and P. B. Moore, *JMB* **112**, 399 (1977).
58. M. J. Miller, A. Niveleau, and A. J. Wahba, *JBC* **249**, 3803 (1974).
59. M. Smolarsky and M. Tal, *BBA* **213**, 401 (1970).
60. J. M. Hermoso and W. Szer, *in* "Methods in Enzymology" (K. Moldave and L. Grossman, eds.), Vol. 60, p. 446. Academic Press, New York, 1979.

61. L. P. Visentin, S. Hasnain, W. Gallin, K. G. Johnson, D. W. Griffith, and A. J. Wahba, *FEBS Lett.* **79**, 258 (1977).
62. I. G. Wool, *in* "Ribosomes, Structure, Function and Genetics" (G. Chambliss, G. R. Carven, J. Davies, K. Davis, L. Kahan, and M. Nomura, eds.), p. 797. University Park Press, Baltimore, Maryland, 1980.
63. P. B. Moore, R. R. Traut, H. Noller, P. Pearson, and H. Delius, *JMB* **31**, 441 (1968).
64. G. R. Craven, P. Voynow, S. J. S. Hardy, and C. G. Kurland, *Bchem* **8**, 2906 (1969).
65. E. Kaltschmidt and H. G. Wittmann, *PNAS* **67**, 1276 (1970).
66. A. R. Subramanian, C. Hasse, and M. Giessen, *EJB* **67**, 591 (1976).
67. L. Giri and A. R. Subramanian, *FEBS Lett.* **81**, 194 (1977).
68. W. Szer, J. O. Thomas, A. Kolb, J. M. Hermoso, and M. Boublik, *in* "Nucleic Acid-Protein Recognition" (H. J. Vogel, ed.), p. 519. Academic Press, New York, 1977.
69. M. Laughrea, D. M. Engelman, and P. B. Moore, *J. Biochem.* **85**, 529 (1978).
70. H. Labischinski and A. R. Subramanian, *EJB* **95**, 359 (1979).
71. R Österberg, B. Sjöberg, and J. Littlechild, *FEBS Lett.* **93**, 115 (1978).
72. J. H. Hermoso, M. Boublik, and W. Szer, *ABB* **175**, 181 (1976).
73. T. Suryanarayana and A. R. Subramanian, *JMB* **127**, 41 (1979).
74. Y. G. Chu and C. R. Cantor, *NARes* **6**, 2363 (1979).
75. P. B. Moore and M. Laughrea, *NARes* **6**, 2355 (1979).
76. A. E. Dahlberg, *JBC* **249**, 7673 (1974).
77. M. Laughrea and P. B. Moore, *JMB* **121**, 411 (1978).
78. J. Littlechild and M. Spencer, *Bchem* **12**, 3102 (1973).
79. S. Giorginis and A. R. Subramanian, *JMB* **141**, 393 (1980).
80. M. J. Miller and A. J. Wahba, *JBC* **249**, 3808 (1974).
81. G. C. Carmichael, *JBC* **250**, 6161 (1975).
82. A. E. Dahlberg and J. E. Dahlberg, *PNAS* **72**, 2440 (1975).
83. G. Jay and R. Kaempfer, *JBC* **250**, 5749 (1975).
84. A. W. Senear and J. A. Steitz, *JBC* **251**, 1902 (1976).
85. S. Goelz and J. A. Steitz, *JBC* **252**, 5177 (1977).
86. A. Krol, C. Branlant, and J. Ebel, *FEBS Lett.* **80**, 255 (1977).
87. R. Lipecky, J. Vohlschein, and H. G. Gassen, *NARes* **4**, 3627 (1977).
88. D. E. Draper and P. H. von Hippel, *JMB* **122**, 339 (1978).
89. P. T. Li, T. Shea, S. Ellis, and T. H. Conway, *EJB* **98**, 155 (1979).
90. G. Felsenfeld and H. T. Miles, *ARB* **36**, 407 (1967).
91. J. C. Thierr, M. Dourlent, and M. Leng, *JMB* **58**, 815 (1971).
92. W. Szer, *JMB* **16**, 585 (1966).
93. S. B. Zimmerman, *JMB* **101**, 563 (1976).
94. K. A. Hartman, Jr. and A. Rich, *JACS* **87**, 2033 (1965).
95. J. O. Thomas, *in* "Principles and Techniques of Electron Microscopy" (M. A. Hayat, ed.), Vol. 9, p. 64. Van Nostrand-Reinhold, New York, 1978.
96. M. Riley, B. Maling, and M. J. Chamberlin, *JMB* **20**, 359 (1966).
97. D. E. Draper and P. H. von Hippel, *in* "Molecular Mechanisms in Gene Expression" (D. P. Nierlich, W. J. Rutter, and C. F. Fox, eds.), p. 421. Academic Press, New York, 1976.
98. D. E. Draper, C. W. Pratt, and P. H. von Hippel, *PNAS* **74**, 4786 (1977).
99. D. E. Draper and P. H. von Hippel, *JMB* **122**, 321 (1978).
100. A. Mülsch, M. Colpan, F. Wollny, H. G. Gassen, and D. Riesner, *NARes* **9**, 2307 (1981).
101. A. R. Subramanian, *JBC* **255**, 3227 (1980).

102. A. R. Subramanian and S. Mizushima, *JBC* **254**, 4309 (1979).
103. J. O. Thomas, M. Boublik, W. Szer, and A. R. Subramanian, *EJB* **102**, 309 (1979).
104. R. Linde, N. Quoc Khan, R. Lipecky, and H. G. Gassen, *EJB* **93**, (1979).
105. J. Shine and L. Dalgarno, *PNAS* **71**, 1342 (1974).
106. J. A. Steitz and K. Jakes, *PNAS* **72**, 4734 (1975).
107. J. A. Steitz and D. A. Steege, *JMB* **114**, 545 (1977).
108. C. Backendorf, G. P. Overbeek, J. H. van Boom, G. van der Marel, G. Veeneman, and J. van Duin, *EJB* **110**, 599 (1980).
109. R. A. Kenner, *BBRC* **51**, 932 (1973).
110. A. P. Czernilowsky, C. G. Kurland, and G. Söffler, *FEBS Lett.* **58**, 281 (1975).
111. A. Bollen, R. C. Heimark, A. Cozzone, R. R. Traut, J. W. B. Hershey, and L. Kahan, *JBC* **250**, 4310 (1975).
112. R. C. Heimark, L. Kahan, K. Johnston, J. W. B. Hershey, and R. R. Traut, *JMB* **105**, 219, 1976).
113. M. Laughrea and P. B. Moore, *JMB* **122**, 109 (1978).
114. D. E. Draper and P. H. von Hippel, *PNAS* **76**, 1040 (1979).
115. C. Backendort, C. J. L. Ravensbergen, J. Van der Plas, J. H. van Boom, G. Veeneman, and J. van Duin, *NARes* **9**, 1425 (1981).
116. J. A. Steitz, A. J. Wahba, M. Laughrea, and P. B. Moore, *NARes* **4**, 1 (1977).
117. M. M. Lamb and B. Daneholt, *Cell* **16**, 373 (1979).
118. S. L. McKnight and O. L. Miller, Jr., *Cell* **17**, 551 (1979).
119. A. L. Beyer, O. L. Miller, Jr., and S. L. McKnight, *Cell* **20**, 75 (1980).
120. A. L. Beyer, A. H. Bouton, L. D. Hodge, and O. L. Miller, Jr., *JMB* **147**, 269 (1981).
121. W. Northemann, M. Scheurlen, V. Gross, and P. C. Heinrich, *BBRC* **76**, 1130 (1977).
122. W. Northemann, H. Klump, and P. C. Heinrich, *EJB* **99**, 447 (1979).
123. W. Northemann, H. Seifert, and P. C. Heinrich, *Hoppe-Seyler's Z. Physiol. Chem.* **360**, 877 (1979).
124. J. Paoletti, J. Rech, C. Brunel, and P. Jeanteur, *Bchem* **19**, 5223 (1980).
125. O. P. Samarina, E. M. Lukanidin, J. Molnar, and G. P. Georgiev, *JMB* **33**, 251 (1968).
126. T. E. Martin, P. B. Billings, J. M. Pullman, B. J. Stevens, and A. J. Kinniburgh, *CSHSQB* **42**, 899 (1978).
127. J. T. Parson and K. S. McCarty, *JBC* **243**, 5377 (1968).
128. J. Pederson, *JMB* **83**, 163 (1974).
129. J. Stevenin and M. Jacob, *EJB* **47**, 129 (1974).
130. J. Stevenin, R. Gattoni, G. Divilliers, and M. Jacob, *EJB* **95**, 593 (1979).
131. A. Kinniburgh and T. Martin, *PNAS* **73**, 2725 (1976).
132. A. Alonso, C. H. Louis, C. Flytzanis, and C. Sekeris, *FEBS Lett.* **93**, 351 (1978).
133. K. Maundrell and K. Scherrer, *EJB* **99**, 225 (1979).
134. T. Pederson and N. G. Davis, *Cell Biol.* **87**, 47 (1980).
135. S. H. Munroe and T. Pederson, *JMB* **147**, 437 (1981).
136. S. Mayrand and T. Pederson, *PNAS* **78**, 2208 (1981).
137. B. W. Walker, L. Lothstein, C. L. Baker, and W. M. LeStourgeon, *NARes* **8**, 3639 (1980).
138. L. H. Augenlicht, *JBC* **253**, 3035 (1978).
139. N. T. Patel, A. Kurosky, and V. Holoubek, *BBA* **533**, 282 (1978).
140. M. E. Christensen, A. L. Beyer, B. Walker, and W. M. LeStourgeon, *BBRC* **74**, 621 (1977).
141. K. E. Peters and D. E. Comings, *J. Cell Biol.* **86**, 135 (1980).

142. J. Stevenin, H. Gallinaro-Matringe, R. Gattoni, and M. Jacob, *EJB* **74**, 589 (1977).
143. J. Rech, C. Brunel, and P. Jeanteur, *BBRC* **88**, 422 (1979).
144. J. P. Calvert and T. Pederson, *JMB* **122**, 361 (1978).
145. J. P. Calvert and T. Pederson, *PNAS* **76**, 755 (1979).
146. V. M. Kish and T. Pederson, *PNAS* **74**, 1426 (1977).
147. W. Jelinek and L. Leinwand, *Cell* **15**, 205 (1978).
148. J. A. Steitz and R. Kamen, *Mol. Cell. Biol.* 1, 21 (1981).
149. M. R. Lerner, J. A. Boyle, S. M. Mount, S. L. Wolin, and J. A. Steitz, *Nature* **283**, 220 (1979).
150. J. H. Weiner, L. L. Bertsch, and A. Kornberg, *JBC* **250**, 1972 (1975).
151. N. Sigal, H. Delius, T. Kornberg, M. L. Gefter, and B. Alberts, *PNAS* **69**, 3537 (1972).
152. C. C. Hentschel and J. R. Tata, *Trends Biochem. Sci.* **1**, 97 (1976).
153. W. M. LeStourgeon, A. L. Beyer, M. E. Christensen, B. W. Walker, S. M. Poupore, and L. P. Daniels, *CSHSQB* **42**, 885 (1978).
154. A. Weissbach, *ARB* **46**, 25 (1977).
155. R. E. Jones, C. S. Okamura, and T. E. Martin, *J. Cell. Biol.* **86**, 235 (1980).
156. A. Klug, *Harvey Lect.* **74**, 141 (1980).
157. L. A. Day and R. L. Wiseman, *in* "The Single Stranded DNA Phages" (D. T. Denhardt, D. Dressler and D. S. Ray, eds.), p. 605. Cold Spring Harbor Laboratory, Cold Spring Harbor, New York, 1978.
158. L. A. Day, R. L. Wiseman, and C. J. Marzec, *NARes* **7**, 1393 (1979).
159. L. A. Day, *Bchem* **12**, 5329 (1973).
160. R. A. Anderson, Y. Nakashima, and J. E. Coleman, *Bchem* **14**, 907 (1975).

Nucleotide Cyclases

LAURENCE S. BRADHAM
AND
WAI YIU CHEUNG

Department of Biochemistry
University of Tennessee Center for Health Sciences, and St. Jude Children's Research Hospital
Memphis, Tennessee

Nucleotide cyclases catalyze the synthesis of cyclic nucleotides by the general reaction

$$\text{NTP} \rightarrow \text{cNMP} + \text{PP}_i$$

Cleavage of the α,β acid-anhydride bond of the nucleoside triphosphate (NTP) is accompanied by simultaneous esterification of the 3′ hydroxyl of the sugar moiety to yield the nucleoside 3′,5′-(cyclic)monophosphate (cNMP). Although cAMP, cGMP, and cCMP have been identified in biological tissues, only adenylate cyclase (ATP pyrophosphate-lyase (cyclizing), EC 4.6.1.1) and guanylate cyclase (GTP pyrophosphate-lyase (cyclizing), EC 4.6.1.2) have been isolated and extensively characterized. Adenylate cyclase was first identified in a particulate fraction from various tissues by Rall and Sutherland (*1*), and its preparation and properties were described in 1962 by Suther-

Progress in Nucleic Acid Research
and Molecular Biology, Vol. 27

ISBN 0-12-540027-6

land *et al.* (2). Guanylate cyclase was identified in a variety of tissues in 1969 by Schultz *et al.* (3), Hardman and Sutherland (4), and White and Aurbach (5). To date, a comparable enzyme catalyzing the synthesis of cCMP has not been discovered.

A unique feature of adenylate and guanylate cyclases is their stimulation by hormones. Stimulation of adenylate cyclase *in vitro* was first reported in 1962 (6, 7), and led to the formulation of the "second messenger" concept. Subsequent research has shown that adenylate cyclase can be regulated by a wide variety of hormones and other agents that influence the activity of the isolated enzyme. Reports of hormonal stimulation of guanylate cyclase *in vitro* are relatively few, although it is well documented that intracellular levels of cGMP are under hormonal control, presumed to be mediated by guanylate cyclase. Therefore, adenylate and guanylate cyclases clearly play central roles in the control of cell function. The following discussion provides a comparison of the properties, regulation, and biological functions of these two enzymes.

I. Adenylate Cyclase

A. Tissue and Cellular Distribution

Adenylate cyclase is widely distributed in nature, having been isolated from or identified in both eukaryotic and prokaryotic cells (for a general review see 8). It has not yet been positively identified in cells of higher plants, but it has been found in every tissue of mammalian organisms, and within each tissue it appears to be present in virtually every subcellular organelle. With one exception, mammalian adenylate cyclase is associated with membranes; little or no activity is found in the cytosol. In testicular cells, there is also a cytosolic form, and bacterial adenylate cyclase is in this fraction. The membrane-bound enzyme of mammalian cells can be solubilized by the use of detergents.

B. Stoichiometry and Reaction Equilibrium

The stoichiometry of the reaction catalyzed by adenylate cyclase was established in experiments with the enzyme from skeletal muscle (9); equimolar amounts of cyclic nucleotide and PP_i are produced from each mole of nucleoside triphosphate. Under standard conditions (1 M reactants and products, 25°, pH 7), enzymes from *Brevibacterium liquifaciens* and *Streptococcus salivarius* catalyze the synthesis of ATP from cAMP (10–14). The equilibrium constant for the forward reaction has been estimated to be 0.065 (*10, 12, 15*). Therefore, under these conditions, the formation of cAMP is endergonic with a $\Delta G°$ of +1.6 kcal/mol at pH 7 (*11, 12, 15*).

No significant reversal of the reaction with the enzyme from *B. liquifaciens* was observed by others (*16*), nor was reversal detected with adenylate cyclase from *Escherichia coli* (*17*) or from frog erythrocytes (*18*). Possible explanations for this discrepancy have been pointed out (*11*). Regardless of the validity of the results, it is doubtful that reversal of the reaction is physiologically relevant, since concentrations of substrates required for reversal do not exist in biological systems (*12*).

The stereochemistry of the reaction catalyzed by a bacterial enzyme has been studied with the *S* diastereoisomer of adenosine 5'-(α-thio)triphosphate (ATPαS) as the substrate (*19*). The data suggest that the reaction occurs by a general base-catalyzed displacement of pyrophosphate accompanied by inversion of configuration at the α-phosphate. Hence, the reaction proceeds in a single step without the formation of an adenylated intermediate.

C. State of Purity and Macromolecular Properties

The most highly purified adenylate cyclase is the crystalline enzyme derived from *B. liquifaciens* (*10*). The 4500-fold purified enzyme catalyzes the formation of 30 μmol of cAMP per minute per milligram of protein. To date, there is no report of crystallization of adenylate cyclase derived from mammalian tissues, but there are a few claims of extensive purification. A combination of hydrophobic and affinity chromatography gave a 5000-fold purification of adenylate cyclase from cardiac tissue (*20, 21*). The claim of a high specific activity for the final product is difficult to assess since the purified enzyme fraction appears to contain no measurable protein (*21*). Affinity columns of various types have also been used to purify the adenylate cyclase of brain (*22*) and liver (*23, 24*). The soluble enzyme from rat testes has been purified to apparent homogeneity by a combination of ion-exchange chromatography, gel filtration, and isoelectric focusing (*25*).

Highly purified as well as relatively crude preparations have been used to estimate the molecular weight (M_r) and to investigate the macromolecular properties of adenylate cyclase. A range of values has been obtained depending upon the source of the enzymes. The smallest bacterial enzyme isolated thus far appears to be the one purified 38-fold from the culture medium of *Bordetella pertussis*, which migrates on gel electrophoresis in dodecyl sulfate as a single component of M_r = 70,000 (26). The crystalline enzyme from B. liquifaciens, on the other hand, has an M_r of 92,400 as estimated by sedimentation equilibrium centrifugation (10).

The molecular weights of adenylate cyclase from several mammalian tissues are shown in Table I (24, 25, 28–37). The classification into types I, II, and III is based upon location in the cell and relative binding of detergent (27). Types I and II are membrane-bound and require detergent for solubilization. However, as indicated by their partial specific volumes, solubilized type I enzymes bind significant amounts of detergent whereas type II enzymes do not. The molecular weights of type I enzymes shown in Table I have been corrected for bound detergent. The only example of type III known is the cytosolic enzyme from rat testes, which is water-soluble and binds no significant amount of detergent (25).

The adenylate cyclase extracted from bovine cerebral cortex membranes with Lubrol PX has been resolved into high and low molecular weight forms (28). Only the properties of the low molecular weight form are described in Table I. The high molecular weight form (M_r = 265,000) has catalytic activity but does not exhibit the usual regulatory properties of adenylate cyclase, and it may be an aggregate with another membrane protein (28).

The extensive binding of detergent by type I adenylate cyclase is probably due to hydrophobic areas in the molecule that facilitate its inclusion in the membrane lipid bilayer (27, 29–31). The enzymes of brain, lymphoma cells, and liver are presumably intrinsic membrane proteins whereas those from kidney, thyroid, and sperm do not have such extensive hydrophobic areas and are only partially buried in the inner membrane surface. The soluble form of the sperm enzyme may be either a cytosolic protein or one that readily detaches from the membrane during disruption of the cell.

The validity of estimations of molecular weight from the hydrodynamic properties of adenylate cyclase has been questioned because of the possibility of its association with other membrane proteins (38). However, electron inactivation analysis suggests M_r's of 150,000, to 160,000 for the enzymes in intact hepatic membranes (39, 40). Such close agreement with values obtained from hydrodynamic measurements suggests that these more conventional techniques provide reliable estimates of M_r regardless of the purity of the enzyme.

There is evidence, however, that adenylate cyclase binds reversibly to intrinsic regulatory components and that the apparent M_r of the enzyme may be affected by its state of activation. Electron inactivation analysis of the enzyme after activation by various effectors indicates an

TABLE I

HYDRODYNAMIC PROPERTIES OF ADENYLATE CYCLASE

Type	Source	Molecular weight ($\times 10^{-5}$)	$s_{20,w}$ (S)	Stokes' radius (nm)	f/f_o	Partial specific volume (ml/g)	Detergent bound (g/g)	References
I	Brain	1.99	7.3	6.8	ND	0.81	0.32[a]	28
		1.76	7.2	6.5	ND	0.80	0.32[b]	28
	Brain[c]	2.51	8.5	7.2	ND	0.79	0.24[a]	28
		2.2	8.1	7.0	1.5	0.79	0.28[b]	29
	S49 lymphoma	2.2	7.5	7.1	1.6	0.78	0.2[a]	30
	Liver	1.5	ND[d]	ND	ND	ND	ND	24
		1.83	6.8	7.0	1.5	0.82	0.40[a]	31
	Liver fluke	1.15	4.5	6.3	1.7	0.80	0.41[a]	32
II	Kidney	1.57	6.1	6.1	1.6	0.71	N.s.[a,d]	33
		1.59	5.9	6.2	1.6	0.74	N.s.[b]	33
		1.7	6.1	6.5	ND	0.76	0.08[b]	34
	Kidney[c]	2.1	7.8	6.5	ND	0.78	0.18[b]	34
	Thyroid	1.19	6.6	4.1	ND	0.75	N.s.[e]	35
	Thyroid[c]	1.59	7.4	4.5	ND	0.75	N.s.[e]	35, 36
	Testes (membrane)	1.91	6.7	6.8	1.6	0.73	N.s.[b]	37
III	Testes	0.56	3.8	3.4	1.2	ND	ND	37
	(cytosol)	0.74	4.3	3.95	1.4	0.74	N.s.	25

[a] Solubilized with Lubrol PX (Lubrol 12A9).
[b] Solubilized with Triton X-100.
[c] Activated with GuoPP[NH]P.
[d] ND, not determined; N.s., not significant.
[e] Solubilized with Triton N-101.

increase in M_r of 80,000–100,000 (39). Different M_r's for the enzyme isolated from thyroid, kidney medulla, and brain have also been obtained before and after activation with a guanine nucleotide (see Table I). The increase in M_r may result from the binding of the enzyme to a protein required for nucleotide activation (27, 34, 35).

The only specimens of adenylate cyclase sufficiently purified to permit analysis of subunit structure are those from B. *liquifaciens* (10) and B. *pertussis* (26). The enzyme from B. *liquifaciens* consists of two subunits of equal mass (46,000 daltons) whereas that from B. *pertussis* consists of a single polypeptide chain. The adenylate cyclase purified from liver membranes (24) and that obtained from rat testes (25) also migrate as a single band on gel electrophoresis in dodecyl sulfate.

D. Enzymic Properties

1. SUBSTRATE SPECIFICITY

The only natural nucleoside triphosphates that serve as substrates for adenylate cyclase are ATP and dATP. The highly purified enzyme from B. *liquifaciens*, for example, uses either nucleotide equally well (10). Activity with the synthetic ATP analog adenosine 5'-[β,γ-imido]triphosphate (AdoPP[NH]P) is 20% of that with the natural substrates. The K_m value for ATP and dATP in the forward reaction is 0.4 mM. In the reverse reaction, both cAMP and cdAMP can serve as substrate, but the K_m values are much higher (14 mM and 13 mM, respectively). The K_m for PP$_i$ in the reverse reaction is 1.9 mM.

Accurate measurement of K_m values for partially purified mammalian adenylate cyclase necessitates elimination of interference from the ATP hydrolase activity, present in all membranes, that competes with adenylate cyclase for ATP. One method of avoiding this interference is the use of a suitable regeneration system to maintain a constant concentration of substrate during the assay. With such a precaution, K_m values in the micromolar range have been obtained (32, 41–49). AdoPP[NH]P, which is resistant to hydrolysis by ATPase, has also been used as a substitute for ATP in the absence of a substrate regenerating system (47), and the K_m for this analog is the same as for ATP but the V_{max} is lower. Possible complications that may arise from the use of substrate regenerating systems in the assay of adenylate cyclase have been noted (50).

2. DIVALENT CATION REQUIREMENTS

a. Magnesium and Manganese Ions. Adenylate cyclase, like other enzymes that catalyze reactions of nucleoside triphosphates, requires a divalent cation for activity. The cation can be either Mg^{2+} or Mn^{2+}, and their relative activity varies considerably depending upon the source and prior treatment of the enzyme. Some preparations of adenylate cyclase have equivalent activity when assayed with either cation, whereas others have higher activity in the presence of Mn^{2+} (2, 8, 10, 26, 37, 43, 48, 51–63). In general, enzyme activity at low concentrations of divalent cation is higher with Mn^{2+} than with Mg^{2+}. The activity of brain adenylate cyclase for example, is maximal with 1 to 3 mM Mn^{2+}, whereas maximal activity with Mg^{2+} is observed at a concentration of 5 mM or higher (8, 59). Divalent cation in excess of ATP is usually required for maximal activity, but Mn^{2+} is sometimes inhibitory at high concentrations. The soluble enzyme from rat testis (37, 53) and the membrane-bound enzyme from *Neurospora crassa* (54) are solely dependent upon Mn^{2+} for activity.

Although adenylate cyclase exhibits activity with either Mg^{2+} or Mn^{2+}, the most likely physiological cation is Mg^{2+}. The intracellular concentration of Mg^{2+} is in the range required for enzyme activity, whereas the physiological concentration of Mn^{2+} is too low. In addition, when it is assayed with Mn^{2+}, adenylate cyclase appears to lose its regulatory properties. When brain adenylate cyclase, for example, is assayed in the presence of Mn^{2+} there is no stimulation by effectors such as fluoride and GuoPP[NH]P (Bradham, unpublished data). These results suggest that the enzyme exhibits maximal activity when assayed with Mn^{2+} and is not affected by the addition of positive effectors. High concentrations of Mn^{2+} inhibit the activity of frog erythrocyte adenylate cyclase when it is assayed with isoproterenol, GuoPP[NH]P, or a prostaglandin without affecting the binding of these agonists with the membrane (64). These findings suggest that Mn^{2+} causes uncoupling of adenylate cyclase from its regulatory mechanism.

It has been proposed that the preferred cation for the catalytic subunit of adenylate cyclase is Mn^{2+}, but that its regulatory properties depend upon Mg^{2+} (39). The molecular weight of the enzyme obtained by electron inactivation analysis is smaller when it is assayed with Mn^{2+}, suggesting that it does not couple with its regulatory subunits in the presence of this cation (39, 65). In addition, the adenylate cyclase from a genetic variant of S49 lymphoma cells (cyc⁻, which lacks a regulatory component) exhibits activity only in the presence of Mn^{2+} (66), and physical separation of the enzyme of other tissues from its regulatory components results in increased activity with Mn^{2+} relative to Mg^{2+} concurrent with loss of its regulatory properties (67–69).

b. Calcium Ion. Adenylate cyclase exhibits no activity when assayed with Ca^{2+} as a substitute for Mg^{2+}, but Ca^{2+} at millimolar concentrations is inhibitory when the enzyme is assayed with Mg^{2+} (43, 45, 46, 48, 56, 58–60, 70–74). This inhibition results in a decrease in V_{max}. There is less inhibition when Mg^{2+} is replaced with Mn^{2+} (58, 76, 79), and there is evidence that Ca^{2+} competes with Mg^{2+} or Mn^{2+} for binding sites on the enzyme (43, 76). It has been proposed that inhibition by Ca^{2+} is important in physiological regulation of the enzyme (76–79).

At lower concentrations, Ca^{2+} appears to be required for full activity of the adenylate cyclase from brain and other tissues. The evidence for this has been reviewed (80, 81). The requirement can be demonstrated by the use of the chelating agent EGTA, which inhibits the enzyme (8, 58, 59, 71, 72, 82–97). Inhibition is characterized by a decrease in V_{max} rather than K_m (98) and occurs at a concentration of EGTA that correlates well with the concentration of endogenous Ca^{2+}. Inhibition by EGTA is completely reversed by Ca^{2+} and other metal ions. The concentration of free Ca^{2+} necessary for half-maximal activity of guinea pig brain adenylate cyclase is calculated to be 0.08 μM (97). At higher concentrations, the ion is inhibitory. The effect of Ca^{2+} on adenylate cyclase, therefore, is biphasic, and maximal activity is observed only within a narrow range of Ca^{2+} concentration. Washing of cultured brain cells (C-6 glioma) with EGTA causes a decrease in their adenylate cyclase activity that is reversed by exogenous Ca^{2+} (99).

The activating effect of Ca^{2+} on brain adenylate cyclase can be attributed to its requirement for the Ca^{2+}-binding protein calmodulin (CaM). In its native state, the enzyme is complexed with $Ca^{2+} \cdot$ calmodulin ($Ca \cdot CaM$) and exhibits full enzymic activity. Treatment with EGTA causes dissociation of the complex and partial inactivation of the enzyme. Dissociation is reversible, and the activity of the enzyme is rapidly altered by adjusting the concentration of $Ca \cdot CaM$ in the assay mixture (100, 101). Calmodulin can be separated from the enzyme by chromatography of detergent-solubilized preparations in the presence of EGTA (100–102) or by extracting membranes with salt solution containing the metal chelator (97, 103). The residual enzyme is activated by Ca^{2+} in the presence of exogenous calmodulin.

There is considerable evidence that brain membranes contain both calmodulin-dependent and -independent forms of adenylate cyclase; approximately 80% of the brain enzyme is calmodulin-dependent (84). The dependent form is more stable, and incubation of membranes at 37° produces an enzyme that is almost totally dependent. Alternatively, the independent form appears to be activated to a greater degree by positive effectors, such as fluoride and guanine nucleotides (83, 84, 86, 103). The two forms can be resolved on a cal-modulin affinity-column (104). The dependent form is adsorbed to the column and is eluted with EGTA. It is stimulated by Ca^{2+} at low concentrations but is inhibited by higher concentrations of the ion. The independent form exhibits only inhibition by Ca^{2+}. In the presence of a guanine nucleotide and another protein fraction, the independent form is converted to the dependent form (105).

The CaM-dependent form of adenylate cyclase in intact cells and isolated membranes is inhibited by chlorpromazine or trifluoperazine (84, 99). These phenothiazines bind to CaM and render it biologically inactive (106). The calmodulin-dependent form is also inhibited by the calmodulin-binding protein, calcineurin (107).

Adenylate cyclase from a prokaryotic organism can be stimulated by CaM from eukaryotic cells. The adenylate cyclase of B. pertussis is activated in a dose-dependent manner by CaM derived from calf brain (108). Stimulation is prevented by EGTA, but once the enzyme·CaM complex is formed it is not readily reversed by chelation of Ca^{2+}. The activity of this enzyme·CaM complex is also inhibited by trifluoperazine.

3. POSITIVE EFFECTORS

a. Fluoride Ions. Although there are a few exceptions, adenylate cyclase from most sources is activated by fluoride ions. The exceptions are most bacterial enzymes (10, 17, 26), the soluble enzyme from sperm (37–52), and the membrane-bound enzyme from *Neurospora crassa* (54). The enzyme purified from S. *salivarius*, on the other hand, is stimulated by the anion (14). The concentration of fluoride required for maximal stimulation is in the millimolar range, but the exact concentration varies from one preparation to another, and higher anion concentrations are often inhibitory (14, 45, 46, 48, 72, 77, 93). With some preparations, the increase in enzyme activity as a function of fluoride concentration is sigmoidal (32, 45, 48, 70, 71, 75, 109). Fluoride increases the V_{max} with little or no effect on the apparent K_m (41, 43, 45, 46, 48, 75, 94), and the stimulation is not additive to that produced by hormones (2, 45, 70–72, 74, 92, 110–112). Where it has been tested, stimulation by fluoride is temperature-dependent (45, 48, 75, 94, 112).

When adenylate cyclase is incubated with fluoride, it rapidly becomes activated, and the activated state persists after dilution of fluoride to an ineffective concentration or its removal by washing or dialysis of the membranes (48, 62, 63, 75, 92, 113–115). The enzyme remains activated at 0°, but loses activity at a higher temperature (62,

114). Under the appropriate conditions, therefore, fluoride activation is reversible. Activation is temperature-dependent and partially dependent upon a divalent cation.

b. *Nucleotides.* The activity of adenylate cyclase from most mammalian sources is affected by guanine nucleotides. In many instances, GTP is required for stimulation of the enzyme by hormones or other positive effectors (*56, 94, 109, 116–128*). Early findings that ATP may serve a regulatory role in hormonal stimulation of bladder (*94*) and liver (*120*) adenylate cyclase may have been due to contamination by GTP. Glucagon stimulation of hepatic adenylate cyclase shows an absolute dependence upon GTP when the substrate ATP has been extensively purified to remove contaminating nucleotides (*127, 128*). In some instances, GTP stimulates the enzyme in the absence of hormones (*94, 109, 116, 117, 119, 122, 126–128*), but these increases are moderate and are further enhanced by hormones.

Adenylate cyclase is also activated by structural analogs of GTP that are not readily hydrolyzed by phosphohydrolases present in membranes or solubilized preparations of the enzyme. Compounds such as guanosine $5'$-[β,γ-imido]triphosphate (GuoPP[NH]P), guanosine $5'$-[β,γ-methylene]triphosphate (GuoPP[CH$_2$]P), and guanosine $5'$-[γ-thio]triphosphate (GuoPPP[S] or GTPγS) all enhance the stimulation of adenylate cyclase by hormones and activate the catalytic unit in the absence of hormones (*29, 32, 36, 42, 44, 78, 116, 129–141*). The effect on the enzyme is an increase in the V_{max} without appreciably changing the K_m. With some enzyme preparations there is a lag period before the onset of activation (*42, 129, 131, 133, 134*). The concentration of nucleotide required for activation is in the micromolar range, with maximal activation occurring at approximately 100 μM.

Incubation of either membrane-bound or solubilized adenylate cyclase with a nucleotide results in slow activation, and the active state persists after washing of the membrane, dialysis, or dilution of the nucleotide to an ineffective concentration (*29, 32, 36, 59, 129–134, 137–139, 141*). The enzyme remains in the activated state throughout solubilization with detergents and various chromatographic procedures (*29, 32, 36, 59, 130–132*). Incubation of membrane fractions with GTP does not activate adenylate cyclase, but GTP prevents activation by GuoPP[NH]P if it is added prior to the analog (*132, 134, 137*). There is evidence that both GTP and the analog bind to the same membrane sites; the difference in their potency for activation of adenylate cyclase is due to a difference in their susceptibility to hydrolysis at these sites (*138, 139*). The GTP is rapidly hydrolyzed by nucleotide phosphohydrolases whereas GuoPP[NH]P bound to the membrane remains intact. The binding constants for the two nucleotides are similar, and both GTP and GDP competitively inhibit the binding of the analog to hepatocyte and adipocyte membranes (133).

    c. Bacterial Enterotoxins. Much of what is known about the mechanism of regulation of adenylate cyclase has been learned from the use of cholera toxin, a potent activator of the enzyme in intact cells and isolated preparations. The structure, the properties, and the activation of adenylate cyclase by this enterotoxin have been reviewed (142). Choleragen is secreted by *Vibrio cholerae* and is the active vector in the clinical symptoms of cholera. It is an oligomeric protein (84,000 daltons) composed of three dissimilar peptides, B, A_1, and A_2. There are five B subunits (11,600 daltons) that bind specifically to GM_1 ganglioside on the cell surface. The single subunit A (23,500 daltons) dissociates into A_1 and A_2 in the presence of thiols. The A_1 subunit is the biologically active component.

    Infection of cells with choleragen increases intracellular cAMP (143–148), and this can be correlated with the water and electrolyte imbalance that causes the watery diarrhea of cholera (144) and the other biological effects of the toxin (144, 145, 149–155). The increase in cAMP results from activation of adenylate cyclase; incubation of intact cells with choleragen or administration of the toxin *in vivo* produces an increase in the basal activity of the enzyme (147, 156–163). Activation is slow, with a characteristic lag phase, and persists after removal of the toxin and isolation of the membranes.

    Activation of adenylate cyclase in isolated membranes or solubilized preparations can be produced by the holotoxin, subunit A, or purified subunit A_1 (161, 162, 164–173). Activation *in vitro* requires NAD^+, ATP, glutathione, and a cytosolic protein (164, 168, 173). Activation by the holotoxin is prevented by prior addition of exogenous ganglioside GM_1 or choleragenoid (inactivated choleragen). These agents, which inhibit binding of choleragen to its receptor (174), do not affect activation by subunits A and A_1 (164, 165).

    In its activated state, adenylate cyclase has properties different from those of the native enzyme. In addition to its increased activity, sensitivity to GTP and to hormonal stimulation are increased (147, 157–159, 172, 175). In contrast, the toxin-activated enzyme is no longer responsive to stimulation by fluoride (157, 158, 172).

    Adenylate cyclase is also activated by an enterotoxin secreted by *E. coli*; this activation and the subsequent increase in intracellular cAMP have been correlated with the clinical symptoms of infection (153, 155, 176–183). The active component of this enterotoxin is a heat-labile protein ($M_r = 23,000–24,000$) that appears to be similar or identical to

subunit A_1 of choleragen (182). Activation of adenylate cyclase in isolated membranes by this toxin exhibits the same cofactor requirements
as choleragen (182).

A heat-stable component of *E. coli* enterotoxin also causes watery
diarrhea and alteration of ion fluxes in intestinal tissue. This component (M_r = 5000) does not activate adenylate cyclase but causes increased cGMP formation in intact cells and activates guanylate cyclase
in the membrane fraction of intestinal epithelial cells (184, 185).

The A_1 subunit of choleragen and the heat-labile toxin of *E. coli*
have enzymic activity; they catalyze the hydrolysis of NAD^+ and the
ADP-ribosylation of several guanidinium compounds such as arginine, arginine methyl ester, and guanidine itself (186–190). Subunit
A becomes ADP-ribosylated[1] in the absence of another acceptor (191).
An ADP-ribosyltransferease that activates brain adenylate cyclase has
been isolated from avian erythrocytes (192, 193). The enzyme
catalyzes the hydrolysis of NAD^+ and ADP-ribosylation of
guanidinium compounds and several proteins. After 500,000-fold
purification by affinity chromatography, the enzyme activity is associated with a component of M_r = 28,300 (193).

E. Regulatory Components of Adenylate Cyclase

The effect of fluoride, guanine nucleotides, and choleragen on
adenylate cyclase appears to be mediated by a nucleotide-binding
protein that was first identified in pigeon erythrocytes (130). The protein can be separated from the adenylate cyclase by chromatography
on a nucleotide-affinity column, resulting in partial loss of enzyme
activation by nucleotides and fluoride (139, 140). Responsiveness is
restored by recombination with a protein fraction eluted from the column with GuoPP[NH]P. Similar proteins have since been identified in
membranes of many tissues, and their properties and function have
been reviewed recently (194).

Genetic variants of cultured cells have been useful in identifying
and characterizing this regulatory component. The cyc⁻ variant of S49
lymphoma cells exhibits adenylate cyclase activity when assayed with
Mn^{2+} but has no activity with Mg^{2+}, nor is it stimulated by fluoride,
nucleotides or hormones (66). Membranes of cyc⁻ cells apparently
have the catalytic subunit of adenylate cyclase but are deficient in the
regulatory component. When cyc⁻ membranes or detergent extracts
are combined with detergent extracts of wild S49 cells (195), rat liver

---

[1] See essay on poly(ADP-ribose) by Mandel, Okazaki, and Niedergang in this volume.
[Ed.]

(66), or other cultured cell lines (196), the physiological properties of the adenylate cyclase are restored. In the reconstituted system, the enzyme exhibits activity in the presence of Mg^{2+} and is stimulated by fluoride, GuoPP[NH]P, and hormones.

Regulatory components of adenylate cyclase have been identified in enzyme preparations derived from other sources. Extraction of brain membranes with detergent solutions results in a diminished response to fluoride (114) and GuoPP[NH]P (197, 198) that is restored by recombination with the detergent extract. The regulatory component of brain has been resolved from the catalytic subunit by gel filtration of a preparation solubilized in a buffer containing cholate and ammonium sulfate (67). A similar technique has been successful in isolating of a regulatory component from hepatic membranes (68). Regulatory components have also been identified in liver fluke (199) and muscle (200).

The biologically active regulatory component is a large protein with a molecular weight of 126,000 (201) to 130,000 (202). These estimates are based upon the hydrodynamic properties of the protein, but are confirmed by the results of electron inactivation analysis of intact erythrocyte membranes (65). A detergent is required to extract the protein from the membrane, but it does not bind a considerable amount of detergent in solution. Other evidence suggests, however, that it is an intrinsic membrane protein (201). It is an elongated molecule (Stokes' radius 61 Å, frictional ratio 1.85) and is located on the inner face of the plasma membrane (203, 204).

A highly purified regulatory component from hepatic membranes is composed of three subunits with molecular weights of 52,000, 45,000, and 35,000 (205). All three polypeptides may be required for biological activity, since they are not resolved by procedures that preserve the functional integrity of the complex. Cholera toxin has been a valuable tool for investigating the role of these subunits in the activity of the regulatory component (206). Activation of adenylate cyclase by the enterotoxin results from modification of the regulatory component rather than of the catalytic subunit. Cholera toxin has no effect on the adenylate cyclase of the cyc⁻ S49 cell, but the enzyme becomes responsive to GTP and insensitive to fluoride when it is combined with extracts of membranes from wild-type cells treated with the toxin (207).

The activating effect of cholera toxin on the regulatory component is probably the result of covalent modification of one or more of its subunits. When [^{32}P]NAD is used as the substrate in assays of ADP-ribosyltransferase[1] activity, several membrane proteins in erythrocyte and lymphoma cells become labeled, but the predominant one is a 42,000- to 45,000-dalton polypeptide (*201, 208–210*). The number of molecules labeled is approximately equivalent to the number of β-adrenergic receptors (*203*). Labeling is correlated with activation of the adenylate cyclase, and reversal of ADP-ribosylation by unlabeled nicotinamide also reverses enzyme activation (*203, 208*). There is no labeling of a peptide having this molecular weight when cyc⁻ cells are treated with the toxin, but labeling does occur after incorporation of the regulatory component from another source into cyc⁻ membranes (*201, 210*).

When the highly purified regulatory component from hepatic membranes is incubated with cholera toxin and [^{32}P]NAD, the 52,000- and 45,000-dalton subunits are predominately labeled (*205*). The 35,000-dalton subunit is not labeled although its presence is required for biological activity. This subunit can be resolved from the others after inactivation of the regulatory component, but recombination does not result in restoration of activity. The precise role of each of these subunits in the activation of adenylate cyclase is unknown, although it seems clear that the intact complex is required for activity.

It is not yet known if the action of nucleotides and fluoride is mediated through the same or separate molecules. In some systems, resolution of the regulatory component from adenylate cyclase results in the loss of responsiveness to both effectors, and reconstitution with a partially purified component restores sensitivity to both. Modification by treatment with cholera toxin produces a simultaneous increase in responsiveness to GTP and loss of sensitivity to fluoride, and the alteration in both properties is reversed upon reversal of ADP-ribosylation[1] (*203, 208*). Fluoride activation of erythrocyte membrane adenylate cyclase requires a nucleotide bound to the regulatory component. Treatment of the membranes with isoproterenol and a high concentration of GMP displaces bound nucleotide from the membrane, and the adenylate cyclase becomes more sensitive to activation by GuoPP[NH]P and insensitive to activation by fluoride (*211, 212*). Responsiveness to fluoride is restored by the addition of either GTP or GDP (*211*).

These results support the argument that nucleotide and fluoride activation are related, and furthermore suggest that they are mediated by the same component. The two activities differ, however, with respect to thermal stability at 50°C and sensitivity to inactivation by N-ethylmaleimide (*195, 207*) suggesting a requirement for separate regulatory components. It is quite possible that the same component mediates the response to both effectors, but does so through different mechanisms.

The regulatory component appears to have catalytic activity. Turkey erythrocyte membranes contain a GTPase that is stimulated by catecholamines (213). Treatment with cholera toxin causes an inhibition of GTPase that coincides with activation of adenylate cyclase (214) and ADP-ribosylation of the 42,000-dalton peptide (203). Inhibition of GTPase activity at the regulatory site accounts for increased responsiveness of the adenylate cyclase to GTP. In the absence of hydrolysis, GTP has the same properties as GuoPP[NH]P or other nonhydrolyzable nucleotide. The involvement of a hormone-sensitive GTPase in the regulation of adenylate cyclase in S49 lymphoma cells has been confirmed indirectly (215).

Similar regulatory components are found in cytoplasmic fractions from several tissues. There is a soluble component that enhances basal activity and epinephrine stimulation of adenylate cyclase in rat liver membranes (216). The factor appears to be a protein that binds GTP, but it has not been further characterized. A protein purified from a supernatant fraction of rat brain enhances fluoride stimulation of the brain adenylate cyclase (217). The component is heat-stable (92°) and has a molecular weight of 59,000. A protein in supernatant fractions from liver, heart, and skeletal muscle reconstitutes fluoride- and nucleotide-stimulated activity in membranes of cyc⁻ S49 cells (218). Approximately 25% of the total reconstituting activity is found in the supernatant fraction. These factors may represent adenylate cyclase regulatory components separated from the membrane during preparation, or they may be unique proteins normally present in the cytoplasm. Relevant to this is the finding that several proteins in a soluble fraction from bovine thymus are substrates for ADP-ribosylation[1] by cholera toxin; among them is a 42,000-dalton polypeptide (219).

E. Hormonal Regulation

Physiologically, the most significant property of adenylate cyclase is its regulation by hormones. In intact cells, the enzyme is stimulated by a wide variety of catecholamine and polypeptide hormones, leading to an increased intracellular concentration of cAMP that triggers the appropriate physiological response of the cell to the hormone. In most systems, this property is retained by isolated membranes, and incubation with a hormone increases the V_{max} of adenylate cyclase. As predicted by an early model (220), regulation is mediated by a multicomponent complex—consisting of the receptor on the external face of the plasma membrane, the catalytic subunit on the internal surface, and a transducer component—that transmits the signal from the hormone-occupied receptor to the catalytic subunit. In the past decade, each of these components has been isolated and identified as a distinct, separable protein. The precise mechanism by which they interact is still unknown, but their organization within the membrane is clearly critical. Stimulation of adenylate cyclase by hormones is usually observed only within the framework of the intact membrane.

In addition to the macromolecular components of this regulatory system, there is a requirement for GTP. The importance of this nucleotide has been demonstrated recently in intact cultured cells (221). When rat kidney cells are treated with inhibitors of inosinate dehydrogenase, such as virazole or mycophenolic acid, the intracellular concentration of GTP decreases, and the responsiveness of the adenylate cyclase to prostaglandin E_1 and isoproterenol is reduced. As described in the following sections, GTP affects both the receptor and the adenylate cyclase, and its effect is mediated by the nucleotide-binding regulatory component.

1. COUPLING OF RECEPTORS WITH ADENYLATE CYCLASE

a. Properties of Receptors. There are many examples of correlation between agonist–receptor binding and activation of adenylate cyclase (49, 93, 121, 222–231). Some tissues contain receptors for only one hormone, whereas others contain multiple receptors. The fat cell membrane, for example, has receptors for catecholamines, corticotropin, luteinizing hormone, glucagon, and secretin, all of which are coupled with adenylate cyclase (232). The β-adrenergic receptor has been most extensively characterized because of the availability of radioactively labeled ligands of known chemical structure. These receptors are found in membranes of a wide variety of tissues including avian and amphibian erythrocytes (229, 233, 234), cardiac tissue (235), and adipocytes (236, 237). They are highly specific for β-adrenergic agents, and there is little or no binding of α-adrenergic agents, cholinergic agents, or inactive catechol compounds; the number of binding sites in frog erythrocyte membranes is estimated to be 1300–1800 (229). Binding of β-antagonists such as alprenolol and propanolol is rapid and reversible, and is inhibited competitively by the β-agonists isoproterenol, epinephrine, and norepinephrine in that order of potency with specificity for the (−) isomers.

In contrast, the binding of agonists to β-receptors in frog erythrocyte membranes is slow and irreversible, and displacement by an antagonist is only partially competitive (238). The binding properties of the receptor in erythrocytes and other cells are affected by guanine nucleotides; GTP and other nucleotides lower the affinity of receptors for agonists but have no effect on the binding of antagonists (238–242). In the presence of GTP, the binding of agonists becomes almost instantaneous, reversible, and competitive with antagonists. Nucleotides reduce the affinity of receptors for the hormone, but this coincides with stimulation of adenylate cyclase (229).

A similar relationship exists between receptors and nucleotides in membranes of hepatic and fat cells (243). Nucleotides reduce the affinity of the receptors for glucagon, but the efficiency of coupling with adenylate cyclase is increased. There is a reciprocal relationship between the occupied receptor and nucleotides. Glucagon increases the activation by nucleotides, and nucleotides increase activation by the hormone.

Receptors for many hormones have been isolated and purified by various techniques (30, 244 –248). The β-adrenergic receptor has been purified 1500-fold by alprenolol–agarose affinity chromatography (248). The receptor protein binds to the column and is eluted with β-adrenergic agonists or antagonists, resulting in complete separation from the catalytic subunit. The hydrodynamic properties of the β-adrenergic receptor partially purified from S49 cells indicate that the solubilized protein binds a considerable amount of detergent, suggesting that it is an intrinsic membrane component (30). After correction for bound detergent, the molecular weight of the receptor from this source is 75,000. A molecular weight of 90,000 for the β-receptor of turkey erythrocytes is suggested by the results of electron inactivation analysis (65).

Although there are reports to the contrary (249, 250), solubilization of membranes usually results in loss of hormonal stimulation of adenylate cyclase despite the fact that both enzyme and receptor are present in the same detergent extract. It is possible, however, to reconstitute hormonal sensitivity with receptors from one cell and adenylate cyclase from another. Thus β-receptors of cyc$^-$ S49 cells couple with the adenylate cyclase from a variant of mouse L cells (B82) when the cyc$^-$ membranes are mixed with a detergent extract of B82 cell membranes (251). Purified β-receptors from turkey erythrocytes can also be incorporated into human erythrocytes by means of similar techniques (252).

Membrane-fusion procedures can also be used to transplant receptors from one cell to another. Turkey erythrocyte ghosts containing β-receptors and inactivated adenylate cyclase can be fused with Friend erythroleukemia cells (F cells) in the presence of Sendai virus (253). The F cells are complementary, since they contain adenylate cyclase but no receptor; after fusion, the enzyme in isolated membranes (253) or in the intact fused cell (254) is responsive to catecholamines. A fusion technique employing polyethylene glycol has been used to implant erythrocyte β-receptors (255) and liver glucagon receptors (256) into membranes of F cells, producing receptor-coupled adenylate cyclase. The properties of the receptor in the hybrid membrane are essentially the same as those in the native membrane. Successful implantation requires phospholipids.

b. *Desensitization of Receptors.* Prolonged exposure of membranes to a hormone results in loss of the responsiveness of the adenylate cyclase to subsequent challenges by the same agonist. Desensitization of amphibian erythrocyte membranes occurs after administration of catecholamines *in vivo* (257) or exposure of whole cells and isolated membranes to catecholamines (258–261) or prostaglandin E_1 (262). The loss of responsiveness to the hormone is accompanied by a decrease in the total number of β-receptors. Desensitization by catecholamines is stereospecific and is prevented by β-antagonists. After washing the desensitized membranes to remove the agonist, the addition of guanine nucleotides restores the response to the hormone (259, 260). Desensitization in erythrocytes may result from the formation of a high affinity complex between the hormone and the receptor, thus decreasing the number of available receptors (239).

Desensitization appears to be somewhat more complex in other cells. In a variety of cultured cells, the rate of decline of hormonal responsiveness of the adenylate cyclase is faster than the rate of reduction in receptor number (263–265). If cells are exposed for short time intervals, desensitization is reversible, but it becomes irreversible after longer exposure. There is no effect upon basal adenylate cyclase activity or upon activation of the enzyme by NaF, GuoPP[NH]P, and cholera toxin (263, 264). Therefore, desensitization occurs in two stages: uncoupling of the receptor and adenylate cyclase, followed by alteration of the binding properties of the receptor.

Desensitization in cultured astrocytoma cells is characterized by agonist-specific alterations in the properties of the receptor and adenylate cyclase as well as nonspecific changes (266, 267). Specific desensitization results in loss of response only to the agonist used to promote desensitization, whereas the nonspecific desensitization decreases the response to other agonists. Nonspecific desensitization is reversible when the cell is disrupted, and may be mediated by intracellular cAMP (267) or by accumulation of an adenylate cyclase inhibitor in the cell (266). In some cell lines, refractoriness to hormonal stimulation is induced by cAMP and reversed by inhibitors of protein and RNA synthesis, suggesting that it is mediated by a rapidly turning-over protein whose synthesis is controlled by intracellular cAMP levels (268).

Desensitization of ovarian adenylate cyclase by exposure to luteinizing hormone depends upon GTP (269, 270). The effect of the nucleotide is concentration-dependent and is not duplicated by GuoPP[NH]P and other nucleotides. The data suggest that luteinizing hormone increases the dissociation of the nucleotide from its binding sites, causing deactivation of the adenylate cyclase (270).

c. *"Down-Regulation" of Adenylate Cyclase.* In the systems discussed above, coupling of the hormone-occupied receptor with adenylate cyclase activates the enzyme. In other systems, agonists inhibit adenylate cyclase. Examples of receptors that produce "down-regulation" of adenylate cyclase are the α-adrenergic, opiate, and muscarinic acetylcholine receptors of NG108-15 neuroblastoma-glioma hybrid cells (271–275).

The effect of agonists on these cells is biphasic. Exposure of the intact cell or its membrane to an agonist results in an immediate inhibition of adenylate cyclase (271, 274), but the enzyme activity returns to normal after prolonged exposure (10 hours or more) (272, 275). Washing the cells to remove the agonist, or adding an antagonist, rapidly increases the enzyme activity, which then slowly returns to normal levels. The inhibitory effects require GTP, and inhibition by opiates requires Na^+ in addition to the nucleotide (276). The binding of agonists and antagonists to solubilized opiate receptors is also inhibited by nucleotides (277). The nucleotide requirement for inhibition suggests that coupling of the receptor with adenylate cyclase occurs by a mechanism similar to that producing activation in other cells, except that the end result is inhibition rather than stimulation. The recovery of adenylate cyclase activity after prolonged exposure to agonists appears to be equivalent to desensitization, even though the end results are opposite.

Adenosine has a bimodal effect on adenylate cyclase. In some cells, this nucleoside and its structural analogs are stimulatory, whereas they are inhibitory in others. The two effects appear to be mediated by separate receptors, since they have different structural specificities (278). The receptors that mediate the stimulatory effect are called "R" receptors because stimulation is affected by structural alterations in the ribosyl moiety of the nucleoside. Alternatively, inhibitory receptors are affected by changes in the purine moiety and are called "P" receptors.

Inhibition and stimulation of adipocyte adenylate cyclase are both mediated by GTP. The nucleotide stimulates the enzyme at low concentrations, but it is inhibitory at higher concentrations (279). Inhibition by GTP is enhanced by adenosine and structural analogs of the nucleoside that exhibit "P" site specificity (280). The inhibitory phase is abolished by cholera toxin, leaving the stimulatory phase intact, whereas stimulation is abolished by organic mercurials (281). Stimulation and inhibition by adenosine therefore appear to be mediated by separate receptors coupled with the same or a similar regulatory mechanism. Adenosine also has a biphasic effect on the adenylate cyclase of turkey erythrocytes, but the inhibitory phase does not require GTP (282).

2. Requirement for the Nucleotide Regulatory Component

The nucleotide regulatory component is widely distributed and is even found in membranes of cells (human and rat erythrocytes) that do not contain hormonally responsive adenylate cyclase (210, 283). The adenylate cyclase from cells in which this component is absent or defective does not respond to hormones, but responsiveness is restored when the component from another source is added. The adenylate cyclase of the cyc⁻ S49 lymphoma membrane becomes responsive to catecholamines after combination with detergent extracts that contain the regulatory component from wild S49 cells, the HC-1 variant of HTC hepatoma cells, or the B82 varient of mouse L cells (66, 196, 206, 251). In these reconstituted systems, coupling of the β-adrenergic receptors of the cyc⁻ membrane is mediated by the exogenous regulatory component, and the reassembled system has all the properties of the wild S49 cell. Similar reconstituted systems can be assembled using cyc⁻ membranes and detergent extracts of avian and human erythrocytes (201, 204, 210).

Another variant of S49 cells (UNC) contains receptors and adenylate cyclase that is stimulated by fluoride and guanine nucleotides but is not responsive to hormones (206, 284). This variant apparently contains a regulatory component that may be defective, since it does not mediate coupling between the receptor and the adenylate cyclase. However, a reconstituted system that is responsive to catecholamines and prostaglandins can be prepared, by the addition of the regulatory component derived from other cells (285).

Membranes of ram sperm apparently do not contain the regulatory component, since the adenylate cyclase is not activated by fluoride, nucleotides, or hormones (286). The catalytic subunit in these membranes uses MnATP as its substrate, but displays little activity with MgATP. When sperm membranes are mixed with human erythrocyte membranes, comparable activity is exhibited with either MgATP or MnATP, and the enzyme becomes responsive to fluoride, GuoPP[NH]P, and prostaglandins. Thus, the sperm enzyme can use the regulatory component and receptors from the erythrocyte membranes.

These experiments demonstrate the importance of the regulatory component in physiological regulation of adenylate cyclase. Regulatory components from various sources appear to be functionally equivalent and reasonably uniform in structure. Peptide mapping of proteolytic digests of the regulatory components from pigeon and human erythrocytes indicates that the proteins have similar, but not identical, structures (287).

3. MECHANISM OF HORMONAL ACTIVATION

Hormonal regulation of adenylate cyclase is the result of the interactions of at least three macromolecular components of the membrane: the hormone receptor (R), the nucleotide-binding regulatory component (N), and the catalytic subunit (C). Much of the knowledge of this regulatory system has been derived from studies of the membranes of nucleated erythrocytes. The kinetics of activation of adenylate cyclase in turkey erythrocyte membranes are best explained by a collision-coupling model in which a freely floating agonist-occupied receptor interacts briefly with adenylate cyclase, resulting in its activation (288). This model is supported by the observation that not all the β-receptors in the membrane are required for activation of the enzyme; incapacitation of the majority of the receptors reduces the rate of activation of the enzyme but has no effect on the maximal activated state (288). In addition, conditions that alter the mobility of the receptor in the membrane also alter enzyme activation. Increasing the fluidity of the membrane by the incorporation of cis-vaccenic acid increases the rate of activation of adenylate cyclase by catecholamines (289). Apoferritin, by contrast, decreases the lateral mobility of membrane proteins, and the incorporation of this protein into erythrocyte membrane decreases catacholamine stimulation of adenylate cyclase (290).

Assuming unrestricted movement of the macromolecular components within the phospholipid bilayer of the membrane, the sequence of events that result in hormonal activation of adenylate cyclase may be described by the following equations (291).

$$N_{GDP} + R_H \rightarrow R_H N_{GDP} \tag{1}$$

$$R_H N_{GDP} + GTP \rightarrow R_H N_{GTP} + GDP \tag{2}$$

$$R_H N_{GTP} \rightarrow R_H + N_{GTP} \tag{3}$$

$$C_{(inactive)} + N_{GTP} \rightarrow C_{(active)} N_{GTP} \tag{4}$$

$$C_{(active)} N_{GTP} \rightarrow C_{(inactive)} + N_{GDP} + P_i \tag{5}$$

These reactions constitute a cycle, since each component is returned to its original state at the end of the sequence. As discussed below, there is evidence supporting each step.

a. Activation of the Regulatory Component (Steps 1–3). Activation
of the regulatory component (N) involves binding of the occupied
receptor (R_H) to the GDP-occupied regulatory component (N_{GDP}), exchange of the nucleotides, and the dissociation of the complex to yield
the GTP-occupied regulatory component (N_{GTP}). In isolated erythrocyte membranes, the nucleotide binding sites are occupied by GDP,
and β-agonists facilitate its displacement by GTP and other nucleoside
triphosphates (*212, 240*). Replacement with GuoPP[NH]P results in
an immediate activation of adenylate cyclase that is not affected by
further addition of hormone. The rates of displacement of GDP and
activation of the enzyme are identical (*212*). When excess nucleotide is
removed, the activated state of the enzyme decays slowly; the rate of
decay is decreased by GMP but is enhanced by GTP or GDP, which
presumably displace the activating ligand. The GDP analog, guanosine 5′-(β-thio)diphosphate (GuoPP[S] or GDPβs), inhibits erythrocyte adenylate cyclase, and the inhibition is competitive with
GTP (*292*).

There is evidence that the 42,000-dalton subunit of the erythrocyte
regulatory component binds to the receptor in the presence of an
agonist. The apparent molecular size of the receptor increases when it
is coupled with an agonist (*293*), and the solubilized receptor from
membranes treated with [^{32}P]NAD and cholera toxin comigrates on gel
filtration with a ^{32}P-labeled polypeptide (*294*). Formation of this complex is prevented by GuoPP[NH]P.

These experimental results indicate the formation of a complex
between the occupied receptor (reaction 1), agonist-directed replacement of GDP by GTP (reaction 2), and dissociation of the complex to
yield the GTP-occupied regulatory component (reaction 3). The GTP-
liganded component is the active species that can interact with and
activate adenylate cyclase.

b. Activation of Adenylate Cyclase (Step 4). Formation of a complex between adenylate cyclase (C) and the GTP-liganded regulatory
component N_{GTP} is supported by several lines of evidence. The
molecular weights of thyroid and kidney adenylate cyclase are increased by about 40,000 after activation by GuoPP[NH]P (see Table I).
Activation of avian erythrocyte adenylate cyclase by a GTP analog also
produces an increase in the sedimentation coefficient of the enzyme,
whereas incubation with GDP or GTP has no effect (*291*). The
42,000-dalton subunit of the erythrocyte regulatory component comigrates with adenylate cyclase upon gel filtration, ion-exchange
chromatography, and sucrose density centrifugation in the presence of
GTP analogs but not GDP (*139, 291*). There is also an increase in the

molecular weight of the partially resolved catalytic subunit of brain adenylate cyclase when it is activated by GuoPP[NH]P (28).

  c. *Hydrolysis of GTP and Termination of Activation (Step 5).* Termination of hormonal activation of adenylate cyclase may be the result of the hydrolysis of GTP at the binding site (295). In frog and turkey erythrocyte membranes, GTPase activity is stimulated by catecholamines, and the receptor specificity is identical to that for stimulation of adenylate cyclase (296). Desensitization of the receptors by prolonged exposure to isoproterenol decreases both hormone-stimulated adenylate cyclase and GTPase activities (296). This process is ligand-specific (desensitization by isoproterenol does not affect stimulation of the enzymes by prostaglandin E_1), suggesting that it is the result of a lesion at the receptor level. Hormonal stimulation of the GTPase is blocked by propanolol (a β-blocker) but not by phentolamine (an α-blocker) (296). Both propanolol and GDPβS increase the rate of decay of hormone-activated adenylate cyclase (270, 295). These results suggest that hormonal stimulation of the GTPase results from facilitated introduction of GTP to the binding site on the nucleotide regulatory protein. If the replenishment of GTP is blocked, adenylate cyclase and GTPase activities both decrease. When GTPase activity is inhibited by choleragen-catalyzed ADP-ribosylation,[1] GTP activates adenylate cyclase as effectively as its nonhydrolyzable analogs.

  Gel filtration of detergent-solubilized brain adenylate cyclase results in comigration of GTPase activity with adenylate cyclase that responds to GuoPP[NH]P (28). Choleragen activation of adenylate cyclase in erythrocyte membranes coincides with the inhibition of GTPase and ADP-ribosylation of the 42,000-dalton subunit. These findings suggest that GTPase resides on one of the subunits of the nucleotide regulatory component. However, after extensive purification, the regulatory component from rabbit liver does not exhibit GTPase activity (205). Thus it is quite possible that this catalytic activity resides on another membrane component.

  Although this hypothetical model can account for many of the properties of the regulatory system for adenylate cyclase, in some respects it is not completely corroborated by experimental data. The model assumes that a nucleotide-binding subunit dissociates from the regulatory protein complex, and that this subunit binds first to the receptor and then to the adenylate cyclase. This assumption is supported by changes in the hydrodynamic properties of the receptor, the regulatory component, and the adenylate cyclase at various stages of the regulatory cycle. However, there is no clear-cut evidence that dis-

sociation actually occurs. The binding of GuoPP[NH]P to the regulatory component of S49 cells produces an alteration in its hydrodynamic properties that is consistent with a change in molecular
weight of about 40,000 (202, 291). However, these changes can be
reversed by removal of the ligand even after subjection of the
liganded-component to procedures that should resolve a subunit with
this mass (202). On the other hand, alteration in the hydrodynamic
properties of the regulatory component may result from a change in the
conformation of the molecule when bound to a nucleotide. Limited
proteolysis of the regulatory component from avian erythrocytes in the
presence of GTP releases different peptides than when it is performed
in the presence of GDP or in the absence of a ligand (297). This
suggests that the binding of GTP causes a conformational change that
exposes different cleavage sites for the proteolytic enzyme.

Dissociation of a subunit may not be a requisite step in hormonal
activation. The results of electron inactivation analysis of turkey erythrocyte adenylate cyclase demonstrate that the target for inactivation
of the enzyme in the presence of isoproterenol has a mass large enough
to include all three macromolecular components of the regulatory system (i.e., R, N, and C). This suggests that the three components exist in
a preformed complex activated by binding of the agonist (65). This
complex could consist of the receptor spanning the membrane and
associating with the regulatory component, which in turn is associated
with the catalytic subunit (298). Binding of an agonist to the receptor
at the external surface of the membrane might produce conformational
changes in the three components that induce binding of GTP to the
regulatory component and activation of the adenylate cyclase. Hydrolysis of GTP would terminate the activation of the enzyme and increase the affinity of the receptor for another molecule of agonist.

Whether this simplified scheme can be applied to adenylate cyclase in other tissues remains unclear. Electron inactivation analysis of
the structure of the system in hepatic (42) and adipocyte (299) membranes indicates that the size of the ground state is much larger than
the sum of the sizes of its various components. It is possible that in
these membranes tne R·N complex exists in an aggregated state prior
to binding of the hormone (298). Hormone binding causes disaggrega-
tion, which permits binding of GTP to RN monomers followed by
interaction with the enzyme to produce activation.

Although a GTPase appears to be important in the termination of
activation in erythrocyte membranes, it is uncertain whether the enzyme is equally important in membranes of other cells. Prostaglandin
stimulation of the GTPase of mononuclear blood cells coincides with
activation of the adenylate cyclase, but there is no correlation between

the concentrations of the hormone required for the two effects (*300*). GDP is a competitive inhibitor of adenylate cyclase activation in turkey erythrocyte membranes, but the nucleotide is a positive effector in hepatic membranes under conditions that do not permit transphosphorylation to GTP (*301–303*). There may be two levels of regulation of adenylate cyclase in hepatic membranes (*301*). Hormonal regulation may be mediated by either GTP or GDP and does not require the participation of a GTPase. Regulation by intracellular nucleotides, on the other hand, may be controlled by a specific GTPase. Although the kinetics of activation of hepatic adenylate cyclase do not rule out the participation of a GTPase, they do not prove it to be absolutely essential (*304, 305*).

Inhibitory regulation by opiates, α-adrenergic agents, cholinergic agents, and adenosine are probably mediated through N since GTP is required. Separate R·N complexes coupled with the same enzyme molecule may mediate stimulatory and inhibitory effects in cells exhibiting this type of regulation (*298*). Alternatively, an inhibitory R·N complex may not interact with the adenylate cyclase, but may affect another phase of the regulatory cycle. Opiates, for example, stimulate GTP hydrolysis in membranes of NG-108-15 cells, and this may account for their inhibition of adenylate cyclase (*306*). Stimulation of GTPase requires Na^+ and exhibits the same receptor specificity as inhibition of adenylate cyclase. Conceivably, inhibitory R·N complexes may couple with the GTPase, promoting hydrolysis of GTP, which, in turn, results in inactivation of adenylate cyclase (*306*).

The role of the regulatory component in desensitization remains to be determined. The cyc⁻ S49 cells, for example, undergo desensitization even though they do not contain an endogenous N (*307*). Furthermore, hormonally responsive adenylate cyclase in desensitized S49 cells is not restored by the addition of exogenous N. This suggests that the lesion produced by desensitization is in a different component of the system. On the other hand, desensitization in ovarian cells decreases the rate of exchange of nucleotides at the binding site, suggesting that coupling between the occupied receptor and the nucleotide regulatory component is impaired (*270*).

II. Guanylate Cyclase

A. General Aspects

Guanylate cyclase, like adenylate cyclase, is widely distributed throughout the animal kingdom (for general reviews, see *308* and *309*). Although the enzyme has not been identified in higher plants, cGMP has been detected in plant cells. In some tissues, guanylate cyclase is exclusively associated with membranes; in others, it is found only in the cytosol or is distributed between the two. Intracellular distribution may also vary during embryological development, during rapid growth, or at different stages of the life cycle of an organism. Its activity is affected by detergents, and solubilization of the membrane-associated enzyme often increases its activity manyfold. It is possible, therefore, that most of the enzyme in the cell is membrane-bound rather than cytoplasmic.

The stoichiometry of the reaction catalyzed by guanylate cyclase has been established by means of an enzyme preparation from lung (310). The extent of reversibility of the reaction is not known.

B. State of Purity and Macromolecular Properties

Highly purified guanylate cyclase has been prepared from rat lung (311), rat liver (312), and sea urchin sperm (313). The enzymes from lung and liver are apparently homogeneous and have specific activities of 700 and 276 nmol per minute per milligram of protein, respectively. The turnover number of these preparations is only a fraction of that obtained with the purified sperm enzyme, which has a specific activity of 12,000 nmol per minute per milligram of protein. Although not yet completely homogeneous, the sperm enzyme is devoid of adenylate cyclase, phosphodiesterase, and GTPase activities (313).

Molecular weights of guanylate cyclase derived from a variety of sources are shown in Table II (311–318). The enzyme from sea urchin sperm appears to be composed of two subunits of 118,000 and 75,000 daltons. The highly purified lung enzyme consists of subunits of 74,000 and 79,000, whereas the liver enzyme is composed of two subunits of 105,000 and 45,000 daltons. Another liver preparation, on the other hand, has three subunits (319), and a preparation from brain has been resolved into four subunits of unequal size (318).

C. Enzymic Properties

1. SUBSTRATE SPECIFICITY

The most effective substrate for guanylate cyclase is GTP; the K_m values for this substrate range between 10 and 300 μM depending upon the source of the enzyme and its state of purity (311, 313, 314, 317, 318, 320–329). GuoPP[NH]P can serve as a substrate, but is less effective (318, 325, 330). Some particulate preparations of guanylate cyclase exhibit positive cooperativity with respect to substrate concen-

TABLE II
MOLECULAR WEIGHTS OF GUANYLATE CYCLASE FROM VARIOUS SOURCES

Source	Molecular weight $(\times 10^{-5})$	Reference
Escherichia coli	0.3	*314*
Caulobacter crescentus	1.4	*315*
Kidney cytosol	1.5	*316*
Lung	1.5	*311*
Liver	1.5	*312*
Platelet	1.8	*317*
Sea urchin sperm	1.8	*313*
Kidney membrane	3.0	*316*
Brain (synaptosomes)	4.8	*318*

tration (*320, 321, 326, 328, 329, 331*), but the enzyme from sea urchin sperm enzyme loses this property after purification (*313*).

2. DIVALENT CATION REQUIREMENTS

The preferred cation for guanylate cyclase activity is Mn^{2+}, but some activity is also exhibited with Mg^{2+}. Activity with Mg^{2+} ranges between 10 and 40% of that obtained with Mn^{2+} and is usually found only in preparations of the soluble enzyme (*314, 315, 317, 318, 320– 322, 324, 326–331*). Activity in the presence of Mg^{2+} appears to be affected by prior treatment of the enzyme; in the presence of detergent or detergent and fatty acids, for example, the activity with Mg^{2+} is proportionately higher than that obtained with Mn^{2+} (*324, 332*). As with adenylate cyclase, the concentration of Mn^{2+} required for activity *in vitro* is unphysiological, and the physiological cation may be Mg^{2+} rather than Mn^{2+}.

Activity of guanylate cyclase is generally low when Ca^{2+} is substituted for Mn^{2+}, but some preparations are stimulated when assayed with Ca^{2+} in addition to Mn^{2+} (*311, 315, 320–323, 326–329, 331, 333*). As examples, the activities of lymphocyte (*333*) and liver (*326*) guanylate cyclase are increased 2.5- to 10-fold by Ca^{2+} when the enzyme is assayed at low concentrations of Mn^{2+}, but Ca^{2+} has little effect when the concentration of Mn^{2+} approaches that of the GTP. Other metals, such as Fe^{3+} (*321, 329, 334*), Cu^{2+} (*321*), and Sn^{2+} (*321*), support the activity of guanylate cyclase from various sources.

The guanylate cyclase of the protozoan *Tetrahymena pyriformis* is membrane-bound and prefers Mg^{2+} as its principal divalent cation (*335*). The enzyme is stimulated by Ca^{2+} and a protein that has been identified as calmodulin (*336–338*). The presence of calmodulin in this organism has been confirmed independently (*339*). It remains to be determined if calmodulin or a calmodulin-like protein mediates the stimulation of mammalian guanylate cyclase by Ca^{2+}.

3. POSITIVE EFFECTORS

a. Activation of Guanylate Cyclase by Redox Reactions. A unique property of guanylate cyclase is sensitivity to oxidizing agents. Simple exposure of the isolated enzyme to air, for example, causes activation that is suppressed by reducing agents (*320, 340*). Activation is also produced by many compounds that are either oxidizing agents or serve as precursors of oxidizing free radicals.

b. Nitric Oxide and Other Nitrogen Compounds. Nitric oxide is a potent activator of guanylate cyclase in both intact cells and isolated preparations. Exposure of either particulate or supernatant fractions from a variety of tissues to the gas produces a rapid and reversible activation of the enzyme (*341*). Activation is usually greater in soluble than in particulate fractions. The soluble enzyme is activated by NO even after extensive purification (*312, 341, 342*). The presence of the gas in high concentration can account for the activation of guanylate cyclase by the vapor phase of tobacco smoke (*343, 344*).

A similar activation is produced by a wide variety of compounds, such as sodium azide (*345–349*), sodium nitroprusside (*312, 350–352*), hydroxylamine (*341, 353, 354*), hydrazines (*355, 356*), *N*-methyl-*N'*-nitro-*N*-nitrosoguanidine (*357–361*), nitrosoureas (*362, 363*), nitriles (*364*), and 4-nitroquinoline 1-oxide (*365*). A common mechanism for the effect of these compounds may be the intracellular generation of NO (*309, 325, 341, 365*). Heme may be an obligatory intermediate in nitric oxide activation (*359–361, 366*). Catalase and other heme proteins are required for activation by azide and other nitrogen compounds (*309, 359–361, 366–368*), and electron spin resonance studies have shown the formation of paramagnetic nitrosyl heme under conditions that activate guanylate cyclase (*359, 360, 366, 368*).

In addition to stimulation, NO and the other nitrogen compounds produce striking changes in the properties of the enzyme. One of the most significant is alteration of divalent cation requirements. Enzyme activity measured in the presence of Mg^{2+} becomes equivalent to that in the presence of Mn^{2+} after exposure to the activating agent (*347, 348, 350–352, 358, 362, 366*). The degree of activation is much higher, therefore, when the enzyme is assayed in the presence of Mg^{2+} rather than Mn^{2+}. Since the concentration of Mn^{2+} that produces maximal activity is unphysiological, it is significant that the enzyme is dependent upon physiological concentrations of Mg^{2+} after activation.

There is also a change in substrate specificity (369, 370). The enzyme catalyzes the synthesis of cAMP from ATP in the presence of the activating agent. This "adenylate cyclase" activity is found in the supernatant fraction, is Mn^{2+}-dependent, is not stimulated by fluoride, and is inhibited by GTP. Its hydrodynamic properties are identical with guanylate cyclase and differ from those of the soluble adenylate cyclase of rat testis (371). Although the mechanism is unknown, the alteration of divalent cation requirements and substrate specificity suggests conformational changes in the active site of the guanylate cyclase, which may result from oxidation of reactive functional groups.

c. Fatty Acid and Prostaglandin Peroxides. Activation of guanylate cyclase through an oxidative mechanism also occurs in the presence of more physiological agents. A notable example of this is activation by peroxides of fatty acids and prostaglandins. Soluble guanylate cyclase from splenic cells is stimulated by the prostaglandin endoperoxides PGG_2 (15-hydroperoxy-9,11-peroxidoprosta-5,13-dienoic acid) and PGH_2 (15-hydroxy-9,11-peroxidoprosta-5,13-dienoic acid) as well as hydroperoxy derivatives of eicosatetraenoic and octadecanoic acids (372). These compounds enhance the rate of spontaneous activation, and the two prostaglandin derivatives produce activation in an inert atmosphere. Maximal stimulation is 2.5- to 5-fold, and half-maximal activation occurs at concentrations of the effector ranging between 3 and 10 μM. The corresponding hydroxy analogs of these compounds are less potent. Both spontaneous and lipid-enhanced activation are prevented and reversed by N-ethylmaleimide and other thiol reagents. These results suggest that activation is caused by oxidation of reactive sulfhydryl groups on the enzyme or on a regulatory component.

Partially purified guanylate cyclase from platelets is activated by peroxides of arachidonic and other unsaturated fatty acids (317, 373). These fatty acids stimulate guanylate cyclase in a number of other systems (332, 374–382), and a portion of this effect is probably due to the generation of fatty acid peroxides and prostaglandin endoperoxides. In some instances, arachidonate activation requires or is potentiated by lipoxidase (EC 1.13.11.12) and phospholipase A_2 (EC 3.1.1.4), and is inhibited by indomethacin and aspirin, which inhibit a step in the biosynthesis of prostaglandins (378, 379).

Oxidation may not account for all the effects of these compounds. In crude fractions from liver, conditions that promote peroxidation diminish activation by arachidonate (380), and peroxidation does not appear to be necessary for stimulation of the highly purified enzyme from this tissue (312).

d. Ascorbic Acid Derivatives. Guanylate cyclase is also activated by dehydroascorbic acid, which increases the rate of spontaneous activation of the soluble and particulate enzymes from spleen and produces activation under an inert atmosphere (*383, 384*). Activation is stable and persists after removal of the agent. Dehydroascorbate enhances the accumulation of cGMP in intact splenic cells, and the guanylate cyclase isolated from these cells has increased specific activity. The effects of H_2 ascorbate on the isolated enzyme and intact cells are prevented and reversed by thiols (dithiothreitol and cysteine) or sulfhydryl reagents, such as *N*-ethylmaleimide, *p*-hydroxymercuribenzoate, and 5,5'-dithio-bis(2-nitrobenzoate).

Ascorbate increases the accumulation of cGMP in intact cells but has no effect on isolated guanylate cyclase (*384*). However, the enzyme isolated from cells treated with ascorbate has an increased specific activity, indicating that the effect is due to its activation. Activation is reversed by thiol compounds, but, after reversal, the isolated guanylate cyclase cannot be reactivated by ascorbate. The activation may require prior conversion of the ascorbate to an oxidizing intermediate, such as the monoanionic free radical or to dehydroascorbate (*384*).

The similarity between activation of splenic cell guanylate cyclase by fatty acid hydroperoxides, prostaglandin endoperoxides, and dehydroascorbic acid suggests that the enzyme is regulated by a redox mechanism involving reactive sulfhydryl groups at separate regulatory sites (*384, 385*). One site is hydrophobic and is regulated by fatty acid and prostaglandin peroxides. The other site is hydrophilic and is affected by water-soluble compounds such as H_2 ascorbate. This hypothesis is consistent with the fact that the effects of the two classes of compounds are additive (*384*).

e. Free Radicals. Spontaneous activation of a soluble lung guanylate cyclase is enhanced by H_2O_2 (*340*), and a partially purified soluble liver enzyme is activated by superoxide dismutase in a reaction requiring H_2O_2 (*386, 387*). Activation by superoxide dismutase may be caused by hydroxyl free radicals generated by the reaction of superoxide ion and H_2O_2 (*387*). Alternatively, superoxide ion may activate the enzyme directly without mediation by peroxide (*388*). Regardless of the identity of the proximal activating agent, it is clear that guanylate cyclase can be regulated by free radicals, and that this may be important in its regulation by various physiological and pharmacological agents. There appears to be more than one mechanism for oxidative control, since the properties of the activated enzyme differ depending upon the nature of the oxidant. This suggests the presence on the enzyme molecule of multiple sites susceptible to oxidation.

D. Hormonal Regulation

Relatively little is known about the mechanism of hormonal regulation of guanylate cyclase in spite of ample evidence that its activity in intact cells is affected by a wide variety of hormones and other agents, including cholinergic agents, catecholamines, prostaglandins, polypeptide hormones, steroids, ionophores, and anesthetics (308). Although these studies *in vivo* strongly suggest coupling between an agonist–receptor complex and the enzyme, there is little supporting evidence to prove it. Until recently, there were few reports of hormonal stimulation of isolated guanylate cyclase. One difficulty stems from the susceptibility of guanylate cyclase to activation by detergents and oxidizing agents. The apparent hormonal stimulation of the enzyme could be due to redox properties of the hormone or to the presence of an unsuspected contaminant. As an example, stimulation of the enzyme *in vitro* by secretin and pancreozymin (389–391) has been attributed to bile salts that contaminate the hormone preparations (392).

One feature of the stimulation of guanylate cyclase *in vivo* by many of these agents is a requirement for Ca^{2+} (308, 309). In a variety of tissues, stimulation by cholinergic agents and other hormones is blocked by tetracaine, which interferes with the movement of ions across cell membranes. On the other hand, intracellular levels of cGMP are increased by the ionophore A23187, which promotes the transport of Ca^{2+}. Removal of Ca^{2+} from the incubation medium causes, in some tissues, a decrease in cGMP and a loss of the effectiveness of phosphodiesterase inhibitors to enhance its levels.

It is not yet clear whether Ca^{2+} affects guanylate cyclase directly or interacts with some other component of the cell. Some preparations of the soluble form of the enzyme are stimulated *in vitro* by Ca^{2+} at low concentrations of Mn^{2+}, but the concentrations of divalent cations required are unphysiological. On the other hand, the membrane-bound enzyme of cultured BALB fibroblast cells is stimulated by physiological concentrations of Ca^{2+} when it is assayed with Mg^{2+} (393). If the physiological cation for guanylate cyclase is Mg^{2+}, an influx of Ca^{2+} caused by a hormone might result in its activation.

Another possibility is that an influx of Ca^{2+} initiates a sequence of reactions that ultimately results in activation of the guanylate cyclase in the cytosol by an oxidative mechanism. The initial event may be Ca^{2+} activation of a membrane-bound phospholipase that catalyzes the release of a fatty acid precursor of a prostaglandin endoperoxide or some other oxidizing intermediate (308, 309). In this context, it is interesting that activation of guanylate cyclase by the heat-stable enterotoxin of

E. coli is inhibited by indomethacin and butylated hydroxyanisole, a free-radical scavenger (*394*). This suggests that the effect of the toxin is mediated by a free radical or some other oxidizing intermediate. Thus, the regulatory system for guanylate may involve a number of intermediate steps.

It is possible that there are separate systems for regulation of guanylate cyclase in the cytosol and the membrane. There is evidence that the two forms of the enzyme may not be identical (*395*). Several differences have been observed in the properties of the guanylate cyclase from the soluble fraction of a liver homogenate and that separated from the membrane by treatment with trypsin (*395*). The two forms of the enzyme differ with respect to kinetic properties and sensitivity to a thiol reagent and nitroso compounds. The cytosolic enzyme is stimulated by nitroprusside, whereas the trypsin-solubilized form is unaffected. Assuming that treatment with trypsin has not altered the properties of the membrane-bound enzyme, these results suggest innate differences between the two forms. Therefore, it is possible that the activities of cytosolic and membrane-bound guanylate cyclase are controlled by different regulatory mechanisms, and that only the membrane-bound enzyme is affected by hormones.

The adrenal cortex is a tissue in which there appear to be distinct mechanisms for regulation of the two forms of guanylate cyclase. The membrane-bound enzyme of normal and adrenocortical carcinoma 494 cells is stimulated *in vitro* by physiological concentrations (10^{-12} to 10^{-10} M) of ACTH (*396, 397*). At such concentrations, the hormone has no effect on the adenylate cyclase in these membranes and does not stimulate the cytosolic guanylate cyclase. Stimulation is absolutely dependent upon exogenous Ca^{2+}, which has no effect on basal activity. Sodium nitroprusside, on the other hand, activates the soluble form but has no effect on the membrane enzyme. These results suggest that the two forms of the enzyme in adrenal tissue have different properties and are regulated by separate mechanisms. The membrane enzyme appears to be directly coupled with the ACTH receptor, and further study of this system may shed light on the general mechanism of hormonal regulation of guanylate cyclase.

III. Concluding Remarks

Considerable knowledge has accumulated about the structure, properties, and mechanism of regulation of adenylate cyclase. It is now clear that the catalytic subunit of the enzyme is part of a multicomponent complex that regulates the synthesis of cAMP. This system is responsive to hormones, and thus transmits the signal generated by one cell into a physiological response by another. Several components of this system have been identified, isolated, and extensively characterized; there may be others that are not yet discovered.

The orientation and organization of these components in the membrane are critical; hormonal responsiveness is rarely observed in a solubilized membrane preparation. The properties of the isolated components suggest that they are intrinsic membrane proteins. These proteins appear not to be tissue-specific. Adenylate cyclase reconstituted with solubilized components exhibits many of the properties of the native enzyme, but is not stimulated by hormones. It is likely that hormonal responsiveness requires a degree of organization found only in intact membranes, and that membrane lipids enable proper orientation of the enzyme components. Alternatively, hormonal activation may require additional membrane proteins that are not easily solubilized by methods currently available. This problem is important and should be a target for future research.

The structural changes in the catalytic subunit of adenylate cyclase that result in its activation need to be explored. Although recent results are encouraging, purification of the enzyme has proved to be difficult, and relatively little is known about its structure. It is clear that binding of the nucleotide regulatory component in the presence of GTP results in activation, but the conformational changes that are responsible for the increased activity are unknown.

The role of calmodulin in the control of brain adenylate cyclase is still not clear, especially since it also regulates the activity of 3',5'-cyclic-nucleotide phosphodiesterase (EC 3.1.4.17), which catalyzes the hydrolysis of cAMP. The common requirement for calmodulin and Ca^{2+} may provide a mechanism by which an influx of Ca^{2+} causes a transient increase in cAMP through sequential activation of the two enzymes. The relationship between activation of adenylate cyclase by calmodulin and that by the nucleotide regulatory component remains to be determined. In some brain cells, Ca^{2+} is partially required for hormonal stimulation of adenylate cyclase, and there is evidence that the enzyme may be either calmodulin-dependent or -independent. Regulation of the enzyme by calmodulin may be independent of the nucleotide regulatory component, although there is some evidence that the two systems are interrelated.

In contrast with adenylate cyclase, relatively little is known about the mechanism of hormonal regulation of guanylate cyclase. Although intracellular cGMP is clearly regulated by hormones, progress in understanding the mechanism of regulation has been hampered by the absence of a clear-cut demonstration of hormonal stimulation in an isolated system. The differences between the membrane-bound and the soluble forms of the enzyme may lead to more fruitful experimentation. The membrane-bound guanylate cyclase may be regulated by a system similar to that for adenylate cyclase, and it is possible that various components can be isolated and reassembled into an active regulatory complex. The recent demonstration of ACTH stimulation of guanylate cyclase in membranes of normal and abnormal adrenal cells appears to be a step in this direction.

In conclusion, research during the past decade has increased dramatically our understanding of the mechanism of hormonal control of cell function. There is still much more to be learned. As in any area of research, attempts to find answers to difficult questions usually raises new ones.

ACKNOWLEDGMENTS

The work from our laboratories has been supported by Grants NS 08059, NS 12122, and GM 28178, and ALSAC. We are grateful to Jane Seifert for editorial assistance.

REFERENCES

1. T. W. Rall and E. W. Sutherland, *JBC* **232**, 1065 (1958).
2. E. W. Sutherland, T. W. Rall, and T. Menon, *JBC* **237**, 1220 (1962).
3. G. Schultz, E. Bohme, and K. Munske, *Life Sci.* **8**, 1323 (1969).
4. J. G. Hardman and E. W. Sutherland, *JBC* **244**, 6363 (1969).
5. A. A. White and G. D. Aurbach, *BBA* **191**, 686 (1969).
6. F. Murad, Y. M. Chi, T. W. Rall, and E. W. Sutherland, *JBC* **237**, 1233 (1962).
7. L. M. Klainer, Y. M. Chi, S. L. Freidberg, T. W. Rall, and E. W. Sutherland, *JBC* **237**, 1239 (1962).
8. J. P. Perkins, *Adv. Cyclic Nucleotide Res.* **3**, 1 (1973).
9. T. W. Rall and E. W. Sutherland, *JBC* **237**, 1228 (1962).
10. K. Takai, Y. Kurashina, C. Suzuki-Hori, H. Okamoto, and O. Hayaishi, *JBC* **249**, 1965 (1974).
11. Y. Kurashina, K. Takai, C. Suzuki-Hori, H. Okamoto, and O. Hayaishi, *JBC* **249**, 4824 (1974).
12. O. Hayaishi, P. Greengard, and S. Colowick, *JBC* **246**, 5840 (1971).
13. K. Takai, Y. Kurashina, C. Suzuki-Hori, H. Okamoto, A. Ueki, and O. Hayaishi, *JBC* **246**, 5843 (1971).
14. H. L. Khandelwal and I. H. Hamilton, *JBC* **246**, 3297 (1971).
15. K. Takai, Y. Kurashina, and O. Hayaishi, *Methods Enzymol.* **38**, 160 (1974).
16. W. Y. Cheung and M. Chiang, *BBRC* **43**, 868 (1971).
17. M. Tao and F. Lipmann, *PNAS* **63**, 86 (1969).
18. O. M. Rosen and S. M. Rosen, *ABB* **131**, 449 (1969).
19. J. A. Gerit, J. A. Coderre, and M. S. Wolin, *JBC* **255**, 331 (1980).
20. C. J. Homcy, S. M. Wrenn, and E. Haber, *JBC* **252**, 8957 (1977).
21. C. J. Homcy, S. M. Wrenn, and E. Haber, *PNAS* **75**, 59 (1978).

22. E. Stellwagen and B. Baker, *Nature* **261**, 719 (1978).
23. J. Ryan, *FP* **35**, 422 (1976).
24. N. I. Swislocki, T. Magnuson, and J. Tierney, *ABB* **179**, 157 (1977).
25. A. R. Kornblihtt, M. M. Flawia, and H. N. Torres, *Bchem* **20**, 1262 (1981).
26. E. Hewlett and J. Wolff, *J. Bact.* **127**, 890 (1976).
27. E. J. Neer, *Adv. Cyclic Nucleotide Res.* 9, 69 (1978).
28. E. J. Neer, D. Echeverria, and S. Knox, *JBC* **255**, 9782 (1980).
29. E. J. Neer, *JBC* **253**, 1498 (1978).
30. T. Haga, K. Haga, and A. G. Gilman, *JBC* **252**, 5778 (1977).
31. D. Stengel and J. Hanoune, *EJB* **102**, 21 (1979).
32. J. K. Northup, M. F. Renart, J. R. Grove, and T. E. Mansour, *JBC* **254**, 11861 (1979).
33. E. J. Neer, *JBC* **249**, 6527 (1974).
34. G. Guillon, P. O. Couraud, and C. Roy, *BBRC* **87**, 855 (1979).
35. A. Goldhammer, G. H. Cook, and J. Wolff, *JBC* **255**, 6918 (1980).
36. R. F. Asbury, G. H. Cook, and J. Wolff, *JBC* **253**, 5286 (1978).
37. E. J. Neer, *JBC* **253**, 5808 (1978).
38. A. F. Welton, P. M. Lad, A. C. Newby, H. Yamamura, S. Nicosia, and M. Rodbell, *BBA* **522**, 625 (1978).
39. W. Schlegel, E. S. Kempner, and M. Rodbell, *JBC* **254**, 5168 (1979).
40. M. D. Houslay, J. C. Ellory, G. A. Smith, T. R. Hesketh, J. M. Stein, G. B. Warren, and J. C. Metcalfe, *BBA* **467**, 208 (1977).
41. E. J. Neer, *JBC* **248**, 4775 (1973).
42. M. Rodbell, *JBC* **250**, 5826 (1975).
43. G. I. Drummond, D. L. Severson, and L. Duncan, *JBC* **246**, 4166 (1971).
44. M. Rendell, Y. Salomon, M. C. Lin, M. Rodbell, and M. Berman, *JBC* **250**, 4253 (1975).
45. L. Birnbaumer, S. L. Pohl, and M. Rodbell, *JBC* **244**, 3468 (1969).
46. G. I. Drummond and L. Duncan, *JBC* **245**, 976 (1970).
47. M. C. Lin, Y. Salomon, M. Rendell, and M. Rodbell, *JBC* **250**, 4246 (1975).
48. D. L. Severson, G. I. Drummond, and P. V. Sulakhe, *JBC* **247**, 2949 (1972).
49. R. Rajerison, J. Marchetti, C. Roy, J. Bockaert, and S. Jard, *JBC* **249**, 6390 (1974).
50. R. A. Johnson, *JBC* **255**, 8252 (1980).
51. K. M. J. Menon and M. Smith, *Bchem* **10**, 1186 (1971).
52. T. Braun and R. F. Dods, *PNAS* **72**, 1097 (1975).
53. C. A. Herman, W. L. Zahler, G. A. Doak, and B. J. Campbell, *ABB* **177**, 622 (1976).
54. M. M. Flawia and H. N. Torres, *JBC* **247**, 6873 (1972).
55. M. M. Flawia and H. N. Torres, *JBC* **248**, 4517 (1973).
56. C. Londos and M. S. Preston, *JBC* **252**, 5957 (1977).
57. D. L. Garbers and R. A. Johnson, *JBC* **250**, 8449 (1975).
58. R. A. Johnson and E. W. Sutherland, *JBC* **248**, 5114 (1973).
59. E. J. Neer, *JBC* **254**, 2089 (1979).
60. B. Burke, *BBA* **220**, 30 (1970).
61. D. F. Malamud, C. C. Dirusso, and J. R. Aprille, *BBA* **485**, 243 (1977).
62. S. J. Pilkes and R. A. Johnson, *BBA* **341**, 388 (1974).
63. R. A. Johnson, S. J. Pilkes, and P. Hamet, *JBC* **250**, 6599 (1975).
64. L. E. Limbird, A. R. Hickey, and R. J. Lefkowitz, *JBC* **254**, 2677 (1979).
65. T. B. Nielson, P. M. Lad, M. S. Preston, E. Kempner, W. Schlegel, and M. Rodbell, *PNAS* **78**, 722 (1981).
66. E. M. Ross, A. C. Howlett, K. M. Ferguson, and A. G. Gilman, *JBC* **253**, 6401 (1978).

67. S. Strittmatter and E. J. Neer, *PNAS* **77**, 6344 (1980).
68. E. M. Ross, *JBC* **256**, 1949 (1981).
69. E. J. Neer, *FEBS Lett.* **125**, 134 (1981).
70. O. D. Taunton, J. Roth, and I. Pastan, *JBC* **244**, 247 (1969).
71. K. D. Hepp, R. Edel, and O. Wieland, *EJB* **17**, 171 (1970).
72. W. J. Rutten, J. J. H. H. M. de Pont, and S. L. Bonting, *BBA* **274**, 201 (1972).
73. L. S. Bradham, D. A. Holt, and M. Sims, *BBA* **201**, 250 (1970).
74. M. Vaughan and F. Murad, *Bchem* **8**, 3092 (1969).
75. J. P. Perkins and M. M. Moore, *JBC* **246**, 62 (1971).
76. M. L. Steer and A. Levitzki, *JBC* **250**, 2080 (1975).
77. M. L. Steer, C. Baldwin, and A. Levitzki, *JBC* **251**, 4930 (1976).
78. V. Stolc, *JBC* **252**, 1901 (1977).
79. E. Hanski, N. Sevilla, and A. Levitzki, *EJB* **76**, 513 (1977).
80. L. S. Bradham and W. Y. Cheung, *Calcium and Cell Function* 1, 109 (1980).
81. D. J. Wolff and C. O. Brostrom, *Adv. Cyclic Nucleotide Res.* **11**, 37 (1979).
82. K. von Hungen and S. Roberts, *Nature NB* **242**, 58 (1973).
83. I. MacDonald, *BBA* **397**, 244 (1975).
84. C. O. Brostrom, M. A. Brostrom, and D. J. Wolff, *JBC* **252**, 5677 (1977).
85. M. A. Brostrom, C. O. Brostrom, B. M. Breckenridge, and D. J. Wolff, *JBC* **251**, 4744 (1976).
86. M. A. Brostrom, C. O. Brostrom, and D. J. Wolff, *ABB* **191**, 341 (1978).
87. L. Birnbaumer and M. Rodbell, *JBC* **244**, 3477 (1969).
88. R. J. Lefkowitz, J. Roth, and I. Pastan, *Nature* **228**, 864 (1970).
89. H. P. Bar and O. Hechter, *PNAS* **63**, 350 (1969).
90. H. P. Bar and O. Hechter, *BBRC* **35**, 681 (1969).
91. T. K. Ray, V. Tomasi, and G. V. Marrinetti, *BBA* **211**, 20 (1970).
92. L. A. Kelly and S. B. Koritz, *BBA* **237**, 141 (1971).
93. B. J. Campbell, G. Woodward, and V. Borberg, *JBC* **247**, 6167 (1972).
94. J. Bockaert, C. Roy, and S. Jard, *JBC* **247**, 7073 (1972).
95. D. J. Franks, L. S. Perrin, and D. Malamud, *FEBS Lett.* **42**, 267 (1974).
96. F. M. Finn, J. A. Montibeller, Y. Ushijima, and K. Hofmann, *JBC* **250**, 1188 (1975).
97. M. J. Plascik, P. L. Wisler, C. L. Johnson, and J. D. Potter, *JBC* **255**, 4176 (1980).
98. L. S. Bradham, *BBA* **276**, 434 (1972).
99. M. A. Brostrom, C. O. Brostrom, and D. J. Wolff, *JBC* **254**, 7548 (1979).
100. W. Y. Cheung, L. S. Bradham, T. J. Lynch, Y. M. Lin, and E. A. Tallant, *BBRC* **66**, 1055 (1975).
101. T. J. Lynch, E. A. Tallant, and W. Y. Cheung, *BBRC* **68**, 616 (1978).
102. C. O. Brostrom, Y. Huang, B. M. Breckenridge, and D. J. Wolff, *PNAS* **72**, 64 (1975).
103. T. J. Lynch, E. A. Tallant, and W. Y. Cheung, *ABB* **182**, 124 (1977).
104. K. R. Westcott, D. C. La Porte, and D. R. Storm, *PNAS* **76**, 204 (1979).
105. W. A. Toscano, K. R. Westcott, D. C. La Porte, and D. R. Storm, *PNAS* **76**, 5582 (1979).
106. R. M. Levin and B. Weiss, *Mol. Pharmacol.* **13**, 690 (1977).
107. R. W. Wallace, T. J. Lynch, E. A. Tallant, and W. Y. Cheung, *ABB* **187**, 328 (1978).
108. J. Wolff, G. H. Cook, A. R. Goldhammer, and S. A. Berkowitz, *PNAS* **77**, 3841 (1980).
109. T. J. Wincek, A. L. Hupka, and F. W. Sweat, *JBC* **250**, 8863 (1975).
110. J. Wolff and A. B. James, *JBC* **246**, 3939 (1971).
111. L. Birnbaumer, S. L. Pohl, and M. Rodbell, *JBC* **246**, 1857 (1971).
112. J. P. Harwood and M. Rodbell, *JBC* **248**, 4901 (1973).

113. M. Schramm and E. Naim, *JBC* **245**, 3225 (1970).
114. L. S. Bradham, *J. Cyclic Nucleotide Res.* **3**, 119 (1977).
115. V. Manganiello and M. Vaughan, *JBC* **251**, 6205 (1976).
116. M. Rodbell, L. Birnbaumer, S. L. Pohl, and H. M. J. Krans, *JBC* **246**, 1877 (1971).
117. F. Leray, A. Chambaut, and J. Hanoune, *BBRC* **48**, 1385 (1973).
118. J. P. Harwood, H. Low, and M. Rodbell, *JBC* **248**, 6239 (1973).
119. J. Wolff and G. H. Cook, *JBC* **248**, 350 (1973).
120. L. Birnbaumer, S. L. Pohl, and M. Rodbell, *JBC* **247**, 2038 (1972).
121. I. D. Goldfine, J. Roth, and L. Birnbaumer, *JBC* **247**, 1211 (1972).
122. G. Krishna and J. P. Harwood, *JBC* **247**, 2253 (1972).
123. D. G. Johnson, W. J. Thompson, and R. H. Williams, *Bchem* **13**, 1920 (1974).
124. J. P. Bilezikian and G. D. Aurbach, *JBC* **249**, 157 (1974).
125. M. Rodbell, M. C. Lin, and Y. Salomon, *JBC* **249**, 59 (1974).
126. J. Hanoune, M. Lacombe, and F. Pecker, *JBC* **250**, 4569 (1975).
127. N. Kimura and N. Nagata, *JBC* **252**, 3829 (1977).
128. N. Kimura and N. Nagata, *JBC* **254**, 3451 (1979).
129. C. Londos, Y. Salomon, M. C. Lin, J. P. Harwood, M. Schramm, J. Wolff, and M. Rodbell, *PNAS* **71**, 3087 (1974).
130. T. Pfeuffer and E. J. M. Helmreich, *JBC* **250**, 867 (1975).
131. M. Schramm and M. Rodbell, *JBC* **250**, 2232 (1975).
132. P. Cuatrecasas, S. Jacobs, and V. Bennett, *PNAS* **72**, 1739 (1975).
133. Y. Salomon, M. C. Lin, C. Londos, M. Rendell, and M. Rodbell, *JBC* **250**, 4239 (1975).
134. R. J. Lefkowitz and M. G. Caron, *JBC* **250**, 4418 (1975).
135. Y. Salomon and M. Rodbell, *JBC* **250**, 7245 (1975).
136. O. Zinder, O. Nikodijevic, P. G. Hoffman, and H. B. Pollard, *JBC* **251**, 2179 (1976).
137. S. Jacobs, V. Bennett, and P. Cuatrecasas, *J. Cyclic Nucleotide Res.* **2**, 205 (1976).
138. P. M. Lad, A. F. Welton, and M. Rodbell, *JBC* **252**, 5942 (1977).
139. T. Pfeuffer, *JBC* **252**, 7224 (1977).
140. E. J. M. Helmreich and T. Pfeuffer, *Adv. Enzyme Regul.* **15**, 209 (1977).
141. J. K. Northup and T. E. Mansour, *Mol. Pharmacol.* **14**, 820 (1978).
142. J. Moss and M. Vaughan, *ARB* **48**, 781 (1979).
143. D. E. Schafer, W. D. Lust, B. Sircar, and N. D. Goldberg, *PNAS* **67**, 851 (1970).
144. M. Field, D. Fromm, Q. Al-Awgati, and W. Greenough, *J. Clin. Invest.* **51**, 796 (1972).
145. L. M. Lichtenstein, C. S. Henney, H. R. Bourne, and W. B. Greenough, *J. Clin. Invest.* **52**, 691 (1973).
146. A. Haksar, D. V. Maudsley, and F. G. Peron, *BBA* **381**, 308 (1975).
147. M. Field, *PNAS* **71**, 3299 (1974).
148. G. L. Johnson, T. K. Harden, and J. P. Perkins, *JBC* **253**, 1465 (1978).
149. M. Vaughan, N. F. Pierce, and W. B. Greenough, *Nature* **226**, 658 (1970).
150. P. Cuatrecasas, *Bchem* **12**, 3567 (1973).
151. E. O'Keefe and P. Cuatrecasas, *PNAS* **71**, 2500 (1974).
152. R. W. Wishnow, E. Lifrak, and C. Chen, *J. Infect. Dis.* **133**, S108 (1976).
153. D. J. Evans, L. C. Chen, G. T. Curlin, and D. G. Evans, *Nature NB* **236**, 137 (1972).
154. R. L. Guerrant, L. C. Chen, and G. W. G. Sharp, *J. Infect. Dis.* **125**, 377 (1972).
155. E. L. Hewlett, R. L. Guerrant, D. J. Evans, and W. B. Greenough, *Nature* **249**, 371 (1974).
156. D. V. Kimberg, M. Field, J. Johnson, A. Henderson, and E. Gershon, *J. Clin. Invest* **50**, 1218 (1971).

157. V. Bennett and P. Cuatrecasas, *J. Membr. Biol.* **22**, 1 (1975).
158. V. Bennett and P. Cuatrecasas, *J. Membr. Biol.* **22**, 29 (1975).
159. V. Bennett, L. Mong, and P. Cuatrecasas, *J. Membr. Biol.* **22**, 107 (1975).
160. V. Bennett, E. O'Keefe, and P. Cuatrecasas, *PNAS* **72**, 33 (1975).
161. E. Berkenbile and R. Delaney, *J. Infect. Dis.* **133**, S82 (1976).
162. J. Fischer, T. R. Kohler, L. G. Lipson, J. Flores, P. A. Witkum, and G. W. G. Sharp, *BJ* **172**, 59 (1978).
163. I. Holmgren and I. Lonnroth, *J. Infect. Dis.* **133**, S64 (1976).
164. S. van Heyningen and C. A. King, *BJ* **146**, 269 (1975).
165. N. Sahyoun and P. Cuatrecasas, *PNAS* **72**, 3438 (1975).
166. S. van Heyningen, *BJ* **157**, 785 (1975).
167. M. W. Bitensky, M. A. Wheeler, H. Mehta, and N. Miki, *PNAS* **72**, 2572 (1975).
168. D. M. Gill, *PNAS* **72**, 2064 (1975).
169. D. M. Gill and C. A. King, *JBC* **250**, 6424 (1975).
170. Y. Matuo, M. A. Wheeler, and M. W. Bitensky, *PNAS* **73**, 2654 (1976).
171. M. A. Wheeler, R. A. Solomon, C. Cooper, L. Hertzberg, H. Mehta, N. Miki, and M. W. Bitensky, *J. Infect. Dis.* **133**, S39 (1976).
172. J. Flores, P. Witkum, and G. W. G. Sharp, *J. Clin. Invest.* **57**, 450 (1976).
173. D. M. Gill, *J. Infect. Dis.* **133**, S55 (1976).
174. P. Cuatrecasas, *Bchem* **12**, 3547 (1973).
175. U. Ganguly and W. B. Greenough, *PNAS* **72**, 3561 (1975).
176. K. Mashiter, G. D. Mashiter, R. E. Hauger, and J. B. Field, *Endocrinology* **92**, 541 (1973).
177. T. V. Zenser and J. S. Metzger, *Infect. Immun.* **10**, 503 (1974).
178. H. S. Kantor, P. Tao, and S. L. Gorbach, *J. Infect. Dis.* **129**, 1 (1974).
179. S. Hynie, H. Raskoya, T. Sechser, J. Vanecek, D. Matejovska, V. Matejovska, M. Treu, and L. Polak, *Toxicon* **12**, 173 (1974).
180. C. N. Kwan and R. M. Wishnow, *Infect. Immun.* **10**, 146 (1974).
181. F. Dorner and P. Mayer, *Infect. Immun.* **11**, 429 (1975).
182. D. M. Gill, D. J. Evans, and D. G. Evans, *J. Infect. Dis.* **133**, S103 (1976).
183. M. J. Bergman, R. L. Guerrant, F. Murad, S. M. Richardson, D. Weaver, and G. L. Mandell, *J. Clin. Invest.* **61**, 227 (1978).
184. J. M. Hughes, F. Murad, B. Chang, and R. L. Guerrant, *Nature* **227**, 755 (1978).
185. M. Field, L. H. Gray, W. J. Laird, and P. L. Smith, *PNAS* **75**, 2800 (1978).
186. J. Moss, V. C. Manganiello, and M. Vaughan, *PNAS* **73**, 4424 (1976).
187. J. Moss, J. C. Osborne, P. H. Fishman, H. B. Brewer, M. Vaughan, and R. O. Brady, *PNAS* **74**, 74 (1977).
188. J. Moss and M. Vaughan, *JBC* **252**, 2455 (1977).
189. J. Moss and S. H. Richardson, *J. Clin. Invest.* **62**, 281 (1978).
190. N. J. Oppenheimer, *JBC* **253**, 4907 (1978).
191. J. B. Trepel, D. M. Chuang, and N. H. Neff, *PNAS* **73**, 5440 (1977).
192. J. Moss and M. Vaughan, *PNAS* **75**, 3621 (1978).
193. J. Moss, S. J. Stanley, and P. A. Watkins, *JBC* **255**, 5838 (1980).
194. E. M. Ross and A. G. Gilman, *ARB* **49**, 533 (1980).
195. E. M. Ross and A. G. Gilman, *JBC* **252**, 6966 (1977).
196. A. C. Howlett, P. C. Sternweis, B. A. Macik, P. M. Van Arsdale, and A. G. Gilman, *JBC* **254**, 2287 (1979).
197. N. Sahyoun, C. J. Schmitges, H. le Vine, and P. Cuatrecasas, *Life Sci.* **21**, 1837 (1978).
198. M. Hebdon, H. le Vine, N. Sahyoun, C. J. Schmitges, and P. Cuatrecasas, *PNAS* **75**, 3693 (1978).

199. M. F. Renart, G. Ayanoglu, J. M. Mansour, and T. E. Mansour, *BBRC* **89**, 1146 (1979).
200. G. I. Drummond, M. Sano, and P. Nambi, *ARB* **201**, 286 (1980).
201. H. R. Kaslow, G. L. Johnson, V. M. Brothers, and H. R. Bourne, *JBC* **255**, 3736 (1980).
202. A. C. Howlett and A. G. Gilman, *JBC* **255**, 2861 (1980).
203. D. M. Gill and R. Meren, *PNAS* **75**, 3050 (1978).
204. Z. Farfel, H. R. Kaslow, and H. R. Bourne, *BBRC* **90**, 1237 (1979).
205. J. K. Northup, P. C. Sternweis, M. D. Smigel, L. S. Schleifer, E. M. Ross, and A. G. Gilman, *PNAS* **77**, 6516 (1980).
206. G. L. Johnson, H. R. Kaslow, Z. Farfel, and H. R. Bourne, *Adv. Cyclic Nucleotide Res.* **13**, 1 (1980).
207. G. L. Johnson, H. R. Kaslow, and H. R. Bourne, *PNAS* **75**, 3113 (1978).
208. D. Cassel and T. Pfeuffer, *PNAS* **75**, 2669 (1978).
209. G. L. Johnson, H. R. Kaslow, and H. R. Bourne, *JBC* **253**, 7120 (1978).
210. H. R. Kaslow, Z. Farfel, G. L. Johnson, and H. R. Bourne, *Mol. Pharmacol.* **15**, 472 (1979).
211. R. W. Downs, A. M. Spiegel, M. Singer, S. Reen, and G. D. Aurbach, *JBC* **255**, 949 (1980).
212. D. Cassel and Z. Selinger, *PNAS* **75**, 4155 (1978).
213. D. Cassel and Z. Selinger, *BBA* **452**, 538 (1976).
214. D. Cassel and Z. Selinger, *PNAS* **74**, 3307 (1977).
215. G. L. Johnson and H. R. Bourne, *BBRC* **78**, 792 (1977).
216. F. Pecker and J. Hanoune, *JBC* **252**, 2784 (1977).
217. M. M. Rasenick and M. W. Bitensky, *PNAS* **77**, 4628 (1980).
218. M. K. Bhat, R. Iyengar, J. Abramowitz, M. E. Bordelon-Riser, and L. Birnbaumer, *PNAS* **77**, 38 (1980).
219. P. A. Watkins, J. Moss, and M. Vaughan, *JBC* **255**, 3959 (1980).
220. L. Birnbaumer, S. L. Pohl, H. M. J. Krans, and M. Rodbell, *Adv. Biochem. Psychopharmacol.* **3**, 185 (1970).
221. G. S. Johnson and V. R. Mukku, *JBC* **254**, 95 (1979).
222. M. Rodbell, H. M. J. Krans, S. L. Pohl, and L. Birnbaumer, *JBC* **246**, 1861 (1971).
223. S. J. Marx, S. A. Fedak, and G. D. Aurbach, *JBC* **247**, 6913 (1972).
224. M. Schramm, H. Feinstein, E. Naim, M. Lang, and M. Lasser, *PNAS* **69**, 523 (1972).
225. J. P. Bilezikian and G. D. Aurbach, *JBC* **248**, 5575 (1973).
226. R. J. Lefkowitz, G. W. G. Sharp, and E. Haber, *JBC* **248**, 342 (1973).
227. J. Bockaert, C. Roy, R. Rajerison, and S. Jard, *JBC* **248**, 5922 (1973).
228. C. Roy, T. Barth, and S. Jard, *JBC* **250**, 3157 (1975).
229. C. Mukherjee, M. G. Caron, M. Coverstone, and R. J. Lefkowitz, *JBC* **250**, 4869 (1975).
230. R. J. Lefkowitz, D. Mullikin, and M. G. Caron, *JBC* **251**, 4686 (1976).
231. M. C. Lin, S. Nicosia, P. M. Lad, and M. Rodbell, *JBC* **252**, 2790 (1977).
232. L. Birnbaumer and M. Rodbell, *JBC* **244**, 3477 (1969).
233. A. Levitzki, D. Atlas, and M. L. Steer, *PNAS* **71**, 2773 (1974).
234. D. Atlas, M. L. Steer, and A. Levitzki, *PNAS* **71**, 4246 (1974).
235. R. W. Alexander, L. T. Williams, and R. J. Lefkowitz, *PNAS* **72**, 1564 (1975).
236. L. T. Williams, L. Jarett, and R. J. Lefkowitz, *JBC* **251**, 3096 (1976).
237. G. S. Levey, M. A. Fletcher, I. Meir, E. Ruiz, and A. Schenk, *JBC* **249**, 2665 (1974).
238. L. T. Williams and R. J. Lefkowitz, *JBC* **252**, 7207 (1977).
239. R. J. Lefkowitz and L. T. Williams, *Adv. Cyclic Nucleotide Res.* **9**, 1 (1978).
240. P. M. Lad, T. B. Nielson, M. S. Preston, and M. Rodbell, *JBC* **255**, 988 (1980).

241. E. M. Ross, M. E. Maguire, T. W. Sturgill, R. L. Biltonen, and A. G. Gilman, *JBC* **252**, 3761 (1977).
242. J. M. Stadel, A. DeLean, and R. J. Lefkowitz, *JBC* **255**, 1436 (1980).
243. M. Rodbell, M. C. Lin, Y. Salomon, C. Londos, J. P. Harwood, B. R. Martin, M. Rendell, and M. Berman, *Adv. Cyclic Nucleotide Res.* **5**, 3 (1975).
244. R. L. Tate, J. M. Holmes, L. D. Kohn, and R. J. Winand, *JBC* **250**, 6527 (1975).
245. L. E. Limbird and R. J. Lefkowitz, *JBC* **252**, 799 (1977).
246. G. Vauquelin, P. Geynet, J. Hanoune, and A. D. Strosberg, *PNAS* **74**, 3710 (1977).
247. A. F. Welton, P. M. Lad, A. C. Newby, H. Yamamura, S. Nicosia, and M. Rodbell, *JBC* **252**, 5947 (1977).
248. M. G. Caron, Y. Srinivasan, J. Pitha, K. Kociolek, and R. J. Lefkowitz, *JBC* **254**, 2923 (1979).
249. G. S. Lévey, *JBC* **246**, 7405 (1971).
250. F. M. Hoffman, *JBC* **254**, 255 (1979).
251. E. M. Ross and A. G. Gilman, *PNAS* **74**, 3715 (1977).
252. D. R. Jeffery, R. R. Charlton, and J. C. Venter, *JBC* **255**, 5015 (1980).
253. J. Orly and M. Schramm, *PNAS* **75**, 4410 (1976).
254. B. Schulster, J. Orly, G. Seidel, and M. Schramm, *JBC* **253**, 1201 (1978).
255. S. Eimerl, G. Neufeld, M. Korner, and M. Schramm, *PNAS* **77**, 760 (1980).
256. M. Schramm, *PNAS* **76**, 1174 (1979).
257. C. Mikherjee, M. G. Caron, and R. J. Lefkowitz, *PNAS* **72**, 1945 (1975).
258. J. Mickey, R. Tate, and R. J. Lefkowitz, *JBC* **250**, 5727 (1975).
259. C. Mikherjee and R. J. Lefkowitz, *PNAS* **73**, 1494 (1976).
260. C. Mukherjee and R. J. Lefkowitz, *Mol. Pharmacol.* **13**, 291 (1977).
261. M. R. Wessels, D. Mullikin, and R. J. Lefkowitz, *JBC* **253**, 3371 (1978).
262. R. J. Lefkowitz, D. Mullikin, C. L. Wood, T. B. Gore, and C. Mukherjee, *JBC* **252**, 5295 (1977).
263. Y. Su, T. K. Harden, and J. P. Perkins, *JBC* **255**, 7410 (1980).
264. M. Shear, P. A. Insel, K. L. Melmon, and P. Coffino, *JBC* **251**, 7572 (1976).
265. V. Hamburger, M. Lucas, B. Cantau, T. Barabe, J. Penit, and J. Bockaert, *JBC* **255**, 10436 (1980).
266. J. P. Perkins, G. L. Johnson, and T. K. Harden, *Adv. Cyclic Nucleotide Res.* **9**, 19 (1978).
267. G. L. Johnson, B. B. Wolfe, T. K. Harden, P. B. Molinoff, and J. P. Perkins, *JBC* **253**, 1472 (1978).
268. W. L. Terasaki, G. Brooker, J. de Vellis, D. Inglish, C. Hsu, and R. D. Moylan, *Adv. Cyclic Nucleotide Res.* **9**, 33 (1978).
269. E. Ezra and Y. Salomon, *JBC* **255**, 653 (1980).
270. E. Ezra and Y. Salomon, *JBC* **256**, 5377 (1981).
271. S. K. Sharma, M. Nirenberg, and W. A. Klee, *PNAS* **72**, 590 (1975).
272. S. K. Sharma, W. A. Klee, and M. Nirenberg, *PNAS* **72**, 3092 (1975).
273. N. M. Nathanson, W. L. Klein, and M. Nirenberg, *PNAS* **75**, 1788 (1978).
274. S. L. Sabol and M. Nirenberg, *JBC* **254**, 1913 (1979).
275. S. L. Sabol and M. Nirenberg, *JBC* **254**, 1921 (1979).
276. A. J. Blume, D. Lichtshtein, and G. Boone, *PNAS* **76**, 5626 (1979).
277. G. Koski, W. F. Simonds, and W. A. Klee, *JBC* **256**, 1536 (1981).
278. C. Londos and J. Wolff, *PNAS* **74**, 5482 (1977).
279. H. Yamamura, P. M. Lad, and M. Rodbell, *JBC* **252**, 7964 (1977).
280. C. Londos, D. M. F. Cooper, W. Schlegel, and M. Rodbell, *PNAS* **75**, 5362 (1978).
281. D. M. F. Cooper, W. Schlegel, M. C. Lin, and M. Rodbell, *JBC* **254**, 8927 (1979).

282. P. M. Lad, T. B. Nielson, C. Londos, M. S. Preston, and M. Rodbell, *JBC* **255**, 10841 (1980).
283. L. E. Limbird, D. M. Gill, J. M. Stadel, A. R. Hickey, and R. J. Lefkowitz, *JBC* **255**, 1854 (1980).
284. T. Haga, E. M. Ross, H. J. Anderson, and A. G. Gilman, *PNAS* **74**, 2016 (1977).
285. P. C. Sternweis and A. G. Gilman, *JBC* **254**, 3333 (1979).
286. D. Stengel and J. Hanoune, *JBC* **256**, 5394 (1981).
287. T. H. Hudson and G. L. Johnson, *JBC* **255**, 7480 (1980).
288. A. M. Tolkovsky and A. Levitzki, *Bchem* **17**, 3795 (1978).
289. E. Hanski, G. Ramon, and A. Levitzki, *Bchem* **18**, 846 (1979).
290. D. Atlas, D. J. Volsky, and A. Levitzki, *BBA* **597**, 64 (1980).
291. T. Pfeuffer, *FEBS Lett* **101**, 85 (1979).
292. F. Eckstein, D. Cassel, H. Levkowitz, M. Lowe, and Z. Selinger, *JBC* **254**, 9829 (1979).
293. L. E. Limbird and R. J. Lefkowitz, *PNAS* **75**, 228 (1978).
294. L. E. Limbird, D. M. Gill, and R. J. Lefkowitz, *PNAS* **77**, 775 (1980).
295. D. Cassel, F. Eckstein, M. Lowe, and Z. Selinger, *JBC* **254**, 9835 (1979).
296. L. J. Pike and R. J. Lefkowitz, *JBC* **255**, 6860 (1980).
297. T. H. Hudson, J. F. Roeber, and G. L. Johnson, *JBC* **256**, 1459 (1981).
298. M. Rodbell, *Nature* **284**, 17 (1980).
299. W. Schlegel, D. M. F. Cooper, and M. Rodbell, *ABB* **201**, 678 (1980).
300. A. J. Bitonti, J. Moss, M. N. Tandon, and M. Vaughan, *JBC* **255**, 2026 (1980).
301. R. Iyengar and L. Birnbaumer, *PNAS* **78**, 3189 (1979).
302. R. Iyengar, J. Abramowitz, M. Bordelon-Riser, and L. Birnbaumer, *JBC* **255**, 3558 (1980).
303. R. Iyengar, J. Abramowitz, M. Bordelon-Riser, and L. Birnbaumer, *JBC* **255**, 10312 (1980).
304. M. S. Rendell, M. Rodbell, and M. Berman, *JBC* **252**, 7909 (1977).
305. L. Birnbaumer, T. L. Swartz, J. Abramowitz, P. W. Mintz, and R. Iyengar, *JBC* **255**, 3542 (1980).
306. G. Koski and W. A. Klee, *PNAS* **78**, 4185 (1981).
307. D. A. Green and R. Clark, *JBC* **256**, 2105 (1981).
308. N. D. Goldberg and M. K. Haddox, *ARB* **46**, 923 (1977).
309. F. Murad, W. P. Arnold, C. K. Mittal, and J. M. Braughler, *Adv. Cyclic Nucleotide Res.* **11**, 175 (1979).
310. D. L. Garbers, T. D. Chrisman, J. L. Suddath, and J. G. Hardman, *ABB* **166**, 135 (1975).
311. D. L. Garbers, *JBC* **254**, 240 (1979).
312. J. M. Braughler, C. K. Mittal, and F. Murad, *PNAS* **76**, 219 (1979).
313. D. L. Garbers, *JBC* **251**, 4071 (1976).
314. V. Macchia, S. Varrone, H. Weissbach, D. L. Miller, and I. Pastan, *JBC* **250**, 6214 (1975).
315. I. C. Sun, L. Shapiro, and O. M. Rosen, *BBRC* **61**, 193 (1974).
316. E. J. Neer and E. Sukiennik, *JBC* **250**, 7905 (1975).
317. T. Asano and H. Hidaka, *BBRC* **78**, 910 (1977).
318. M. Nakane and T. Deguchi, *BBA* **525**, 275 (1978).
319. S. Tsai, V. Manganiello, and M. Vaughan, *JBC* **253**, 8452 (1978).
320. T. D. Chrisman, D. L. Garbers, M. A. Parks, and J. G. Hardman, *JBC* **250**, 374 (1975).
321. J. Durham, *EJB* **61**, 535 (1976).

230 LAURENCE S. BRADHAM AND WAI YIU CHEUNG

322. S. J. Strada, L. Kirkegaard, and W. J. Thompson, *Neuropharmacology* **15**, 261 (1976).
323. H. Kimura and F. Murad, *Metabolism* **24**, 439 (1975).
324. W. H. Frey, B. M. Boman, D. Newman, and N. D. Goldberg, *JBC* **252**, 4298 (1977).
325. G. K. Mittal, H. Kimura, and F. Murad, *JBC* **252**, 4384 (1977).
326. H. Kimura and F. Murad, *JBC* **250**, 4810 (1975).
327. K. Nakazawa and M. Sano, *JBC* **249**, 4207 (1974).
328. H. Kimura and F. Murad, *JBC* **249**, 6910 (1974).
329. D. L. Garbers, E. L. Dyer, and J. G. Hardman, *JBC* **250**, 382 (1975).
330. J. A. Nesbitt, W. B. Anderson, Z. Miller, I. Pastan, T. R. Russell, and D. Gospodanowicz, *JBC* **251**, 2344 (1976).
331. S. J. Sulakhe, N. L. Leung, and P. V. Sulakhe, *BJ* **157**, 713 (1976).
332. D. Wallach and I. Pastan, *JBC* **251**, 5802 (1976).
333. T. Katagiri, T. Terao, and T. Osawa, *J. Biochem. (Tokyo)* **79**, 849 (1978).
334. F. Marks, *BBA* **309**, 349 (1973).
335. K. Nakazawa, H. Shimonaka, S. Nagao, S. Kudo, and Y. Nozawa, *J. Biochem. (Tokyo)* **86**, 321 (1979).
336. Y. Suzuki, T. Hirahayashi, and Y. Watanabe, *BBRC* **90**, 253 (1979).
337. S. Nagao, Y. Suzuki, Y. Watanabe, and Y. Nozawa, *BBRC* **90**, 261 (1979).
338. S. Kakiuchi, K. Sobue, R. Yamazaki, S. Nagao, S. Umeki, Y. Nozawa, M. Yazawa, and R. Yagi, *JBC* **256**, 19 (1981).
339. G. A. Jamieson, T. C. Vanaman, and J. J. Blum, *PNAS* **76**, 6471 (1979).
340. A. A. White, K. M. Crawford, C. S. Patt, and P. J. Lad, *JBC* **251**, 7304 (1976).
341. W. P. Arnold, C. K. Mittal, S. Katsuki, and F. Murad, *PNAS* **74**, 3203 (1977).
342. J. M. Braughler, C. K. Mittal, and F. Murad, *JBC* **254**, 12450 (1979).
343. W. P. Arnold, R. Aldred, and F. Murad, *Science* **198**, 934 (1977).
344. C. A. Gruetter, B. K. Barr, D. B. McNamara, P. J. Kadowitz, and L. J. Ignarro, *J. Pharmacol. Exp. Ther.* **214**, 9 (1980).
345. H. Kimura, C. K. Mittal, and F. Murad, *JBC* **250**, 8016 (1975).
346. W. E. Criss, F. Murad, and H. Kimura, *J. Cyclic Nucleotide Res.* **2**, 11 (1976).
347. F. R. De Robertis and P. A. Craven, *JBC* **251**, 4651 (1976).
348. H. Kimura, C. K. Mittal, and F. Murad, *JBC* **251**, 7769 (1976).
349. J. Levilliers, J. Pairault, F. Lecot, and M. Laudat, *FEBS Lett.* **63**, 323 (1976).
350. C. Struck and H. Glossman, *Naunyn-Schmiedeberg's Arch. Pharmacol.* **304**, 51 (1978).
351. E. Bohme, H. Graf, and G. Schultz, *Adv. Cyclic Nucleotide Res.* **9**, 131 (1978).
352. D. Leiber and S. Harbon, *BBRC* **89**, 598 (1979).
353. T. Deguchi, *JBC* **252**, 598 (1977).
354. C. K. Mittal, H. Kimura, and F. Murad, *J. Cyclic Nucleotide Res.* **1**, 261 (1975).
355. D. L. Vesely and G. S. Levey, *BBRC* **74**, 780 (1977).
356. D. L. Vesely, L. E. Rovere, and G. S. Levey, *Enzyme* **23**, 289 (1978).
357. F. R. De Robertis and P. A. Craven, *Science* **193**, 897 (1976).
358. F. R. De Robertis and P. A. Craven, *JBC* **252**, 5804 (1977).
359. F. R. De Robertis, P. A. Craven, and D. W. Pratt, *BBRC* **83**, 158 (1978).
360. F. R. De Robertis, P. A. Craven, and R. Saito, *Cancer* **45**, 1052 (1980).
361. R. G. Briggs and F. R. De Robertis, *BBA* **628**, 425 (1980).
362. F. R. De Robertis and P. A. Craven, *BBA* **499**, 337 (1977).
363. D. L. Vesely, *Res. Commun. Chem. Pathol. Pharmacol.* **24**, 329 (1979).
364. D. L. Vesely, W. R. Benson, E. B. Sheinin, and G. S. Levey, *PSEBM* **161**, 319 (1979).

365. F. R. De Robertis and P. A. Craven, *J. Natl. Cancer Inst.* **59**, 1741 (1977).
366. P. A. Craven and F. R. De Robertis, *JBC* **253**, 8433 (1978).
367. N. Miki, M. Nagano, and K. Kuriyama, *BBRC* **72**, 952 (1976).
368. P. A. Craven, F. R. De Robertis, and D. W. Pratt, *JBC* **254**, 8213 (1979).
369. C. K. Mittal and F. Murad, *JBC* **252**, 3136 (1977).
370. C. K. Mittal, J. M. Braughler, E. Ichihara, and F. Murad, *BBA* **585**, 333 (1979).
371. E. J. Neer and F. Murad, *BBA* **583**, 521 (1979).
372. G. Graff, J. H. Stephenson, D. Glass, M. K. Haddox, and N. D. Goldberg, *JBC* **253**, 7662 (1978).
373. H. Hidaka and T. Asano, *PNAS* **74**, 3657 (1977).
374. T. Asakawa, I. Scheinbaum, and R. Ho, *BBRC* **73**, 141 (1976).
375. A. J. Barber, *BBA* **444**, 579 (1976).
376. D. B. Glass, W. Frey, D. W. Carr, and N. D. Goldberg, *JBC* **252**, 1279 (1977).
377. T. Asakawa, M. Takenoshita, S. Uchida, and S. Tanaka, *J. Neurochem.* **30**, 161 (1978).
378. J. A. Rillema, *Prostaglandins* **15**, 857 (1978).
379. D. V. Gruetter and L. J. Ignarro, *Prostaglandins* **18**, 541 (1979).
380. K. Ichihara, M. El-Zayat, C. K. Mittal, and F. Murad, *ABB* **197**, 44 (1979).
381. D. Leiber and S. Harbon, *BBRC* **89**, 598 (1979).
382. J. S. Cantieri, G. Graff, and N. D. Goldberg, *J. Invest. Dermatol.* **74**, 234 (1980).
383. M. K. Haddox, J. H. Stephenson, M. E. Moser, and N. D. Goldberg, *JBC* **253**, 3143 (1978).
384. N. D. Goldberg, G. Graff, M. K. Haddox, J. H. Stephenson, D. B. Glass, and M. E. Moser, *Adv. Cyclic Nucleotide Res.* **9**, 101 (1978).
385. N. D. Goldberg, G. Graff, M. K. Haddox, J. H. Stephenson, D. B. Glass, and M. E. Moser, *Adv. Enzyme Regul.* **16**, 165 (1978).
386. C. K. Mittal and F. Murad, *PNAS* **74**, 4360 (1977).
387. F. Murad, C. K. Mittal, W. P. Arnold, S. Katsuki, and H. Kimura, *Adv. Cyclic Nucleotide Res.* **9**, 143 (1978).
388. D. L. Vesely, B. Watson, and G. S. Levey, *J. Pharmacol. Exp. Ther.* **209**, 162 (1979).
389. W. J. Thompson, R. H. Williams, and S. A. Little, *BBA* **302**, 329 (1973).
390. S. L. Howell and W. Montague, *BJ* **142**, 379 (1974).
391. M. S. Amer, *Gastroenterology* **67**, 333 (1974).
392. K. Ichihara, J. Larner, H. Kimura, and F. Murad, *BBA* **481**, 734 (1977).
393. D. Wallach and I. Pastan, *BBRC* **72**, 859 (1976).
394. R. L. Guerrant, J. M. Hughes, B. Chang, D. C. Robertson, and F. Murad, *J. Infect. Dis.* **142**, 220 (1980).
395. R. Hauguenauer-Tsapis, A. Ben Salal, M. Lacombe, and J. Hanoune, *JBC* **256**, 1651 (1981).
396. P. Nambi and R. K. Sharma, *Endocrinology* **108**, 2025 (1981).
397. P. Nambi and R. K. Sharma, *BBRC* **100**, 508 (1981). [See Erratum, *BBRC* **101**, 330 (1981)].

Cyclic Nucleotide Control of Protein Kinases

R. K. Sharma

Department of Biochemistry
University of Tennessee Center
for the Health Sciences
Memphis, Tennessee

One of the marvels of nature is the development in a eukaryotic cell of a complex set of homeostatic controls that respond precisely and in a coordinated fashion to the intra- and extracellular signals of the cell. These sensory signals are recognized by the plasma membrane, transduced into an intracellular message, and then translated into an appropriate physiological response. Sutherland and Rall's (*1*) second messenger hypothesis of cyclic AMP (cAMP) action has revolutionized

Progress in Nucleic Acid Research
and Molecular Biology, Vol. 27

our thinking on the understanding of the control processes involved in
these stimulus-secretion cellular processes.

An important contribution to the "second messenger concept" is
the discovery of cAMP-dependent protein kinase (2), bridging the gap
in our understanding of the mechanism by which cAMP elicits a response to a wide range of polypeptide hormones, the catecholamines,
and other cellular stimuli.

This review concentrates on the current knowledge about the structure, function, and regulation of cAMP- and cGMP-dependent protein
kinases. However, for the sake of completeness, I also briefly review
the initial studies that led to the discovery of cAMP-dependent protein
kinase and its mode of regulation by cAMP. In addition, I critically
evaluate, in selected hormonal systems, the observations that correlate
the rise of cAMP with the activation of cAMP-dependent protein
kinase and the phosphorylation of a substrate protein with the biological response. In view of the voluminous literature, it is not practical to
cover all the references on this topic, but many excellent reviews cov-
ering the work of eminent researchers in the field are available (3–14).

I. General Aspects

Early studies (15) showed that particulate preparations of rat liver,
consisting predominantly of nuclei and mitochondria supplemented
with ATP and Mg^{2+}, could incorporate phosphate into fractions of
phospholipids and "pentose nucleic acid," implying the presence of a
kinase activity in the nuclear or mitochondrial fractions. Subsequent
studies showed that the serine residue of casein is phosphorylated by
the crude liver enzyme (16). The protein-kinase-induced transfer of
the γ-phosphate group of ATP to the serine residues of casein was not
indiscriminate, since the phosphorylation of α-casein was over twice
that of β-casein. Slight phosphorylation of ovalbumin was also observed, but not of other proteins, such as β-globulin, serum albumin,
and lysozyme. These investigations established not only the presence
of a specific casein kinase enzyme in the mammalian system, but also
laid the foundation for an exciting area of research dealing with the
potential role of protein kinases in cellular regulation.

The discovery (17, 18) of a specific protein kinase, phosphorylase
kinase, that catalyzes the phosphorylation and activation of glycogen
phosphorylase marked the start of a new era in biochemistry in which
the inquiries were directed toward understanding the functional significance of protein kinase(s) in the control mechanisms of biological
systems. With the discovery (19) of phosvitin kinase three types of

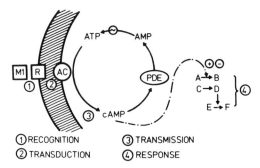

FIG. 1. A schematic representation of the original second-messenger hypothesis in which hormone–receptor interaction leads to generation of the single second messenger, cAMP. The system can also be represented as a four-step information transfer system: recognition → transduction → transmission → response. Adapted from Rasmussen and Goodman (*314*).

specific protein kinases—casein kinase, phosphorylase kinase, and phosvitin kinase—were recognized, although the last enzyme phosphorylated both casein and phosvitin. The finding that serine-bound phosphate in the phosphoproteins of phosvitin can phosphorylate ADP to ATP (*20*), indicated that the protein kinase reaction is reversible, and that the phosphate covalently linked by it to the substrate protein is a "high-energy" phosphate. This observation indicated that the protein-kinase-induced transfer of phosphate between ATP and an acceptor protein may play an important physiological role in the regulation of well-coordinated chemical reactions in biological systems.

II. Cyclic-AMP-Dependent Protein Kinases

One key finding that was a landmark in the understanding of the mechanism of hormone action was the demonstration (*21*) that activation of liver phosphorylase by epinephrine and glucagon in a cell-free system occurs in two stages. In the first stage, the hormone increases the formation of a heat-stable, dialyzable factor in the particulate fraction, and in the second stage, this factor stimulates phosphorylase. The heat-stable factor was later identified as 3′,5′-cyclic AMP (cAMP) (*22, 23*). These and other pioneering studies (*24*) laid the groundwork for the "second messenger hypothesis" for hormonal action (*25*), which depicts the peptide hormone action as illustrated in Fig. 1. The model proposes that cAMP, generated by the interaction of a hormone and its receptor, mediates all subsequent intracellular events. Although this

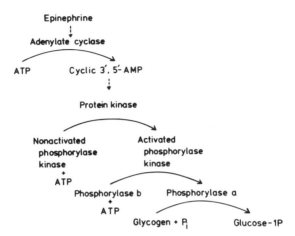

FIG. 2. The mechanism of action of epinephrine in the regulation of skeletal muscle glycogenolysis. Adapted from Walsh and Krebs, (6).

concept did not apply to certain hormones, it nonetheless provided a useful conceptual framework that inspired many tests of its validity.

Another landmark in the area of hormonal biochemistry was the discovery of a cAMP-dependent protein kinase (26) that catalyzes the activation of skeletal muscle phosphorylase kinase. The finding of this enzyme led to the elucidation of an epinephrine-regulated glycogenolytic pathway (6). This scheme is depicted in Fig. 2.

The cAMP-dependent protein kinase not only phosphorylates the skeletal muscle phosphorylase kinase, but also phosphorylates casein and protamine, which indicates a broader specificity (26). Also, it activates the phosphorylation of both phosphorylase kinase and glycogen synthetase (27, 28). These latter investigations explained the earlier observations (29–32) that cAMP activates the phosphorylation of glycogen synthetase; evidently the effect of cAMP in each case occurred by the activation of cAMP-dependent protein kinase (33, 34).

It is now recognized, as originally shown (35), that cAMP-dependent protein kinase exists in two isoenzyme forms, called type I and type II and referred to here as cAMP-PK I and cAMP-PK II. They can be resolved by ion-exchange chromatography on DEAE-cellulose, eluting at pH 6.5 at conductivities of 2.5 mmho and 6.0 mmho, respectively (36). Their relative concentrations vary from tissue to tissue in a given species, and also from species to species for a given tissue. For example, in rabbit skeletal muscle, isozyme I is four times more abundant than isozyme II (35), whereas in rabbit heart, they are present in almost equal proportion (36). Cyclic-AMP-PK I accounts for some 80%

of the total kinase activity in rat and mouse hearts, whereas there is only type II in beef or guinea pig heart (37).

Immunologic data (38) suggest that cAMP-PK II may further be subclassified into two types, one present in nervous system and neuroendocrine cells and the other present in the nonneural tissues such as heart, liver, kidney, and skeletal muscle. Cyclic-AMP-PK I from brain and neuroendocrine tissues was 15- to 30-fold more potent than cAMP-PK II from nonneural tissues in displacing ^{125}I-labeled brain R-II from anti-brain R-II IgG.

A. Subunit Composition

The cAMP-dependent protein kinase from beef heart, appears to be composed of two subunits, a regulatory (R) and a catalytic (C) moiety; cAMP appears to bind to R, dissociating the inactive holoenzyme into R and C subunits (39). A similar conclusion was reached for the beef adrenal enzyme (40). Reticulocyte protein kinase (41) and liver holoenzyme (42) are dissociated by cAMP into catalytic and cyclic AMP-binding subunits. Skeletal muscle protein kinase (43) and beef heart protein kinase (44) also show complete dissociation of R from C in the presence of cAMP. All these studies establish that the holoenzyme of cAMP-dependent protein kinase comprises a regulatory subunit and a catalytic subunit, and offer a molecular mechanism by which cAMP acts in various cellular functions.

The first studies on the stoichiometry of R and C in the cAMP-dependent protein kinase yielded varying results. It was initially reported (45) that the molecular weight of adrenocortical protein kinase is 144,000, with the R subunit equivalent to 92,000 and the C subunit equivalent to 60,000. This suggested a one-to-one ratio of R and C. Similar results were obtained for reticulocyte protein kinase (41). In contrast, purified beef heart protein kinase displayed a molecular weight of 280,000 with R equal to 55,000 and C equal to 42,000, suggesting R_4C_2 as the subunit composition of the native enzyme (46). However, later studies on a similar enzyme indicated a molecular weight of 174,000, and it was proposed that the native holoenzyme contains four polypeptide chains, a dimer of R and two C monomers (47).

A homogeneous form of skeletal muscle protein kinase has a molecular weight of 170,000, and under denaturing conditions, the molecular weights of R subunit and C subunit are 48,000 and 41,000, respectively (48). Densitometer measurements of the resolved (dodecyl sulfate) R and C subunits indicated that the native enzyme consists of approximately equal amounts of R and C subunits.

In saturating concentrations of cAMP, the enzyme binds with two molecules of cAMP, one binding to each regulatory subunit (48). The net result is the dissociation of the catalytic monomers. The regulation of cAMP-dependent protein kinase by cAMP is depicted (48) as follows:

$$R_2C_2 + 2 \text{ cAMP} \rightleftharpoons R_2 \text{ (cAMP)}_2 + 2 \text{ C}$$

Independent studies (49–51) confirmed these results (48): one molecule of cAMP binds with each monomer of the regulatory subunit. In most studies, cAMP binding was measured by Millipore filtration (40, 52).

However, subsequent investigations (54, 55) demonstrate that the R subunit isolated from cAMP-PK II binds two moles of cAMP, corresponding to a stoichiometry of four cAMP molecules bound to the regulatory subunit dimer (R_2). Further, the monomer of cAMP-PK I isolated from rabbit skeletal muscle also binds two moles of cAMP (56), and studies (57) with the R subunit of bovine skeletal muscle cAMP-PK I have further corroborated these results (54, 55). The apparent discrepancy in the stoichiometry has been attributed (57) to the Millipore filter technique. Thus the stoichiometry depicted in the above equation should be modified to

$$R_2C_2 + 4 \text{ cAMP} \rightleftharpoons R_2 \text{ (cAMP)}_4 + 2 \text{ C}$$

B. Catalytic Subunits

1. COMPARISON OF cAMP-PK I AND cAMP-PK II CATALYTIC SUBUNITS

Homogeneous C subunits derived from cAMP-PK I and cAMP-PK II have the same molecular weights, varying from 37,000 to 42,000 (47, 51, 58–63). They also show identical isoelectric profiles (64) and are reported to be functionally (60, 64, 65) and structurally (66) similar. These results indicate that the C subunits of cAMP-PK I and cAMP-PK II are homologous.

Other characteristics of the C subunit of beef heart cAMP-PK II are that (a) none of the three sulfhydryl groups is obligatory for catalytic activity, although the second and third may contribute to it; (b) the molecule contains three cysteine residues, but none is involved in the catalytic activity of the enzyme (67). A frictional ratio (f/fo) of 1.19–1.23 has been calculated (61) for the C subunit of beef liver cAMP-PK II, indicating that the molecule is asymmetric. Circular-dichroic spectroscopy shows that the C subunit is comprised of 29% α-helical, 18% β-helical, and 53% aperiodic structure. The C subunit of rabbit skeletal muscle cAMP-PK I displays a frictional ratio of 1.30 (60), a volume close to that found for the type II C subunit (61).

Although the two types of C subunits of pig skeletal muscle have extensive similarities, they are not identical. Tryptic digestion of carboxymethylated C subunits yielded an acid peptide and several neutral peptides from the type II that were not detected in the corresponding map from the C subunit of type I (66). Similarly, some other peptides were found only in (digests of) type I C subunits. There were also some minor differences in the amino-acid composition of the two types of C subunits; type I C subunits contained 16.6 serine and 22.5 glycine residues, whereas type II subunits had 24.5 serine and 29.3 glycine residues. A similar amino-acid composition was previously reported for skeletal muscle (60) cAMP-PK I C subunit and for cardiac cAMP-PK II C subunit (67). The amino-terminal residue of type II beef heart C subunit is blocked (67), as are those of both type I and type II C subunits of pig skeletal muscle (66).

There are also minor differences between the isoelectric profiles of type I and type II C subunits. The homogeneous C subunit of rabbit skeletal muscle cAMP-PK I shows two pI peaks of 7.4 and 8.5 by isoelectric focusing (60). On the other hand, the C subunit of beef cAMP-PK II can be resolved into three major peaks corresponding to pI values of 7.78, 7.48, and 7.01 (67). The migration of the three isozymes was identical in dodecyl sulfate on polyacrylamide gels, indicating similar molecular weights. Hence, although the C subunits of cAMP-PK I and cAMP-PK II are similar, they are probably not identical. Comparison of the two types of C structures by amino-acid sequencing, or by physical techniques such as nuclear magnetic resonance spectroscopy and X-ray crystallography will ultimately establish the extent of their similarity.

2. PHOSPHORYLATION

The isolated C subunit of rabbit skeletal muscle cAMP-PK I contains an average of 2.2 moles of tightly bound phosphate per mole of protein (60). The phosphate bond was stable when the C subunit was treated with 16% trichloroacetic acid at 90° for 15 min or with 0.1 M HCl for 60 minutes. On the other hand, 0.1 M sodium hydroxide released 60% of the bound phosphate in 40 min at 90°. These data indicate that the endogenous phosphate of the C subunit is relatively acid-stable and alkali-labile. At least 60% of the phosphate occurs as O-phosphoserine or O-phosphothreonine in the enzyme subunit (60).

Alkaline phosphatase had no effect on the release of phosphate from the protein. No incorporation of ^{32}P into the protein in the presence of [γ-^{32}P]ATP and magnesium ions was observed, thus excluding self-phosphorylation of the C subunit. It was suggested that phosphorylation might occur during the synthesis of the C subunit polypeptide, and that, after assuming the native configuration, the phosphorylation site(s) are no longer available.

The type II C subunit of beef heart also contains 1.7 mole of acid-stable endogenous protein-bound phosphate, and the C subunit does not self-phosphorylate (67).

3. SELF-PHOSPHORYLATION

There is some evidence in favor of self-phosphorylation of the type I C subunit of rabbit skeletal muscle. A small but significant incorporation of ^{32}P occurs when C subunit is incubated with Mg^{2+} and [γ-^{32}P]ATP (68). When the C subunit was treated in advance with Escherichia coli phosphatase, there was 0.6 mole of phosphate incorporated into the enzyme per mole of subunit. The phosphorylated catalytic subunit did not transfer its phosphate to histone, a characteristic that distinguishes it from the phosphoenzyme intermediate in the kinase-catalyzed reaction. The phosphate bond was acid-stable and base-labile, a characteristic of a phosphoserine or phosphothreonine (68).

Threonine and serine are the phosphorylated sites in the C subunit of beef cardiac cAMP-PK II (69). The threonine site, located approximately 180 residues from the blocked amino terminus, contains one of the sulfhydryl groups in the sequence -Gly-Arg-Thr-Trp-Thr(P)-Leu-Cys-. The other phosphorylated site is located toward the carboxyl terminus in the sequence-Val-Ser(P)-Ile-Asn-, where the two cysteine residues reside. These two CNBr-cleaved fragments contain all the cysteine residues present in the C subunit. These observations indicate that the first phosphorylation occurs on a threonine residue one residue away from the first cysteine, and that the phosphoserine is located toward the carboxyl end of the molecule, where the other two cysteine residues reside.

The physiological significance of self-phosphorylation of the C subunit is not clear, but self-phosphorylation could play a role in determining its conformation.

4. PHOSPHOENZYME INTERMEDIATE

It has been reported (70, 71) that the C subunit of pig brain cAMP-dependent protein kinase can be phosphorylated in the presence of ATP and Mg^{2+} and that the phosphorylated residue is an acid-labile and base-stable N-phosphohistidine. It appeared that the phosphorylated C subunit is a phosphoenzyme intermediate of the phosphotransferase reaction, since the phosphate could be transferred to histone. These results (70, 71) are in apparent contrast to others (60, 67) that could not detect incorporation of phosphate from [γ-^{32}P]ATP into either type II C subunit or type I C subunit. The existence of a phosphoenzyme is therefore still an open question.

C. Regulatory Subunits

Although it is apparent that the C subunit of cAMP-PK I and cAMP-PK II are almost identical, there is strong evidence that the regulatory (R) subunits of the two types of isoenzymes are different. Evidently, the differences in the biological properties of the holoenzymes are attributed to the type of regulatory subunit in the holoenzyme. The two types of R subunits (R-I and R-II) can be distinguished from one another on the basis of their size, charge, binding affinity for MgATP, the property of phosphorylation, spectroscopic characteristics, fragmentation pattern, and distinct immunochemical characteristics.

1. SIZE AND CHARGE

Molecular weights of 48,000 for R-I and 55,000 for R-II from rabbit skeletal muscle and beef heart muscle, have been reported (46, 58), and 47,000 and 55,000, respectively for the pig R-I and R-II (66). Phosphorylation of the 55,000-dalton R-II subunit gave a molecular weight of 59,000 as determined by dodecyl sulfate/polyacrylamide gel electrophoresis, using Tris-glycine as a buffer (58). When the buffer was sodium phosphate, a molecular weight of 55,000 was observed. A change in apparent molecular weight from 54,000 to 56,000 upon phosphorylation of the R-II from beef heart muscle has also been observed (72). The R subunit of beef adrenal cortex is acidic with a pI of 4.5 (75a). The pI of the membrane R subunit beef cerebral cortex is 4.8, whereas that of R-II of calf brain and heart is 3.8 (51).

R-I and R-II also differ in molecular asymmetry, their frictional ratios being 1.47 and 1.67, respectively (66).

2. MgATP BINDING

The holoenzyme of cAMP-PK I has a MgATP binding site, but that of cAMP-PK II does not (see Section II,D,2). Isolated R-I, in contrast to the holoenzyme, binds neither ATP nor MgATP (48, 58).

3. AUTOPHOSPHORYLATION

In contrast to the R-I subunit, the R-II subunit in the intact holoenzyme can be self-phosphorylated (see Section II,D,3). However, the isolated R-II subunit does not possess this property (73).

4. SPECTROSCOPIC CHARACTERISTICS

A comparison of the spectroscopic characteristics of the cAMP binding sites of isolated R-I and R-II subunits, using the intrinsic tryptophan fluorescence and the fluorescent analog εcAMP as probes, not only provided evidence for differences between the R-I and R-II cAMP binding sites, but also showed the apparent nonidentical nature of the two cAMP-binding sites residing in R-I (74). Binding of cAMP to R-I caused a significant reduction in tryptophan fluorescence with a corresponding blue shift from 332 to 330 nm without affecting the fluorescence lifetime. Binding of εcAMP to R-I also caused a decrease in εcAMP fluorescence that was accompanied by a 20 nm shift. These observations indicate that one of the R-I cAMP binding sites contains a tryptophan residue. The binding of cAMP to R-II did not significantly affect the tryptophan fluorescence. In contrast, the binding of εcAMP to R-II gave a biphasic quenching of the ligand. These studies indicate that the two binding sites of cAMP in R-I are different. One of the sites apparently contains a tryptophan residue, while the other contains one or more of those amino acids, such as tyrosine, cysteine, or methionine, that quench εcAMP fluorescence. In contrast, none of the cAMP binding sites of R-II contains a tryptophan residue, although it may contain other amino acid residues that quench εcAMP fluorescence in both cAMP sites.

5. FRAGMENTATION PATTERN

Studies from various laboratories indicate that proteolysis of the native cAMP-PK yields regulatory subunit fragments that differ in size as well as in the capacity to bind cAMP and inhibit the catalytic activity (54, 75). Recently, fragmentation of R-I and R-II by specific proteolytic enzymes has been utilized to compare the structures of the two types of subunits. Such a study has not only provided some insight into the structural differences between the two types of subunits, but has also revealed the nature of certain relationships between the structural and functional domains of the two molecules.

Two-dimensional carboxymethylated tryptic maps of pig R-I and R-II, obtained by high-voltage paper electrophoresis in one dimension and by paper partition chomatography in the other dimension, were examined; the resolved peptides of the two proteins were non-superimposable, indicating a structural dissimilarity between the two subunits (66). The structural differences between the two molecules were further substantiated by the different amino-acid compositions obtained for the two molecules.

Isolated skeletal muscle R-I was trypsin-treated, and the peptide fragments were separated by Sephadex G-75 chromatography, yielding two major cAMP-binding peaks corresponding to 32,000 and 16,000 daltons (76). The 32,000-dalton fragment, further treated with trypsin, gave a 16,000-dalton cAMP-binding fragment, indicating that the origin of the 16,000-dalton peptide is the 32,000-dalton fragment. Hemin inhibited the binding of cAMP to both fragments.

Under similar restricted proteolysis, R-II from beef heart yielded three cAMP-binding fragments (76). The first peak contained aggregates of 39,000-dalton peptides; the second peak corresponded to the mass of a 15,000–16,000 fragment; and the third peak contained a single 14,000-dalton peptide. Further proteolysis of the 15,000- to 16,000-dalton peptide yielded the 14,000-dalton species. The masses of the 16,000- and 14,000-dalton fragments remained unchanged when these fragments were specifically labeled by a ^{32}P-containing photoaffinity probe, 8-azido-cAMP. The 14,000-dalton fragment, absent from the R-I proteolytic products, was not affected by hemin in its ability to bind to cAMP, in contrast to the 16,000-dalton R-I fragment. These facts agree with the conclusion that not only are the physical characteristics of the structural domains of R-I and R-II different, but also indicate that the natures of the cAMP-binding domains of the two types of proteins are distinct, although considerable homology between the two types of subunits exists.

All the fractions of the fragmented R-I and R-II fail to inhibit the catalytic activity of C (76). This is in contrast to the finding that a 10,000-dalton cAMP-binding fragment derived from the fragmentation of the liver enzyme inhibits the catalytic activity of C (75).

Thermolysin-treated pig R-I subunit yielded a 35,000-dalton fragment that bound cAMP and a 10,500-dalton fraction that did not (77). The larger fragment did not dimerize, but the smaller fragment was dimeric. The amino-terminal sequence of the 35,000-dalton fraction was Ile-Ser-Ala-Glu-Val-Tyr-Thr-Glu-Glu-Asp-(Ala)-Ala-X-Tyr-Val, corresponding to the carboxyl terminus of the original polypeptide chain.

Proteolytic cleavage of this same R-I with chymotrypsin yielded a 31,000-dalton peptide that bound cAMP and a 15,000-dalton peptide that did not. Proteolysis by trypsin yielded a 34,500-dalton fragment.

The fragments corresponding to 34,500 and 30,500 daltons bound cAMP, but the 11,000-dalton fragment did not. There was no major cAMP-binding fragment of mass less than 30,000 daltons (77). The smaller fragment did not come from further proteolysis of the 35,000-dalton fragment. On the other hand, the tryptic digestion of skeletal muscle R-I subunit results in 32,000-dalton and a 16,000-dalton fragments, both of which bind cAMP (76). The 16,000-dalton fragment came from the 32,000-dalton fragment. Both groups (76, 77) found no inhibition of the catalytic activity of C by any of the cAMP-binding fractions.

In summary, these studies indicate that (a) in both R-I and R-II the cAMP-binding domains reside in the carboxyl-terminus, while the amino terminus of the polypeptide chain is in part associated with the dimeric structure of the native regulatory subunits; (b) the functional domains in the native R-I and R-II that specify the inhibition of the catalytic activity of C are labile to proteolysis; (c) despite structural and functional similarities, the two types of subunits are structurally different and variations exist in their functional domains.

One of the major differences between the R-I and the R-II is that the native R-II of the holoenzyme serves as a substrate for phosphorylation catalyzed by the C subunit (5, 78, 79). The primary sequence of the major site of phosphorylation has been determined to be Asp-Arg-Arg-Val-Ser(P)-Val (5, 80).

When porcine R-II was autophosphorylated with $[\gamma\text{-}^{32}P]ATP$ by the C subunit and then cleaved by chymotrypsin, the 37,000-dalton fragment bound cAMP and retained ^{32}P (80). Gel filtration indicated that this fragment was monomeric. In contrast to the native R subunit, which could not be dansylated, Edman degradation of the dansylated 37,000-dalton fragment revealed that the phosphorylated residue was serine, and that it was the fifth amino-acid residue from the amino-terminal end of the proteolytic fragment. These studies thus indicate that the autophosphorylated site of R-II is close to the site sensitive to chymotrypsin, and that the dephosphorylated 37,000-dalton fragment can be phosphorylated by the C subunit. This last finding is interesting since the 37,000-dalton fragment cannot inhibit the catalytic activity of the C subunit (77).

Several studies indicated that the monomeric R binds two molecules of cAMP (54, 55, 57). Subsequently, the possibility was considered (81) that R-II may contain duplicate phosphorylation sites. Native beef heart R-II subunit was phosphorylated with catalytic C subunit in the presence of $[\gamma\text{-}^{32}P]ATP$. The phosphorylated subunit was treated with trypsin and the ^{32}P-labeled 39,000-dalton fragment was isolated and subjected to Edman degradation. The third residue from the amino terminus was found to be phosphorylated. This substantiates the conclusion (80) that the phosphorylated residue is proximal to the proteolytic labile site of the R subunit. The total amount of phosphate incorporated was two moles per mole of R monomer. In the native state, R contains as much as one mole of phosphate per mole of R subunit. There was evidence for the existence of two types of phosphorylated sites (81), the first preferentially phosphorylated at 0° and the second slowly at 30°. The possibility remains that the same serine in two conformations of the polypeptide is phosphorylated at different rates. In accordance with the earlier results (80), the 56,000-dalton native R-II subunit appeared to be a dimer, but the 39,000-dalton fragment was a monomer (81). These results support the earlier conclusion (80) that the structure necessary for the dimerization of the R subunit lies toward the amino-terminal end of the chain.

The inhibitory activity of the R subunit toward C was thermolabile at 60°C, and the site of R-II phosphorylatable by C was not (81). These observations distinguish the two sites of R-II: one binds cAMP and is proximal to the phosphorylation site, and the other inhibits the catalytic activity of C.

Based on these studies, a hypothetical model for the structure of cAMP-PK II R subunit has been proposed (81). According to this model, the R subunit is a dimer. Each monomer binds two molecules of cAMP and contains two phosphorylatable sites. Trypsin cleaves bonds between two arginines proximal to one of the phosphorylatable sites. The site of the second phosphorylatable site is arbitrary. Both phosphorylatable sites are located on the fragment that binds two cAMP-molecules.

Use of a specific photoaffinity probe, 8-azido-cAMP, which specifically binds to R, demonstrated that cAMP binds to the tyrosine in the sequence Lys-Arg-Asn-Ile-Ser-His-Tyr-Glu-Glu-Gln-Leu-Val-Lys-Hse (82).

6. IMMUNOCHEMICAL CHARACTERISTICS

Immunological studies with R-I and R-II provide additional evidence that these two subunits are distinct (83–85). In a radioimmunoassay for R-II, R-II competed for ^{125}I-R-II, but the DEAE-cellulose fraction containing partially purified cAMP-PK I did not, thus indicating that R-I and R-II are antigenically different. The possibility that R-II yielded R-I proteolytically and thus lost the antigenic sites (11) was ruled out by other studies (84).

With a high affinity antiserum against beef skeletal muscle R-I, it was demonstrated that R-II, up to 10,000-fold greater concentration, does not compete with ^{125}I-R-I (84). This indicates a clear immunological difference between R-I and R-II. Further, even R-II from the same species did not recognize sera against R-I.

Studies with beef R-I antisera showed that there is some cross-reactivity with protein kinases from rat tissue extracts, indicating some interspecies heterogeneity of R-I subunits (84). Despite this species-specific difference between the R-I subunits, these subunits possess considerable structural homology, as beef R-I antisera precipitates R-I subunits from crude rat extracts (84). One interesting feature of these studies is that one of the five antisera screened showed site-specific effects of cAMP and C subunit on the immunoreactivity of R-I. Addition of cAMP, or C subunit, to a concentration of 30 pM to 0.1 μM caused a significant decrease in the immunoreactivity of R-I, suggesting that binding of cAMP and C to R-I can block antigenic determinants, or change the conformation of the antigen (84).

D. Holoenzymes

In sections II, B and C, we discuss the evidence indicating that the C subunits of cAMP-PK I and cAMP-PK II are almost identical, but that the R subunits of the two types of holoenzymes are different. Although no functional difference in the physiological role of the two types of holoenzymes has yet been ascertained, it has been clearly demonstrated that the R subunits confer upon the holoenzyme the properties characteristic of a typical cAMP-PK I or cAMP-PK II. There are certain intriguing intrinsic features of the respective holoenzymes that are unique. Some of the salient characteristics of the two enzymes are that (a) the isolated R-II subunit does not self-phosphorylate, but does when a part of the holoenzyme, whereas type I holoenzyme does not autophosphorylate; (b) isolated R-I subunit has no affinity for MgATP, but the holoenzyme possesses a MgATP-binding site, whereas type II holoenzyme has no MgATP binding site; (c) high salt and histone favor the dissociation of cAMP-PK I to a greater extent than cAMP-PK II.

In this section I review briefly some of the characteristics of these holoenzymes.

Originally, it was observed that cAMP-dependent protein kinase exists in two principal forms, peak I and peak II (35, 86). On the basis of their different physical and kinetic characteristics, they were designated type I and type II isozymes (37, 87). Both types of holoenzymes are composed of two identical regulatory (R) subunits and two catalytic (C) subunits; the regulatory subunit complex exists as a dimer

(48). Cyclic AMP binds to the R subunit and dissociates it from the C subunit, which is the active form of the enzyme. The function of the R subunit is not only to act as a receptor for cAMP, but also to inhibit the C subunit in the absence of cAMP. The equation depicting the mode of regulation of the holoenzyme by cAMP has been discussed earlier (Section II,A).

1. SIZE AND PHYSICAL PROPERTIES

Since the only apparent difference in the tetrameric structure of cAMP-PK I and cAMP-PK II resides in the R subunit, the type II isozyme has a molecular weight approximately 14,000 greater than that of the type I isozyme (62). Both cAMP-PK I and cAMP-PK II enzymes are acidic, with pI values ranging from 4.6 to 5.1 (51, 63). Cyclic-AMP-PK I is invariably eluted before cAMP-PK II on an anion-exchange column, indicating a relatively more acidic nature of cAMP-PK II. Since C subunits of type I and type II enzymes are almost identical, the charge difference between R-I and R-II subunits also indicates a firmer binding of R-II than of R-I to C. The validity of this interpretation is reinforced by the findings (37, 87) that histone or 0.5 M NaCl dissociates cAMP-PK I but not cAMP-PK II. The reassociation of the dissociated R-I and C occurs more slowly than the reassociation of R-II and C subunits. Also, MgATP prevents the salt or histone-induced dissociation of the cAMP-PK I (87). One way of interpretating these results is that MgATP binds with the R-I subunit with a greater affinity and prevents the interaction of salt or histone with the R-I receptor site(s); however, other results (92) indicate that ATP binds only to the catalytic subunit (see next Section).

2. MgATP BINDING

MgATP reduces the affinity of partially purified cAMP-PK I enzyme for cAMP (88). The purified enzyme binds MgATP with high affinity, having a K_d of 35 nM (58). MgATP does not bind to cAMP-PK II (58) or to isolated R-I and R-II (48). The binding of MgATP to cAMP-PK I is different from that to C, where it serves as a substrate in the phosphotransferase reactions. The affinity of MgATP for C is relatively low with a K_m of 10 μM. The binding of MgATP to cAMP-PK I increases the apparent dissociation constant for cAMP 10- to 40-fold (89). Thus, MgATP promotes the association of R-I and C (48, 89). In summary, these results indicate that cAMP-PK I has a high-affinity binding site for ATP.

The activity of the cAMP-dependent kinase activity of the type I holoenzyme is modified by the binding of ATP; this occurs only in the holoenzyme, as the isolated subunits do not bind ATP with high affinity. Apparently ATP acts in a manner opposite to cAMP, as the former inhibits the dissociation of the enzyme. Two obvious questions arise. First, is the site of ATP binding the same as that of cAMP binding? Second, is there any relationship between the high-affinity ATP-binding site that resides in the cAMP-PK I and the phosphotransferase activity of the dissociated C subunit?

The first question was answered by a comparison of the cyclic AMP-binding and ATP binding maps, which showed no overlap of the two types of binding sites (90). This indicated that the sites of binding for cAMP and ATP are different. This conclusion was reinforced by the observation (90) that there is no direct competition between the two nucleotides.

The second question was approached by comparing the structural requirements of the ATP site in the holoenzyme with that in the catalytic subunit (91). Mapping experiments with analogs of ATP showed a remarkable similarity for both sites with respect to the adenine moiety, and it was suggested that ATP binding to the holoenzyme occurs via binding of the adenine moiety to the catalytic subunit. In further experiments (92), cAMP-PK I was labeled with 8-azido-[γ-^{32}P]ATP and then dissociated. All radioactivity was found in the C subunit, indicating that the ATP-binding site resides exclusively in the C subunit. The azido-ATP bound to the C subunit could donate the phosphate group to the substrate, histone. These observations indicate that ATP binds to a site in the C subunit, and, when bound to the holoenzyme, ATP inhibits the binding of cAMP to the R-I subunit, but upon dissociation of the holoenzyme, the bound ATP participates in the phosphotransferase reaction. It was suggested (92) that the high-affinity binding site of ATP might be located near the interface of the subunits. It was proposed (92a) that ATP causes a decrease in the dissociation of the holoenzyme into its subunits that in turn increases the K_d of cAMP and a decrease of the apparent cooperativity of cAMP binding to the holoenzyme. According to this proposal, R-I interacts with an ATP whose adenine moiety is bound to the C subunit. Such an interaction of ATP with the holoenzyme would result in a decrease in dissociation of the two subunits, R-I and C.

The overall interaction of MgATP and cAMP with cAMP-PK I is given in the following equation:

$$R_2C_2(MgATP)_2 + 4\ cAMP \rightleftharpoons R_2\ (cAMP)_4 + 2\ C + 2\ MgATP$$

This equation is slightly modified from that originally described (48) to take into account the recently revised stoichiometry of cAMP binding with the R subunit (54–57).

3. AUTOPHOSPHORYLATION

The original observation (78) that beef heart cAMP-PK-II phosphorylates itself, has been extended to type II enzymes of other tissues (51, 58). In contrast, cAMP-PK I does not autophosphorylate (58, 93). The substrate for this reaction is MgATP, and two moles of phosphate are donated by ATP to the R-II subunit (78). The phosphoenzyme can be dephosphorylated by phosphoprotein phosphatase (78) or by a reverse of the phosphotransferase reaction (73). The process of autophosphorylation appears to be predominantly intramolecular (94) at the level of the holoenzyme (73). However, there is some evidence for intermolecular self-phosphorylation, since native cAMP-PK II catalyzes the phosphorylation of its heat-denatured enzyme (49).

Phosphorylation of R-II decreases the rate of its association with C (95). This indicates that self-phosphorylation increases the sensitivity of the holoenzyme to dissociate in response to cyclic AMP. The phosphoenzyme has an altered binding affinity for cAMP as compared to the dephosphoform (58). On the other hand, there seems to be no difference in the affinity for cAMP between the phospho and dephospho state of the enzyme (73).

The physiological significance of the autophosphorylation of cAMP-PK II is not clear. The concentration of ATP in most tissues is in the millimolar range, whereas ATP required for self-phosphorylation is in the nanomolar range. This led to the conclusion (96) that the native state of cAMP-PK II is the phosphorylated form. It is, however, possible that under certain conditions such a phenomenon is physiologically relevant.

Initial studies (97) with cultured S49 lymphoma cells indicated that the R-I subunit serves as a substrate in the phosphotransferase reaction. Subsequent in vitro studies (98) demonstrated that cGMP-dependent protein kinase catalyzes the phosphorylation of the R-I subunit. This raised the possibility of in vivo phosphorylation of R-I. R-I, isolated from beef skeletal muscle is predominantly dephosphorylated whereas that from rat skeletal muscle is largely phosphorylated (99). When R-I from rat or beef skeletal muscle is phosphorylated in vitro by cGMP-dependent protein kinase, two moles of phosphate are incorporated per mole of monomer, indicating a total of four phosphorylated sites in the holoenzyme. Although earlier studies (78) indicated that the catalytic subunit phosphorylates one site on each R-II monomer, some preliminary observations (Huang and Krebs, unpublished; cf. 99) suggest that there may be an additional relatively inert phosphorylated site. Thus, it appears that both R-I and R-II may serve as self-substrates in the phosphotransferase reaction. The possibility exists that an as yet undescribed protein kinase can phosphorylate the R-I subunit of the holoenzyme *in vivo*. It is conceivable that the interaction of different kinases on each other's phosphorylated state plays an important role in their metabolic activities.

4. SUBSTRATE SPECIFICITY

Investigations from various laboratories indicate that cAMP-dependent protein kinase exhibits a broad specificity; the substrates used include casein (*100*), histones (*101–104*), protamine (*105*), phosphorylase kinase (*106*), glycogen synthase (*107, 108*), and pyruvate kinase (*109*) (for a review see ref. 5).

One of the most challenging problems in regulatory biology is to understand the nature of the factors that dictate the specificity of cAMP- dependent protein kinase. Many investigators have examined the nature of the specific substrates. An initial assumption was that the configuration of the protein substrate was an essential feature (*9, 110*). Denatured proteins are better substrates than their native forms (*111, 112*), and small peptides can also be phosphorylated (*113*). It became obvious that the primary, but not the tertiary, structure of the protein is an important factor in determining specificity.

To understand the principal elements that dictate substrate specificity, various investigators have used synthetic peptides as substrates for cAMP-dependent protein kinase. Such studies indicate that the principal determinants of substrate specificity reside in sequences adjacent to the phosphorylated residues (*100, 115–117*), and that in synthetic peptides, such as Leu-Arg-Arg-Ala-Ser-Leu-Gly (*115*) and Leu-Arg-Arg-Ala-Ser-Ala (*117*), the proximal arginine plays an important role in the phosphorylation of serine or threonine. Natural substrates studied thus far also contain one or more arginine residues close to the phosphorylated serine or threonine (*107*). Other investigations (*115, 117*) have also emphasized the important contribution of the two adjacent arginine residues to phosphorylation, and have led to the proposal (*106*) that two adjacent basic residues are required at the phosphorylation site. This hypothesis is consistent with the results of the studies obtained with synthetic peptide analogs of the pyruvate kinase phosphorylation site sequence (*115, 117*).

To date, there is strong evidence that the substrate specificity for protein kinase requires at least one arginine residue, but the argument that substrate specificity is absolutely determined by diarginyl residues or even by two basic residues may not be entirely valid. Other basic residues could substitute for the arginines, albeit less effectively (*115*). The diarginine-containing synthetic peptide Arg-Arg-Lys-Ala-Ser-Gly-Pro, corresponding to the phosphorylation site sequence around Ser-38 in histone H1 is a poorer substrate than the analog peptide of pyruvate kinase (118). Similarly, studies with a series of synthetic peptide analogs of the heart troponin inhibitory subunit, Arg_{12}-Pro-Ala-Ala-Val-Val-Arg_{18}-Arg-Ser_{20}-Asp_{21}-Arg_{22}-Ala, indicate that this peptide is a poor substrate compared to Leu-Arg-Arg-Ala-Ser-Leu-Gly or the carboxy-terminal analog of pyruvate kinase, indicating that the presence of multiple arginines is not the only criterion for the effective phosphorylation of a synthetic peptide substrate (119). In contrast, a peptide containing a single arginine (Lys-Arg-Lys-Gln-Ile-Ser-Val-Ala-Gly-Leu), is as good a substrate as the pyruvate kinase peptide (119). Thus, these studies raise the possibility that, in addition to a single arginine, some configurational arrangement of the protein substrate molecule, such as a β turn, is necessary (120).

To further assess the contribution of two arginine residues to the substrate specificity of cAMP-dependent protein kinase, a series of synthetic dodecapeptide analogs of the general structures, $(Gly)_x$-Arg-Arg-$(Gly)_y$Ala-Ser-Leu-Gly in which $x + y = 6$ was employed (121). Kinetic analysis indicated that the optimal substrate contains one amino-acid residue between the phosphorylated serine and the multiple basic residues. There was a marked increase in the apparent K_m or a decrease in V_{max}, or both, when the arginine residue was situated either immediately adjacent to the serine or separated by two or more residues. The position of the arginine residue in the synthetic peptide not only affected the kinetics of phosphorylation but also the binding characteristics of the peptide with the C subunit of protein kinase. The peptide having only one amino-acid residue between the serine and the basic residue had a much higher binding affinity than the one in which three residues separated the arginine and the serine. Also, the spatial arrangement of the -Arg-Arg-residue in relation to the serine phosphorylation site influenced greatly both the binding and the kinetic constants of the peptides (121). Thus, the specificity of the phorphorylation of serine is dependent on three factors: first, the presence of an arginine residue near the amino terminus of serine; second, the separation of arginine and serine by one amino acid; and third, the nature of the amino acids between the basic residues and the serine. The third criterion might be important with respect to the secondary structure of the substrates (120, 122).

5. MECHANISM OF ACTIVATION

According to one model (48), as modified (54), four molecules of cAMP bind to the R dimer, dissociating the inactive holoenzyme (R_2C_2) into a dimeric R_2cAMP complex and two C catalytic subunits

(Section II,A). It has been postulated on theoretical grounds that there are at least nine possible modes of interaction between cAMP and protein kinase (123). Currently, the following two models are being debated seriously. In view of the recent evidence that the R subunit of both cAMP-PK I and cAMP-PK II bind two moles of cAMP (54–57), we have postulated the interaction of four molecules of cAMP with the holoenzyme.

Model 1: $R_2C_2 \rightleftharpoons R_2 + 2 C \xrightleftharpoons{4\,cAMP} R_2cAMP_4$ (123–125)

Model 2: $R_2C_2 + 4\,cAMP \rightleftharpoons R_2cAMP_4 + 2 C$ (5, 126)

Equilibrium isotope exchange has been used to evaluate critically these two models with respect to the regulation of the holoenzyme by cAMP (127). MgATP and C markedly increased the rate of isotope exchange of [^{3}H]cAMP, with nonradioactive cAMP in the R_2 of protein kinase, leading to the postulate of the formation of the ternary complex, $R_2C_2cAMP_4$, and its dissociable species. Independent investigations (128, 129) also suggest a short-lived ternary complex between R, C, and cAMP. Thus, these studies favor Model 2 for the interaction between cAMP and protein kinase.

6. PROTEIN INHIBITORS

We have already discussed some of the factors that affect the activity of cAMP-PK I and cAMP-PK II isozymes. These included MgATP, salt, and histone for the type I enzyme and MgATP-catalyzed self-phosphorylation of the type II enzyme. In addition to these agents, there are several heat-stable endogenous protein inhibitors present in tissue that specifically inhibit the cAMP-dependent protein kinase activity. These inhibitors are potential regulators of the enzyme.

A heat-stable inhibitor protein specific for cAMP-dependent protein kinase has been isolated from rabbit skeletal muscle (130) and purified to homogeneity (131). The molecular weight of this preparation is 11,300 (131), in contrast to the values of 26,000 determined (130) for the partially purified enzyme, and half the value determined (132) for the protein kinase inhibitor isolated from beef heart.

It was originally found that the inhibitor suppressed the activity of protein kinase noncompetitively with respect to histone (133). With a homogeneous preparation, the cAMP-dependent protein kinase was inhibited competitively in a manner such that the inhibitor bound to the catalytic subunit ($K_i = 2 \times 10^{-9}$ M), and low concentrations of guanidine·HCl competitively inhibited the activity of the protein inhibitor at the catalytic site (131). The concentration of the inhibitor on a molar basis was 10 to 20% that of the kinase; thus, the inhibitor could at best block only 20% of the protein kinase activity. It is proposed (89) that the inhibitor binds the free C subunit, and that this could counteract the effect of the basal cAMP levels present in the tissues. The concentration of the inhibitor appears to change with physiological conditions (134–136). Testis has yielded another acidic inhibitor protein with a molecular weight of 26,100 (137) that, in contrast to the one isolated earlier (130), activates cAMP phosphodiesterase. Another heat-stable inhibitor has been purified some 1500-fold (138). It has a molecular weight of 15,000, inhibits cAMP-dependent, cGMP-dependent, and cyclic-nucleotide-independent protein kinase activities.

The presence of these endogenous inhibitors of protein kinase in tissues raises the possibility of a regulatory role for them in the expression of cyclic-nucleotide-dependent and cyclic-nucleotide-independent protein kinase activities.

III. Cyclic-GMP-Dependent Protein Kinase

The level of cGMP-dependent protein kinase in lobster muscle is comparable to that of cAMP-dependent protein kinase in various arthropods (139, 140). However, the fat bodies of silk-moth pupae and larvae contain exclusively cGMP-dependent protein kinase (140). Mammalian cGMP-dependent protein kinase was first identified in rat cerebellum (141). Other mammalian tissues that contain relatively high levels of cGMP activity are lung (142), femoral artery (143), and small intestine (144); to date, only the fetal and neonatal lung appear to contain more cGMP-dependent protein kinase than cAMP-dependent protein kinase (143).

The molecular weights of a homogenous cGMP-dependent protein kinase from beef lung are 145,000 to 165,000 (145–147) and 150,000 for the beef heart enzyme (148). All these values correspond well with the value of 140,000 originally reported for the cerebellum enzyme (149). The enzyme is composed of two equivalent subunits and has an isoelectric point of 5.7 (149). The molecule is highly asymmetric, with a frictional ratio of 1.42 and an axial ratio of 7.4 (150). The apparent activation K_a by cGMP is 1 to 9×10^{-8} M (145, 146, 151–153) and the reported K_m for ATP is 5–100 μM (150).

A. Subunit Composition

Early studies (154–159) indicated that cGMP binds to the holoenzyme and dissociates it into regulatory and catalytic subunits, a mechanism analogous to the activation of cAMP-dependent protein kinase. However, the activation of the enzyme does not involve dissociation of the enzyme into separate R and C subunits (152). Similar results were obtained for the enzyme isolated from lung (145, 146) and from beef adrenal cortex (153). Limited proteolysis of the enzyme yielded separate cGMP-binding and catalytic fragments (160), indicating that the two domains reside at different locations on the enzyme, but probably within the same polypeptide chain.

Investigations from various laboratories indicate that the enzyme binds with two molecules of cGMP, one binding with each subunit (145, 146, 148).

B. Autophosphorylation

Cyclic GMP-dependent protein kinase is capable of self-phosphorylation (147). One molecule of phosphate is incorporated into the serine residue of each subunit, thus accounting for two moles of phosphate for the holoenzyme (161). However, more recent studies (98) indicate that four moles of phosphate are incorporated per mole of holoenzyme, indicating an uptake of two moles of phosphate for each subunit of enzyme. The R-subunit of cAMP-PK I (98) or cGMP (147, 162) inhibits self-phosphorylation. Since the rate of phosphorylation is unaffected by dilution of the enzyme (161) but is inhibited by cGMP, an intramolecular rather than intermolecular mechanism was proposed (147, 161). An intermolecular mechanism may also operate, since the C subunit of cAMP-dependent protein kinase catalyzes the phosphorylation of cGMP-dependent protein kinase (161). Further, when a fully self-phosphorylated cGMP-dependent protein kinase was incubated with the C subunit of cAMP-dependent protein kinase, no additional uptake of phosphate by the enzyme was noted. These studies indicate that inter- and intramolecular phosphorylation take place at the same site of the enzyme. Arginine residues on the amino terminus side of the phosphorylatable serine appear to be essential for self-phosphorylation, since 2,3-butanedione inhibits this property of the enzyme (161).

The physiological significance of self-phosphorylation of cGMP-dependent protein kinase or of cAMP-PK II is unknown at this time. But, if the self-phosphorylation phenomenon plays a regulatory role in the protein kinase activity, the modes of control by this process of the two enzymes, cAMP-PK II and cGMP-dependent protein kinase, may be entirely different (98). This proposal is based on the premise that the phospho- and dephospho- forms of R-II have different binding affinities for cAMP (58) and for the catalytic subunit (73). In the case of cGMP-dependent protein kinase, the enzyme is not physically dissociated by interacting with cGMP. Although ATP reduces the binding affinity of cGMP for cGMP-dependent protein kinase, the effect is independent of self-phosphorylation (163).

C. Functional Domains

Partial proteolysis has been used to characterize the cGMP-binding, catalytic, and autophosphorylated domains of the cGMP-dependent protein kinase (162). Chymotrypsin- or trypsin-treated enzyme yielded a fragment corresponding to a molecular weight of 65,000 that contained both the catalytic and cGMP-binding domains. Another fragment of M_r 16,000 contained the ^{32}P originally incorporated into the holoenzyme in the self-phosphorylation reaction. These results clearly demonstrate that the holoenzyme consists of a self-phosphorylating domain distinct from the binding and catalytic domains. Taken together with the earlier studies (160) showing the separation of the catalytic fragment from the binding fragment, the proteolytic studies (163) indicate that the three functional domains of the enzyme—cGMP-binding, catalytic, and self-phosphorylating—are all separated from each other, but are located on the same polypeptide chain.

D. Substrate Specificity

The cGMP- and cAMP-dependent protein kinases phosphorylate the same serine hydroxyl groups in H1 histone (163a). The manner by which H2B histone is phosphorylated by the two kinases appears to be different. The cAMP-dependent protein kinase phosphorylated Ser-32 as well as Ser-36, whereas cGMP preferentially phosphorylated Ser-32 and only slightly Ser-36. A synthetic polypeptide corresponding to H2B gave essentially similar results: Ser-32 and Ser-36 were both phosphorylated by the two kinases, but their extent of phosphorylation was different (164, 165). Studies from many laboratories indicate that cGMP- and cAMP-dependent protein kinases can phosphorylate the same protein. Examples include cardiatroponin (166, 167), phosphorylase b kinase (168, 169), glycogen synthase (168), pyruvate kinase (168), the hormone-sensitive lipase (169), fructose 1,6-bisphosphatase (170), and cholesterol esterase (169). However, the structural determinants for the phosphorylation of serine are not necessarily similar for the two enzymes (168, 171, 164). The studies in general demonstrate that an arginine residue near the phosphorylatable serine is a good substrate for cGMP-dependent protein kinase, just as in the case of cAMP-dependent protein kinase. However, the shortest pyruvate kinase peptide phosphorylated by cGMP-dependent protein kinase was Arg-Arg-Ala-Ser-Val-Ala (171); this peptide contains one more amino acid than the minimal substrate phosphorylated by cAMP-dependent protein kinase.

Collectively, these studies suggest that although there is considerable similarity in the substrate specificities of the two kinases, the exact specificities are not identical. The latter view is further supported by the finding of a 23,000-dalton endogenous cerebellum peptide that is specifically phosphorylated by cGMP and by cGMP-dependent protein kinase, (172). Earlier studies with smooth muscle (173) and with brush border epithelium (174) also identified the substrates in the membranous fractions specific for cGMP-dependent protein kinase.

E. Mechanism of Activation

The preceding discussion of the cGMP-dependent protein kinase indicates that the enzyme (a) is dimeric; (b) is composed of two identical subunits; (c) is not dissociated into R and C subunits; and (d) binds two moles of cGMP per mole of holoenzyme. These characteristics of the enzyme led to the following proposal for the mechanism of activation by cGMP (168, 145):

$$(\text{cGMP-PK}) + 2 \text{ cGMP} \rightleftharpoons (\text{cGMP-PK})(\text{cGMP})_2$$
$$\text{(inactive)} \qquad\qquad \text{(active)}$$

where cGMP-PK is the cGMP-dependent protein kinase. The phosphate donor in this kinase reaction is ATP, and GTP cannot substitute for it (146).

F. Protein Modulator

A partially purified acid-stable, heat-labile modulator protein from lobster muscle stimulates cGMP-dependent protein kinase and inhibits cAMP-dependent protein kinase (174a, 174b). Subsequently, the modulator protein was isolated from mammalian tissues (175–177) and purified to homogeneity (175). It has a molecular weight of 34,000, an isoelectric point of 4.0 and is an asymmetric molecule with a frictional ratio of 2.27.

Earlier studies indicated an absolute requirement of the modulator for cGMP-dependent protein kinase (142, 176, 178). However, more recent studies from various laboratories conclude that the enzyme can be activated by cGMP without the addition of the modulator protein (146, 148, 152, 153, 179). The apparent discrepancy is probably due to differences in assay conditions. The earlier group (*142, 176, 178*) used submaximal concentrations of ATP and an arginine-rich histone as substrate. Other investigators used saturating concentrations of ATP and histone H2B, H1, or mixed histone. Indeed, it has been noted (*175*) that the modulator activates cGMP-dependent protein kinase only when histones are used as substrate.

G. Immunochemical Characteristics

The cGMP-dependent protein kinase is immunologically distinct from the regulatory subunits of cAMP-PK I, cAMP-PK II, and the C subunits of cAMP-dependent protein kinase (*180, 181*).

Antiserum against beef lung cGMP-dependent protein kinase showed undetectable cross-reactivity with beef heart C subunit of cAMP-dependent protein kinase and beef lung regulatory subunit of cAMP-PK I or beef heart cAMP-PK II. These observations are not in accord with the earlier observations (*150*) of a strong cross-reactivity of rabbit lung anti-cGMP-dependent protein kinase against beef lung regulatory subunit of cAMP-PK II, but no cross-reactivity with beef lung cAMP-PK I. It was concluded (*150*) that cGMP-dependent protein kinase and cAMP-PK II share certain common antigenic determinants.

IV. Structural Models of cGMP-Dependent and cAMP-Dependent Protein Kinases

Since cGMP-dependent protein kinase is similar to cAMP-dependent protein kinase, especially to cAMP-PK II, in many chemical and physical characteristics—such as molecular weight, asymmetry of the molecules, affinity for their respective cyclic nucleotides and for ATP, ability to autophosphorylate, similarity in amino-acid composition and substrate specificity—it has been proposed (*75a, 150, 167, 182*) that the two kinases are homologous proteins that have evolved from a common ancestral gene. Based on theories of protein evolution, two schemes, depicted in Fig. 3, have been proposed for the evolution of cGMP-dependent and cAMP-dependent protein kinases (*182, 183*). According to scheme A, the ancestral gene was a "cGMP-like kinase composed of a single type of subunit." A split in the gene yielded separate regulatory and catalytic genes coding for the R and C subunits of cAMP-dependent protein kinases. The cGMP-dependent kinase evolved as a dimer composed of two identical subunits. According to scheme B, the ancestral enzyme was "cAMP-like" and consisted of nonidentical subunits. Fusion of the regulatory and catalytic genes

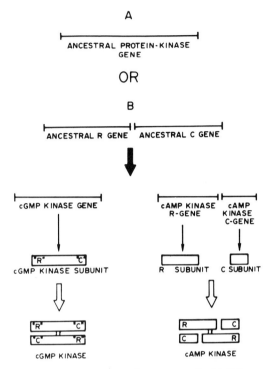

FIG. 3. Possible evolutionary schemes for cAMP and cGMP kinases. Adapted from Lincoln and Corbin (*182*).

yielded a single gene characteristic of a cGMP-dependent protein kinase gene. Favoring scheme A (*182*) is the fact that cGMP-dependent kinase is more abundant in arthropod tissues than in mammalian tissues (*139, 140, 152, 184*), and arthropods precede mammalian cells in evolutionary development.

Based on the concept of allosteric proteins (*185*), the structural model of cGMP-dependent protein kinase depicted in Fig. 4 was proposed (*75a*). According to this model, the enzyme is composed of two identical polypeptide chains associated with each other in antiparallel fashion. The configurational arrangement of the two symmetrical chains is such that the cGMP-receptor located on one chain interacts with the catalytic site of the opposite chain. Disulfide bonds hold the chains together so that binding of cGMP does not dissociate the enzyme into separate regulatory and catalytic subunits, but merely exposes the catalytic site. The structural similarities between the two proposed models of cGMP-dependent protein kinase and cAMP-

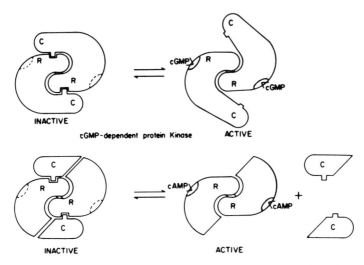

FIG. 4. Two-dimensional structural models of cGMP- and cAMP-dependent protein kinases. Adapted from Gill (75a).

dependent protein kinase are emphasized (75a). The cAMP-dependent protein kinase model contains discontinuous polypeptide chains also arranged in an antiparallel fashion (Fig. 4). The model predicts that the discontinuous chains, composed of R and C, could originate from proteolytic cleavage or from discontinuous synthesis. Such a model would postulate the dissociation of the enzyme into R and C, as is the case with the cAMP-dependent protein kinase.

The above models of cGMP-dependent and of cAMP-dependent protein kinases assume that the two are homologous proteins and have striking similarities in their physical and chemical characteristics. However, there are certain significant structural and catalytic dissimilarities between the two enzymes. The most obvious is the structure. Cyclic GMP-dependent protein kinase is a nondissociable enzyme, whereas cAMP-dependent protein kinase is dissociable. In regard to the differences in the catalytic properties of the two enzymes, cGMP-dependent protein kinase specifically phosphorylates certain endogenous substrates, and there is differential substrate specificity toward synthetic peptides and histone H2B of cAMP-dependent and cGMP-dependent protein kinases (165, 172–174, 186). Also, the stoichiometry of cGMP-binding to cGMP-dependent protein kinase is two moles of cGMP for one mole of enzyme (145, 146, 148), whereas four moles of cAMP bind one mole of cAMP-dependent protein kinase (54–57). Finally, there are distinct antigenic differences between cGMP- and cAMP-dependent kinases. Sera against cGMP-dependent protein kinase do not react with C or R subunits derived from cAMP-dependent protein kinase. Conversely, antisera against the R subunit of cAMP-PK I or cAMP-PK II did not cross-react with cGMP-dependent protein kinase (181). These results indicate that cGMP-dependent protein kinase has a physiological role distinct from cAMP-dependent protein kinase. Indeed, there is evidence that cGMP, presumably via cGMP-dependent protein kinase, mediates certain aspects of ACTH action related to the process of adrenal steroidogenesis (187). It is therefore quite likely that the hypothesis (40, 167, 182) that the cAMP- and cGMP-dependent protein kinases are homologous proteins that evolved from a common ancestral protein will have to be modified.

V. Biological Role of cAMP-Dependent and cGMP-Dependent Protein Kinases

Soon after the discovery (26) that cAMP-dependent protein kinase phosphorylates skeletal muscle phosphorylase kinase, a rate-limiting step in the breakdown of glycogen, it was proposed (188) that the physiological effects of cAMP are mediated by cAMP-dependent protein kinase. Although it is too early to evaluate the universal validity of this hypothesis, most, if not all, of the actions of cAMP known do appear to be mediated by cAMP-dependent protein kinase. In an extension of this hypothesis, it has been postulated (13) that phosphorylated proteins not only mediate the effects of cAMP but also certain effects of other regulatory agents, such as Ca^{2+}, cGMP, and the steroid hormones. This concept is illustrated in Fig. 5.

Since this review is concerned only with the mode of action by which cAMP and cGMP elicit their physiological responses, we have depicted in Fig. 6 the mechanism by which cAMP-dependent- and cGMP-dependent protein kinase may mediate the actions of the respective nucleotides. According to this scheme, phosphorylated proteins play a key role in mediating the effect of the protein kinase. The literature on the importance of phosphorylation-dephosphorylation in the control of key metabolic reactions has been reviewed (5).

Inasmuch as cAMP-dependent protein kinase has a broad substrate specificity *in vitro*, it is difficult to determine whether phosphorylation of a protein is related to a specific physiological activity of cAMP. Five criteria have been proposed (134, 189) to determine if a given physiological response to cAMP is mediated via phosphorylation of a protein. We extend the same criteria to the physiological response of cGMP.

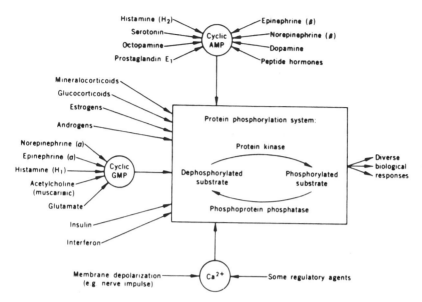

FIG. 5. Schematic diagram of postulated role played by protein phosphorylation in mediating some of the biological effects of a variety of regulatory agents. The diagram gives examples of regulatory agents, some of whose effects may be mediated through regulation of the phosphorylation of specific proteins, and is not intended to be complete. In addition to cAMP and a variety of neurotransmitters and hormones whose effects are mediated through cAMP, these regulatory agents include cGMP, Ca^{2+}, and agents whose effects are mediated through Ca^{2+}, as well as several classes of steroid hormones, insulin, and interferon. For brevity, the numerous peptide hormones whose effects are known to be mediated through cAMP, and the various regulatory agents believed to act through translocation of Ca^{2+} are not listed individually. It seems likely that some, but not necessarily all, of the biological responses elicited by any given regulatory agent are mediated through the protein phosphorylation system; for simplicity, pathways from regulatory agent to biological response that do not involve protein phosphorylation are not shown. From Greengard (13).

These criteria are as follows:

1. The cell contains the cyclic-nucleotide-dependent protein kinase, which catalyzes the phosphorylation *in vitro* of a specific protein that bears a biological relationship to the cyclic nucleotide process.

2. *In vitro* phosphorylation of the protein alters its function.

3. There is a stoichiometric relationship between *in vitro* phosphorylation and the modified function.

4. The cyclic nucleotide phosphorylates the protein substrate *in vivo*.

5. The cyclic nucleotide exerts the physiological function *in vivo*.

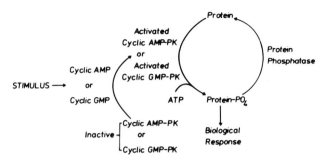

FIG. 6. A schematic diagram illustrating a general mechanism by which a stimulus signal is translated into a physiological response. This model postulates that those hormones that propagate their signal by cAMP or cGMP do so by the activation of their respective protein kinases.

To date, the only protein that satisfies all these criteria is phosphorylase kinase, a key enzyme in glycogen degradation.

It is beyond the scope of this review to catalog all the proteins that are phosphorylated by cAMP-dependent protein kinase *in vitro* and *in vivo*. The reader is referred to other reviews on this subject (*3, 5, 7, 11, 13*). However, we have chosen three different biological systems in which a considerable amount of work has been done to evaluate the mediatory role of cAMP, presumably via cAMP-dependent protein kinase, in translating the hormonal signal into the biological response. Skeletal muscle, adrenal cortex, and reticulocytes represent a nonendocrine system, an endocrine system, and a simplified translation control system, respectively. We summarize very briefly the present state of knowledge in these systems.

A. Skeletal Muscle Phosphorylase Kinase and Glycogen Synthase

Phosphorylase kinase has a molecular weight between 1.28 and 1.33×10^6 (*191, 192*), and is composed of four subunits α, β, γ, δ. The molecular weights reported for the subunits are: $\alpha = 118,000$ (*192*), 136,000 (*193, 194*), and 145,000 (*191*); $\beta = 108,000$ (*192*), 120,000 (*193, 194*), 128,000 (*191*); $\gamma = 42,000$ (*193, 194*) and 41,000 (*191, 192*); $\delta = 17,000$ (*195*). The δ subunit is identical to calmodulin (*196, 197*). The stoichiometry of the subunit composition is (a, β, γ)$_4$. The stoichiometry of the δ subunit appears to be 0.70 mole of δ per mole of α, β, or γ subunit (*195*).

Skeletal muscle phosphorylase kinase is stimulated by cAMP (*197a*). The activation of the enzyme is related to its phosphorylation

(*198, 199*). The discovery of cAMP-dependent protein kinase and the demonstration that phosphorylase kinase is its substrate (*26*) represents a landmark in the recognition that the physiological role of cAMP is exerted via the cAMP-dependent protein kinase. The cAMP-dependent protein kinase also catalyzes the phosphorylation of glycogen synthase. Unlike phosphorylase kinase, phosphorylation of glycogen synthase inactivates it (*200*). Thus, the cAMP-dependent protein kinase initiates the breakdown of glycogen and simultaneously stops its synthesis.

As mentioned earlier, phosphorylase kinase is the only protein that meets all the criteria (*189*) to qualify as a phosphoprotein that mediates the hormonally induced biological response. Below are summarized the reasons for accepting this unique qualification of this protein.

1. The cAMP-dependent protein kinase phosphorylates phosphorylase kinase, *in vitro* (*200a*).
2. The *in vitro* phosphorylation of the protein is associated with altered function, i.e., in an increased activity (*200a*).
3. There is a stoichiometric relationship between *in vitro* phosphorylation of the enzyme and increased activity (modified function) (*200a*).
4 and 5. Administration of epinephrine causes an increment of cAMP *in vivo* that is associated with the activation of phosphorylase kinase, and in an increase in the level of phosphorylase kinase activity (*201, 202*). Activation of phosphorylation *in vivo* occurs as a result of phosphorylation catalyzed by cAMP-dependent protein kinase; in addition, the phosphorylated sites of the enzyme are identical to those obtained *in vitro* (*203*).

More recently, a new set of criteria for an enzyme that undergoes biologically significant phosphorylation-dephosphorylation has been proposed, as quoted below (*5*).

1. Demonstration *in vitro* that the enzyme can be phosphorylated stoichiometrically at a significant rate in a reaction catalyzed by appropriate protein kinase(s).
2. Demonstration that functional properties of the enzyme undergo meaningful changes that correlate with the degree of phosphorylation.
3. Demonstration that the enzyme can be phosphorylated and dephosphorylated *in vivo* or in an intact cell system with functional changes.

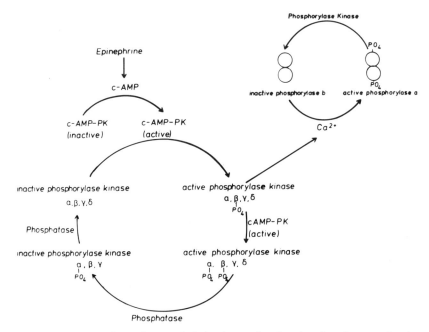

FIG. 7. Hormonal regulation of skeletal muscle phosphorylase kinase via phosphorylation → dephosphorylation enzymic reactions.

4. Correlation of cellular levels of protein kinase and/or phosphoprotein phosphatase effectors and the extent of phosphorylation of the enzyme.

Figure 7 illustrates in a simplified manner the purported mode of hormonal regulation of phosphorylase kinase. However, it is to be noted that the molecular mechanisms involved in the regulation of the phosphorylase kinase are complex and need further clarification. The figure depicts that the increment of cAMP in response to epinephrine stimulus activates the cAMP-dependent protein kinase. No distinction has been made as to which of the protein kinases, cAMP-PK I or cAMP-PK II, is activated by cAMP. The activated kinase selectively phosphorylates the β subunit and then the α subunit (204). It is proposed (205) that phosphorylation of the α subunit is essential for the subsequent dephosphorylation of the β subunit, which in turn results in the inactivation of the enzyme. Dephosphorylation of the β subunit is achieved by a general phosphoprotein phosphatase. A time interval between the phosphorylation of the β subunit and of the α subunit is required for the activation of phosphorylase b to a. Dephosphorylation of the α subunit occurs by a specific α-phosphorylase kinase phosphatase (206).

The activated phosphorylase kinase specifically catalyzes phosphorylation of the serine residue of phosphorylase b, thus converting it to active phosphorylase a. Dephosphorylation of phosphorylase a by a phosphoprotein phosphatase returns the enzyme to the b form.

Phosphorylase kinase activity is also regulated by Ca^{2+}, mediated through the δ subunit, calmodulin (207). This may explain how α-adrenergic stimulation of hepatic glycogenolysis is related to the influx of Ca^{2+}, which then activates phosphorylase kinase independently of cAMP (208–211).

Figure 8 depicts the regulation of glycogen synthase; it summarizes the findings of several investigators (33, 211–215). (For reviews on this topic the reader is referred to 11, 191, 216, 217.) It is noteworthy that regulation of glycogen synthase is complex and involves both cAMP-dependent and -independent protein kinases.

As an added complexity, it is now recognized that phosphorylase kinase, a calcium-sensitive enzyme (207), phosphorylates glycogen synthase in a calcium-dependent manner (216, 218–221). There is also a calmodulin-dependent glycogen synthase kinase in liver (222). This opens up the possibility of α-adrenergic inactivation of glycogen synthase (223) via a calcium-mediated process (224). The enzyme is phosphorylated at several sites. Therefore, it should be recognized that Fig. 8 is a very much simplified illustration of the factors involved in the regulation of glycogen synthase.

Figure 8 illustrates that the active glycogen synthase a can be con-

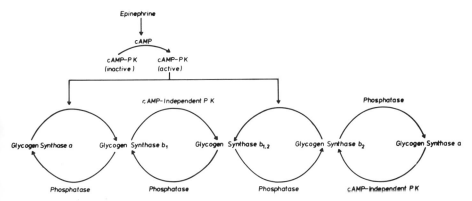

FIG. 8. Hormonal regulation of glycogen synthase via phosphorylation/dephosphorylation enzymic reactions.

verted to the partially inactive forms (glycogen synthase b_1 or glycogen synthase b_2) by the cAMP-dependent and cAMP-independent protein kinases, respectively. The only difference between the two partially inactive forms b_1 and b_2 is their site of phosphorylation. The cAMP-independent and cAMP-dependent protein kinases catalyze the transformation of glycogen synthase b_1 and glycogen synthase b_2, respectively, to the inactive diphosphorylated glycogen synthase $b_{1,2}$.

The essential feature of the regulation of activity of glycogen synthase is its phosphorylated or nonphosphorylated state, implying that phosphoprotein phosphatase plays an essential role. Hutson *et al.* (*223a*) reported that both forms of muscle glycogen synthase, b_1 or b_2, dephosphorylate at a slow rate, and phosphorylation at site b_1 enhances the rate of dephosphorylation at site b_2 by phosphoprotein phosphatase.

B. Adrenocortical Steroid Metabolism

Liver and the adrenal gland are the two tissues in which the original studies were conducted that led Sutherland to formulate the "Second Messenger" concept of cAMP for hormonal action. In the preceding section, I discussed the almost perfect correlation of the predictions of this hypothesis with the results in the regulation of skeletal muscle phosphorylase kinase, the enzyme that controls glycogenolysis. In this section, I review very briefly the applicability of the concept to the regulation of adrenal steroidogenesis. I hope that this discussion will serve as a model to evaluate the concept in other endocrine systems. The reader is referred to excellent reviews for details (*225–228*). These reviews have concentrated on the mediatory role of cAMP in adrenal steroidogenesis. For contrasting ideas that emphasize the discrepancies of the data concerning the role of cAMP in the regulation of adrenal steroidogenesis, the reader is referred to another review (*229*).

ACTH is a pituitary polypeptide hormone that regulates the rate of secretion of corticosteroids in the adrenal cortex. Despite rapid advances in our understanding of the control processes in this gland, the critical question of how ACTH triggers steroidogenesis is still unanswered.

Since the original discovery (*21*) that cAMP mediates the actions of some hormones, the intermediary role of this agent as a second messenger in the regulation of adrenal steroidogenesis has been under continued investigation. The criteria for acceptance of a second-messenger role for cAMP in adrenal steroidogenesis are the following:

1. ACTH activates adenylate cyclase *in vitro*.
2. ACTH increases the concentration of cAMP in the adrenal cell,

which in turn increases an endogenous cAMP-dependent protein kinase.

3. Exogenous cAMP stimulates endogenous protein kinase and steroidogenesis.

4. Cyclic nucleotide phosphodiesterase inhibitors potentiate the steroidogenic response to submaximal concentrations of ACTH.

In addition to satisfying these criteria, the additional criteria (in Section V,A) (189) regarding phosphoprotein as a mediator for cAMP-dependent protein kinase should also be considered.

After the demonstration that ACTH increases cAMP levels in beef adrenal cortex slices (230), it was proposed (231) that cAMP is the mediator of ACTH in adrenal steroidogenesis. Subsequent studies from various laboratories provided evidence that this view does not meet the criteria for the second messenger concept (for a review, see 229). Briefly, in an isolated adrenal cell, this evidence includes the following points.

1. There is a marked dissociation between corticosterone stimulation by low ACTH concentrations and cAMP production (232–238).

2. Exogenous cAMP, in concentrations of less than 100 μM, does not stimulate steroidogenesis, but stimulates endogenous protein kinase in a typical concentration-dependent manner (239), demonstrating a dissociation of cAMP-dependent protein kinase from corticosterone synthesis.

3. Exogenous concentrations of cAMP of less than 100 μM do not stimulate steroidogenosis, whereas the endogenous rise in cAMP in response to even supramaximal steroidogenic concentrations of ACTH ranges only from 100 to 300 nm (232), which indicates that the level of exogenous cAMP required for maximal steroidogenic activity is at least 1000-fold greater than what is endogenously elevated by a maximal steroidogenic concentration of ACTH.

4. The phosphodiesterase inhibitors, caffeine and theophylline, instead of potentiating ACTH-induced steroidogenesis, markedly inhibit ACTH-stimulated corticosterone formation and also block the cAMP-induced steroidogenesis (240, 241). On the other hand, 3-isobutyl-1-methylxanthine, a phosphodiesterase inhibitor ten times more potent than theophylline, potentiates the ACTH-induced accumulation of cAMP and corticosterone *in vitro* and *in vivo* (242). However, the concentrations of ACTH used in these studies were pharmacological.

5. A direct effect of cAMP-dependent protein kinase on the phosphorylation of a specific protein that regulates steroidogenesis has not been demonstrated.

6. Comparative studies with isolated adrenocortical carcinoma and normal adrenal cells clearly demonstrate that certain actions of ACTH are independent of cAMP (243, 243a). These neoplastic cells do not respond to ACTH or cAMP in stimulating corticosterone synthesis (for a review, see 229), but respond with respect to other biochemical parameters to both ACTH and cAMP. Some of the ACTH-dependent processes are mediated by cAMP and some are independent of the nucleotide, indicating that cAMP is not the sole mediator of ACTH.

7. Studies with isolated adrenal cells demonstrate that high concentrations of Ca^{2+} increase cAMP levels but do not stimulate the formation of corticosterone, indicating independence of the production of corticosterone and the formation of cAMP (237).

8. $ACTH_{5-24}$ at low concentration stimulates steroidogenesis without causing an increment in cAMP in isolated adrenal cells (281a). The rise in cAMP only occurs at a peptide-hormone concentration more than 100-fold higher than that required for stimulation of steroidogenesis, indicating again that cAMP at low steroidogenic concentrations of ACTH is not the mediator of adrenocortical steroidogenesis.

These arguments against the notion that cAMP is an obligatory second messenger in adrenal steroidogenesis appear strong, but they are not conclusive.

Attempts have been made to resolve the dissociation of adrenal steroidogenesis from cAMP formation by quantitation of free cAMP and cAMP bound to its receptor, presumably the regulatory subunit of cAMP-dependent protein kinase (244, 245). ACTH at 10^{-12} to 10^{-10} M increased the formation of corticosterone with a concomitant rise of receptor bound, intracellular bound, and extracellular cAMP. The free receptor sites for cAMP, measured by [³H]cAMP binding, decreased with an increase of the endogenous cAMP induced by ACTH. These results apparently satisfy the criterion that submaximal steroidogenic concentrations of ACTH elevate cAMP.

However, there was no rise in intracellular or bound cAMP in response to half-maximal steroidogenic concentration of ACTH (10^{-10} M) in the freshly prepared adrenal cells (244); in fact, between 2 and 15 minutes, there was actually a decline of cAMP and an increased production of corticosterone. After two hours, there was a 20-fold increase in steroid production, but no rise of cAMP. These results, therefore, demonstrate a dissociation between cAMP formation and corticosterone production. There also remain some problems with the cAMP data obtained on previously incubated adrenal cells in response to the low concentration of ACTH (10^{-10} M). The extracellular, intracellular, and receptor-bound rise at 30- and 60-minute intervals was only marginal.

The procedures used in support of the idea of an association of cAMP with the submaximal steroidogenic concentrations of ACTH (245) differ in two significant respects from those that also showed association (244). In the former, the cells were not incubated in advance to show a rise in cAMP, whereas in the latter, it was necessary to incubate the adrenal cells before any rise in cAMP could be demonstrated. Furthermore, the latter did not find it essential to add the phosphodiesterase inhibitor, 3-isobutyl-1-methylxanthine ("IBMX") to demonstrate an ACTH-activated rise of cAMP, but the former (245) found that, when the cells were incubated with the inhibitor in the presence of ACTH, the increment of cAMP was greater than that in cells incubated without it. Other than these differences, the extrapolation of the data (Figs. 1 and 2 of ref. 245) shows that the pattern of rise of cAMP to submaximal steroidogenic ACTH concentrations is similar to that found by both laboratories (244, 245). There is only a marginal rise in the cAMP level in response to near-maximal (1.34×10^{-12} M) or less than half-maximal steroidogenic ACTH concentration. As little as 4×10^{-13} M ACTH elicited steroidogeneis in isolated adrenal cells (245). Without the xanthine inhibitor, the half-maximal steroidogenic concentration of ACTH was 3×10^{-12} M, and again, extrapolation of the data shows that there was neither an extracellular nor an intracellular change of cAMP in response to this concentration of the hormone. Similarly, only very marginal changes were found in receptor-bound cAMP, from 72 to 80 femtomoles, in response to the half-maximal steroidogenic concentration of ACTH (1.3×10^{-12} M ACTH). It is to be noted that the cell yield from one adrenal gland was not given, but 10^5 cells were incubated and maximal steroidogenesis was obtained with 9×10^{-12} M ACTH (a rise of 5 to 85 ng of corticosterone per 10^5 cells in the presence of the xanthine inhibitor (245). The half-maximal steroidogenic ACTH concentration (1.3×10^{-12} M) caused a rise of 17 to 37 ng of corticosterone per 10^5 cells. If no inhibitor was added to the cells, the half-maximal and maximal steroidogenic concentrations of ACTH were 3×10^{-12} and 9×10^{-12} M, respectively. Similarly, extrapolation of the data (Fig. 2 of ref. 245) on the time course of formation of cAMP indicates again a marginal rise, if any, of receptor-bound cAMP.

In contrast to the above, other investigators (246) did not find a significant rise in the extracellular, intracellular, or receptor-bound cAMP at 5-, 10-, 30-, and 60-minute time intervals in response to submaximal steroidogenic concentration of ACTH (7×10^{-12} M). There was also no change in the free receptor sites for cAMP with increasing concentrations of ACTH. In addition, low steroidogenic concentrations of ACTH do not activate adenylate cyclase in particulate adrenal fraction (247, 247a). These critical questions should be resolved before the obligatory mediatory role of cAMP to the physiological levels of ACTH in adrenal steroidogenesis is completely accepted.

C. Regulation of Protein Synthesis

The studies with reticulocyte lysates indicate that heme deficiency and double-stranded RNA (dsRNA) inhibit the activation of protein synthesis (248–252). Thus, reticulocytes, which are nonnucleated, require hemin for the synthesis of globin. There is strong evidence that inhibition in protein synthesis is due to the activation of a cyclic-nucleotide-independent protein kinase, called "heme-controlled repressor" (HCR), that catalyzes the phosphorylation of the α-subunit of the initiation factor eIF-2 (253–259). The phosphorylated eIF-2α does not form a ternary complex with GTP and formylmethionine transfer RNA, thus preventing the interaction of the ternary complex with 40 S ribosomal subunit and the initiation of protein synthesis (260–265). It has been proposed (266, 267) that the mechanism by which hemin regulates the synthesis of globin is that hemin interferes with the binding of cAMP to cAMP-dependent protein kinase, thus preventing the activation of cAMP-dependent protein kinase. As a consequence, HCR will not be activated, the phosphorylation of eIF-2α will cease, and the initiation of protein synthesis will continue. The scheme illustrated in Fig. 9 depicts this type of control in the regulation of globin synthesis in reticulocytes (268). This attractive hypothesis rationalized the mechanism by which cAMP-dependent protein kinase indirectly controls the translation of globin synthesis.

The heme-controlled repressor (HCR) has been highly purified (253–257, 270); it has a molecular weight of 150,000 in dextran gels, but migrates as a 80,000-dalton protein in dodecylsulfate/polyacrylamide gels (271). On the other hand, a molecular weight of 250,000 to 300,000 and a subunit molecular weight of 90,000 have been observed (272). The enzyme phosphorylates itself and also catalyzes the phosphorylation of the α-subunit (270, 273). Hemin inhibits the self-phosphorylation as well as the phosphorylation of eIF-2α (270, 272, 273). Although HRI and dsRNA-activated inhibitor (dsRI) catalyze the phosphorylation of the same site of purified eIF-2α in vitro (256, 274, 275), physiological and immunological criteria indicate that dsRI and HRI are different molecular entities (276). The phosphorylation and activation of HRI seems not to be mediated by a

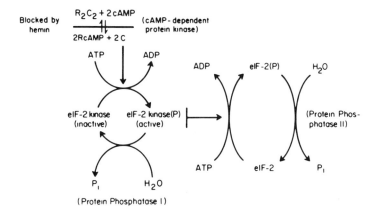

FIG. 9. A model for the regulation of eIF-2 phosphorylation in reticulocytes. From Ochoa and De Haro (*268*).

cAMP-dependent protein kinase (*273, 277*), in contrast to the findings of others (*266, 267*). It therefore appears that the hypothesis depicted in Fig. 9 regarding the control of protein synthesis via cAMP-dependent protein kinase deserves further scrutiny.

A cyclic-nucleotide-independent protein kinase, PK 380, from adrenal cortex has a molecular weight of 380,000 and specifically phosphorylates eIF-2α (*278*). The initial evidence indicates that PK 380 is different from HCR and dsRI (*279*) in that PK 380, but not HCR (*273, 277*), depends on sulfhydryl groups for activity (*279*). The dsRNA-activated inhibitor (dsRI) also phosphorylates histone (*280*); PK 380, on the other hand, does not catalyze the phosphorylation of histone (*278*).

Evidence has been adduced for the presence of an endogenous substrate for a cAMP-dependent protein kinase associated with polyadenylated messenger ribonucleoproteins of adrenal cortex (*280a*). It is anticipated that future studies with purified kinases will clarify the biological roles of cyclic-nucleotide-dependent and -independent protein kinases that control synthesis in eukaryotic cells.

D. Nuclear Translocation of cAMP-Dependent Protein Kinase

Initial studies from several laboratories indicate that the increment in the levels of cAMP in response to hormones (including catecholamines) accompanied translocation of cAMP-dependent protein kinase from the cytoplasm to the nuclei (*281–284*). Such a phenomenon has important biological implications as to how cAMP may control nuclear events. These observations give credence to the original discovery that nuclear proteins serve as substrates for cAMP-dependent protein kinase (27). Subsequently, several investigators demonstrated that phosphorylation of nuclear proteins modifies their regulatory activity (285–289). This indicated that nuclear events mediated by a phosphoprotein could be terminated by a phosphoprotein phosphatase. In support of such a mechanism, it has been shown (290) that nonhistone phosphoprotein phosphatase dephosphorylates the nonhistone phosphorylated protein and specifically alters the patterns of gene transcription in reconstituted chromatin (290). Thus there is a rationale for the proposal that gene expression in eukaryotic cells is regulated by cAMP-dependent protein kinase.

It is not the purpose of this review to cover the comprehensive literature on this topic. The reader is referred to several excellent reviews (291–294). We will only summarize very briefly the experimental studies that have led to the concept of the translocation of cAMP-dependent protein kinase from cytoplasm to nucleus in response to certain hormones, and then briefly describe the hypotheses concerning the mechanisms by which this may take place. Hormones that increase liver cAMP and induce liver enzymes also catalyze the phosphorylation of histones (295, 296). This finding provides a basis for the view that cAMP-dependent protein phosphorylation in the nucleus is important in transcriptional control. Subsequently it was shown (282, 297, 298) that hypophysectomized rats treated with gonadotropin specifically bind cAMP-binding protein and the C subunit to certain chromatin sites. A similar effect is obtained when neonatal pig ovaries are incubated with 8-(p-chlorophenyl)thio-cAMP. A correlation exists between the increase of cAMP, the activation of cAMP-dependent protein kinase, nuclear translocation of the catalytic subunit, activation of RNA synthesis, and transynaptic induction of tyrosine hydroxylase (281, 299–302). The cAMP-mediated translocation of protein kinase into the nucleus might play an important role in the induction of ornithine decarboxylase (303, 304). When rat liver is perfused with glucagon or dibutyryl cAMP, the major portion of the catalytic activity of protein kinase is isolated with a nuclear fraction (283, 284). Since the isolated nuclei as such contain no intrinsic cAMP-dependent protein kinase activity, the possibility arose that the nuclear translocation of protein kinase is cAMP-mediated step (291, 297, 305–307). According to this proposal, cAMP in the cytoplasm binds to the cAMP-dependent protein kinase, causing the holoenzyme to dissociate into regulatory and catalytic subunits; the dissociated subunits are then individually translocated into the nucleus (293). This proposal differs from the one (283, 284) that favors nuclear translocation of the catalytic subunit only (7). The nuclear translocation of the holoenzyme has been considered (291) an improbable event, since in any cAMP-mediated event the production of cAMP at the plasma membrane followed by activation of cAMP-dependent protein kinase would require the dissociation of the enzyme into its subunits in the cytoplasmic fraction of the cell.

Direct evidence for the penetration of the cAMP-bound regulatory subunit across the nuclear membrane comes from studies using a dimethylbenzanthracene-induced mammary tumor cell system, which also indicated phosphorylation of a 76,000-dalton protein in the nucleus (308). This phosphorylation presumably was brought about by the catalytic subunit of the cAMP-dependent protein kinase. In addition, these studies showed that when the tumor nuclei were incubated with cAMP-dependent protein kinase type II holoenzyme, there was incorporation of a cAMP-binding regulatory subunit corresponding to a 56,000-dalton protein and the phosphorylation of a 76,000-dalton nuclear protein substrate. In contrast, there was no phosphorylation of the nuclear protein substrate when the nuclei were incubated only with the catalytic subunit of the cAMP-dependent protein kinase (308). From these observations, it was concluded that the protein kinase catalytic subunit cannot penetrate the nucleus by itself, and it was suggested that an "activated" holoenzyme is formed that is then able to penetrate the nucleus. This hypothesis is depicted in Fig. 10 (309). It was proposed that the formation of such a complex depends on the temperature and on the cAMP concentration; it would be possible at the physiological levels of cAMP, which were considered to be between 10^{-9} to 10^{-6} M (309). The essential feature of this hypothesis is that the "cAMP receptor protein (presumably type II regulatory subunit) that can penetrate into the nucleus must have two functional domains; one for the cAMP binding and the other for an interaction with the catalytic substrate of protein kinase. The activated tertiary complex may then bind to the nuclear acceptor sites through its R subunit; then, owing to a conformational change of the complex upon binding, the C subunit may be released, in which case it would be free to interact with an adjacent chromatin protein, most probably resulting in the phosphorylation of a nuclear protein, such as the 76,000-dalton one. The R and C subunits in the nucleus would then function either independently or cooperatively in regulating gene activity . . . ." (309).

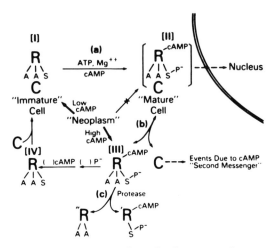

FIG. 10. Model of cAMP action to show the formation of a ternary complex, the cAMP phosphoreceptor·catalytic subunit of protein kinase, which enters the nucleus in rat mammary tumors. RC, protein kinase type II holoenzyme; R, regulatory subunit of protein kinase, the 56,000-dalton cAMP binding protein; R', proteolytic fragment of R (39,000 daltons); R', proteolytic fragment of R (17,000 daltons); C, catalytic subunit of protein kinase; →, forward or reverse reactions and sequence of events; A, arginine; S, serine. Since pure protein kinase was not isolated from the tumors, the structural identification of the enzyme was deduced from the enzyme of normal tissues. Symbols represent qualitative entity, not stoichiometry. From Cho-Chung (309).

VI. Biological Regulation by cGMP-Dependent Protein Kinase

Original studies (310) implicated cGMP as a biological effector molecule mediating the effect of acetylcholine through adrenergic receptors. These investigations catalyzed very intense activities in many laboratories seeking unique biological systems in which cGMP might play an important mediatory role. The "Yin Yang" hypothesis (311), which postulated that the biological regulation of a cell is governed by the opposing biological activities of cAMP and cGMP, created great excitement in the area of regulatory biology. However, the biological role of cGMP became seriously compromised since (a) the previous attempts to demonstrate a hormonally dependent guanylate cyclase failed in every tested system (312, 313); (b) the guanylate cyclase activity from several sources is nonspecifically stimulated by polyunsaturated fatty acids, peroxides, hydroperoxides, free radicals, ascorbic acid, sodium nitroprusside, and several other agents that presumably affect the oxidation-reduction potential of the biochemical reactions

(*313*); and (*c*) there is a general consensus that cGMP-dependent protein kinase does not phosphorylate a specific substrate protein clearly distinct from that of the cAMP-dependent protein kinase (*150*). Here we briefly discuss two systems, one pertaining to neuronal and the other to endocrine (adrenal cortex), where there is evidence of a mediatory role for cGMP. The reader is referred to other reviews for contrasting views and for comprehensive coverage of the literature on cGMP (*312–314*).

A. cGMP and Neurotransmission

There is now some evidence that cGMP plays a mediatory role in neuronal function (*315–317*) through activation of cGMP-dependent protein kinase (*13*). Some studies that have identified the specific substrates for cGMP-dependent protein kinase in some tissues dependent on neurotransmitters are presented below.

Acetylcholine causes a marked increase in cGMP levels in mammalian smooth muscle (*318, 319*). There is a selective phosphorylation of two proteins (designated proteins G-I and G-II) by low concentration of cGMP in guinea pig ductus deferens membrane (*173*). The cGMP concentration that elicit half-maximal increase in the phosphorylation of these proteins is approximately 4 to 5×10^{-8} M, whereas the cAMP concentration required to cause a similar stimulation is 10 to 20 times higher. Similar results were obtained with membrane preparations from uterus (*173*), small intestine (*173*), and aorta (*320*). Subsequently, an acetylcholine-dependent rise of cGMP in phosphorylation of proteins G-I and G-II was observed (*320*). From these observations, it was concluded that acetylcholine-induced increases in cGMP and the cGMP-induced increase in the phosphorylation of proteins G-I and G-II are associated with the acetylcholine-dependent physiological response of smooth muscle. More recently, it was shown that 25% of the total cGMP-dependent protein kinase in the rabbit aortic medial tissue is present in the particulate fraction, and four endogenous particulate substrates were identified: G_0, 250,000 daltons; G_1, 130,000 daltons; G_2, 85,000 daltons; G_3, 75,000 daltons (*321*).

The endogenous phosphorylation of specific protein substrates by cGMP-dependent protein kinase has also been observed in intestinal epithelium brush border (*322*) and the cytosol fraction of rabbit cerebellum (*172*). The half-maximal concentration of cGMP that phosphorylated the 23,000-dalton polypeptide was 60 nM; in contrast, an equivalent concentration of cAMP was ineffective in phosphorylating the polypeptide (*172*).

Some of these endogenous substrates have also been identified by immunological techniques. Antiserum against cGMP-dependent protein kinase inhibits the phosphorylation of G_0, G_1, G_2, and G_3 polypeptides of bovine pulmonary arteries (181), confirming the earlier biochemical findings (321).

There is immunological evidence for the specific substrates of cGMP-dependent protein kinase in smooth muscle membranes and rat aorta. Antiserum against cGMP-dependent protein kinase inhibits cGMP-stimulated phosphorylation of these proteins (181).

These studies indicate that acetylcholine-induced cGMP increases the phosphorylation of certain proteins, leading to specific physiological response. Admittedly, the mechanism by which the effector protein causes the biological response needs to be elucidated.

B. cGMP and Adrenocortical Steroid Metabolism

Submaximal steroidogenic concentrations of ACTH induce a rise in cGMP with a concomitant stimulation of steroidogenesis in isolated rat fasciculata cells (233, 236, 323). Subsequently, the correlation of the rise of cGMP levels with steroidogenesis was observed *in vivo* in the rat adrenal gland (324, 325) and in human (326), crocodile (327), blue and mako shark (328), and bovine adrenal cells (329). These studies indicate that cGMP is one of the mediators of ACTH-induced steroidogenesis.

In the following section, we evaluate the experimental evidence that cGMP mediates adrenal steroidogenesis.

Physiological concentrations (5 to 17×10^{-12} M) of ACTH elevate the levels of cGMP and the production of corticosterone (187, 236, 239, 330). The increment in cGMP preceded the production of corticosterone. Exogenous cGMP stimulates steroidogenesis in quartered adrenal glands (331, 332) and in isolated adrenal cells (333, 334). In addition, cGMP stimulates the transformation of cholesterol to corticosterone in isolated fasciculata cells (335). Since the adrenal cells used in these studies contain relatively little phosphodiesterase (241), the effect of this enzyme on the degradation of the cyclic nucleotides is small.

To satisfy fully the criteria that cGMP mediates ACTH-induced steroidogenesis, it is necessary to show that ACTH stimulates adrenal guanylate cyclase. Indeed, an ACTH-sensitive guanylate cyclase in a particulate fraction of rat adrenal gland has been found (247). Although sodium nitroprusside and ascorbic acid stimulate guanylate cyclase in other tissues (312, 313), they were inactive for the adrenal particulate guanylate cyclase (247). Calcium ion was obligatory for the

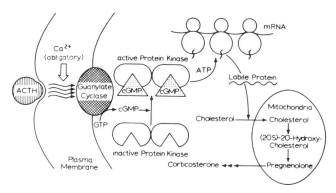

FIG. 11. Postulated role of Ca^{2+} and cGMP in ACTH-activated steroidogenesis. Adapted from Perchellet and Sharma (187).

stimulation of a particulate guanylate cyclase and for the formation of cGMP and corticosterone by ACTH, but calcium alone was inactive (187). These observations constitute strong evidence that cGMP is at least one of the essential components in ACTH-dependent steroidogenesis.

Physiological concentrations of ACTH (5 to 17 × 10^{-12} M) stimulate protein kinase and steroidogenesis in a typical sigmoidal response curve (239, 330). Stimulation of protein kinase preceded the elevation of cGMP, which preceded the production of corticosterone. Thus, induction of corticosteroidogenesis does correlate with cellular levels of cGMP and protein kinase.

Steroidogenic concentrations of cGMP increase endogenous protein kinase activity first, and then corticosterone production in isolated adrenal cells (239). The excellent temporal correlation supports the notion that activation of cGMP-dependent protein kinase is obligatory to ACTH-induced steroidogenesis.

A cGMP-dependent protein kinase from beef adrenal cortex has been characterized (153). It is important to identify its endogenous substrate and to establish the relationship of this phosphoprotein to ACTH-induced steroidogenesis. Only then would the molecular mechanism by which cGMP controls steroid production be fully understood. A hypothetical model depicting the mediatory role of cGMP in adrenal steroidogenesis is shown in Fig. 11. According to this model, Ca^{2+}, cGMP and cGMP-dependent protein kinase are all important components of the fasciculata cell in the control of ACTH-induced steroidogenesis.

There are two apparent weaknesses in the concept of the mediatory role of cGMP in adrenal steroidogenesis. First, exogenous cGMP is only 30% as potent as cAMP in eliciting steroidogenesis in isolated adrenal cells (333). This appears to be technical; the relative uptake of the two nucleotides into the adrenal cell is not known, and the uptake of cGMP may be far lower than that of the cAMP. In addition, the concentrations of both nucleotides required to elicit maximal steroidogenesis are at least six orders of magnitude higher than the endogenous level induced by a maximal steroidogenic concentration of ACTH. Second, 100 μM cGMP failed to stimulate steroidogenesis but did stimulate protein kinase (239). It is conceivable that certain adrenocortical functions of ACTH are independent of cGMP and cAMP.

VII. Concluding Remarks

During the last three decades, we have begun to recognize the sophisticated molecular control mechanisms by which protein kinases, through their substrate proteins, regulate the cellular activity of eukaryotic cells. Three important biological mediators, cyclic AMP, cyclic GMP, and calcium may well exhibit their physiological responses by regulation of their respective protein kinases. Cyclic-AMP-dependent protein kinase has been, and is being, extensively studied, and its key role in the propagation of certain cellular stimuli is well established.

Relatively less is known about the biological importance of cyclic GMP in cellular regulation. The main reluctance to ascribe a mediatory role to this nucleotide in biological responses arises from the failure to identify specific cyclic GMP stimuli and cyclic GMP components in eukaryotic cells. One identified component, cGMP-dependent protein kinase, shows peptide substrate specificity similar to that of cAMP-dependent protein kinase, but the latter kinase is known to be a more efficient phosphorylating enzyme. In addition, the guanylate cyclase responds nonspecifically to such diverse agents as sodium nitroprusside, ascorbic acid, catalase, and cigarette smoke. It is only recently that the hormonally dependent membrane guanylate cyclase has been identified in the adrenal cortex and that specific substrate proteins in the neuronal tissue have been identified. These initial studies indicate that cGMP, like its counterpart cAMP, has an important regulatory role in the mediation of certain cellular responses, and that its effect may be exerted through regulation of cGMP-dependent protein kinase.

The concept that the biological function of calcium is mediated by the intracellular receptor of calcium, calmodulin, has added a new dimension to the protein-kinase-mediated cellular responses. In this hypothesis, calmodulin is the regulatory protein that, by interaction with calcium, becomes an active species, presumably by helical change in its conformation; it in turn activates various cyclic-nucleotide-independent protein kinases. Three protein kinases—myosin light-chain kinase, phosphorylase kinase, and glycogen-synthase kinase—appear to be regulated by calmodulin. Owing to the limited scope of this chapter, it is not possible to discuss more recent developments in this important area of research.

Finally, it must be recognized that the control of various biochemical reactions by protein kinases may not be due to a singular type of protein kinase. The cyclic-nucleotide-dependent protein kinases might control the activity of a certain cyclic-nucleotide-independent protein kinase, and vice versa. The molecular model (Fig. 9) of the control of the initiation of protein synthesis is an example of this. Although this model may not stand the test of further experimentation, it is still a strong possibility that this type of "cascade" control of protein kinases is an important mechanism in the regulation of protein kinase activity. It is anticipated that future research will clarify this aspect of cellular regulation.

ACKNOWLEDGMENTS

Appreciation is expressed to Dr. Alberte L. Ungar for editorial assistance, to Mrs. Joan M. Sharma for the art work, and to Ms. Greta Byars for the excellent typing and editing.

Portions of the experimental work described in this chapter were supported by grants from the National Cancer Institute (CA-16091) and the National Science Foundation (PCM-8008730).

REFERENCES

1. E. W. Sutherland and T. W. Rall, *Pharmacol. Rev.* **12**, 265 (1960).
2. D. A. Walsh, J. P. Perkins, and E. G. Krebs, *JBC* **243**, 3763 (1968).
3. C. S. Rubin and O. M. Rosen, *ARB* **44**, 831 (1975).
4. E. G. Krebs, *Curr. Top. Cell. Regul.* **5**, 99 (1972).
5. E. G. Krebs and J. A. Beavo, *ARB* **48**, 923 (1979).
6. D. A. Walsh and E. G. Krebs, *Enzymes* **8**, 555 (1973).
7. D. A. Walsh and R. H. Cooper, *in* "Biochemical Action of Hormones" (G. Litwack, ed.), Vol. 6, pp. 1–75. Academic Press, New York, 1979.
8. D. A. Walsh, *Biochem. Pharmacol.* **27**, 1801 (1978).
9. T. A. Langan, *Adv. Cyclic Nucleotide Res.* **3**, 99 (1973).
10. G. Taborsky, *Adv. Protein Chem.* **28**, 1 (1974).
11. H. G. Nimmo and P. Cohen, *Adv. Cyclic Nucleotide Res.* **8**, 145 (1977).
12. G. M. Carlson, P. J. Bechtel, and D. J. Graves, *Adv. Enzymol.* **50**, 41 (1979).
13. P. Greengard, *Science* **199**, 146 (1978).
14. E. M. Johnson, *Adv. Cyclic Nucleotide Res.* **8**, 267 (1977).
15. M. Friedkin and A. L. Lehninger, *JBC* **177**, 775 (1949).

16. G. Burnett and E. P. Kennedy, *JBC* **211**, 969 (1954).
17. E. G. Krebs and E. H. Fischer, *BBA* **20**, 1150 (1956).
18. T. W. Rall, E. W. Sutherland, and W. D. Wosilait, *JBC* **218**, 483 (1956).
19. T. A. Sundaranjan, K. S. V. Kumar, and P. S. Sarma, *BBA* **29**, 449 (1958).
20. M. Rabinowitz and F. Lipmann, *JBC* **235**, 1043 (1960).
21. T. W. Rall, E. W. Sutherland, and J. Berthet, *JBC* **224**, 463 (1957).
22. D. Lipkin, W. H. Cook, and R. Markham, *JACS* **81**, 6198 (1959).
23. D. Lipkin, R. Markham, and W. H. Cook, *JACS* **81**, 6075 (1959).
24. G. A. Robison, R. W. Butcher, and E. W. Sutherland, "Cyclic AMP." Academic Press, New York, 1971.
25. E. W. Sutherland, G. A. Robison, and R. W. Butcher, *Circulation* **37**, 279 (1968).
26. D. A. Walsh, J. P. Perkins, and E. G. Krebs, *JBC* **243**, 3763 (1968).
27. T. A. Langan, *Science* **162**, 579 (1968).
28. K. K. Schlender, S. H. Wei, and C. Villar-Palasi, *BBA* **191**, 272 (1969).
29. D. L. Friedman and J. Larner, *Bchem* **2**, 669 (1963).
30. F. Hiujing and J. Larner, *BBRC* **23**, 259 (1966).
31. M. Rosell-Perez and J. Larner, *Bchem* **3**, 81 (1964).
32. E. Belcopitow, *ABB* **93**, 457 (1961).
33. T. R. Soderling, M. F. Jett, N. J. Hutson, and B. S. Khatra, *JBC* **252**, 7517 (1977).
34. C. Villar-Palasi, J. Larner, and L. C. Shen, *Ann. N. Y. Acad. Sci.* **185**, 74 (1971).
35. E. M. Reimann, D. A. Walsh, and E. G. Krebs, *JBC* **246**, 1986 (1971).
36. A. Burchell, P. T. W. Cohen, and P. Cohen, *FEBS Lett.* **67**, 17 (1976).
37. J. D. Corbin and S. L. Keely, *JBC* **252**, 910 (1977).
38. J. Erlichman, D. Sarkar, N. Fleischer, and C. S. Rubin, *JBC* **255**, 8179 (1980).
39. M. A. Brostrom, E. M. Reimann, D. A. Walsh, and E. G. Krebs, *Adv. Enzyme Regul.* **8**, 191 (1970).
40. G. N. Gill and L. D. Garren, *BBRC* **39**, 335 (1970).
41. M. Tao, M. L. Salas, and F. Lipmann, *PNAS* **67**, 408 (1970).
42. A. Kumon, H. Yamamura, and Y. Nishizuka, *BBRC* **41**, 1290 (1970).
43. E. M. Reimann, C. D. Brostrom, J. D. Corbin, C. A. King, and E. G. Krebs, *BBRC* **42**, 187 (1971).
44. J. Erlichman, A. H. Hirsch, and O. M. Rosen, *PNAS* **68**, 731 (1971).
45. G. N. Gill and L. D. Garren, *PNAS* **68**, 786 (1971).
46. C. S. Rubin, J. Erlichman, and O. M. Rosen, *JBC* **247**, 36 (1972).
47. J. Erlichman, C. S. Rubin, and O. M. Rosen, *JBC* **248**, 7607 (1973).
48. J. A. Beavo, P. J. Bechtel, and E. G. Krebs, *Adv. Cyclic Nucleotide Res.* **5**, 241 (1975).
49. O. M. Rosen and J. Erlichman, *JBC* **250**, 7788 (1975).
50. J. Ramseyer, C. B. Kanstein, G. M. Walton, and G. N. Gill, *BBA* **446**, 358 (1976).
51. I. Uno, T. Ueda, and P. Greengard, *JBC* **252**, 5164 (1977).
52. A. G. Gilman, *PNAS* **67**, 305 (1970).
54. J. D. Corbin, P. H. Sugden, L. West, D. A. Flockhart, T. M. Lincoln, and D. McCarthy, *JBC* **253**, 3997 (1978).
55. W. Weber, C. W. Vogel, and H. Hilz, *FEBS Lett.* **99**, 62 (1979).
56. W. Weber and H. Hilz, *BBRC* **90**, 1073 (1979).
57. S. E. Builder, J. A. Beavo, and E. G. Krebs, *JBC* **255**, 2350 (1980).
58. F. Hofmann, J. A. Beavo, P. J. Bechtel, and E. G. Krebs, *JBC* **250**, 7795 (1975).
59. S. S. Taylor and P. H. Stafford, *JBC* **253**, 2284 (1978).
60. P. J. Bechtel, J. A. Beavo, and E. G. Krebs, *JBC* **252**, 2691 (1977).

61. P. H. Sugden, L. A. Holladay, E. M. Reimann, and J. D. Corbin, *BJ* **159**, 409 (1976).
62. F. Hofmann, P. J. Bechtel, and E. G. Krebs, *JBC* **252**, 1441 (1977).
63. M. V. Nesterova, L. P. Sashchenko, V. Y. Vasiliev, and E. S. Severin, *BBA* **377**, 271 (1975).
64. H. Yamamura, K. Nishiyama, R. Shimomura, and Y. Nishizuka, *Bchem* **12**, 856 (1973).
65. P. Cohen, J. F. Antoniw, H. G. Nimmo, and S. J. Yeaman, *in* "Metabolic Interconversions of Enzymes" (S. Shaltiel, ed.), pp. 9–18. Springer-Verlag, Heidelberg, 1976.
66. M. J. Zoller, A. R. Kerlavage, and S. S. Taylor, *JBC* **254**, 2408 (1979).
67. K. A. Peters, J. G. Demaille, and E. H. Fischer, *Bchem* **16**, 5691 (1977).
68. Y. S. Chiu and M. Tao, *JBC* **253**, 7145 (1978).
69. S. Shoji, K. Titani, J. G. Demaile, and E. H. Fischer, *JBC* **254**, 6211 (1979).
70. S. N. Kochetkov, T. V. Bulargina, L. P. Sashchenko, and E. S. Severin, *FEBS Lett.* **71**, 212 (1976).
71. S. N. Kochetkov, T. V. Bulargina, L. P. Sashchenko, and E. S. Severin, *EJB* **81**, 111 (1977).
72. R. Rangel-Aldao, J. W. Kupiec, and O. M. Rosen, *JBC* **254**, 2499 (1979).
73. R. Rangel-Aldao and O. M. Rosen, *JBC* **251**, 7526 (1976).
74. D. C. LaPorte, S. E. Builder, and D. R. Storm, *JBC* **255**, 2343 (1980).
75. A. K. Srivastava and R. H. Stellwagen, *JBC* **253**, 1752 (1978).
75a. G. N. Gill, *J. Cyclic Nucleotide Res.* **3**, 153 (1977).
76. S. R. Rannels and J. D. Corbin, *JBC* **254**, 8605 (1979).
77. R. L. Potter and S. S. Taylor, *JBC* **254**, 2413 (1979).
78. J. Erlichman, R. Rosenfield, and O. M. Rosen, *JBC* **249**, 5000 (1974).
79. H. Maeno, P. L. Reyes, T. Veda, S. A. Rudolf, and P. Greengard, *ABB* **164**, 551 (1974).
80. R. L. Potter and S. S. Taylor, *JBC* **254**, 9000 (1979).
81. D. A. Flockhart, D. M. Watterson, and J. D. Corbin, *JBC* **255**, 4435 (1980).
82. A. R. Kerlaage and S. S. Taylor, *JBC* **255**, 8483 (1980).
83. N. Fleischer, O. M. Rosen, and M. Reichlin, *PNAS* **73**, 54 (1976).
84. C. L. Kapoor, J. A. Beavo, and A. L. Steiner, *JBC* **254**, 12427 (1979).
85. U. Walter, P. Miller, F. Wilson, D. Menkes, and P. Greengard, *JBC* **255**, 3757 (1980).
86. L. J. Chen and D. A. Walsh, *Bchem* **10**, 3614 (1971).
87. J. D. Corbin, S. L. Keely, and C. R. Park, *JBC* **250**, 218 (1975).
88. M. K. Haddox, N. E. Newton, D. K. Hartle, and N. D. Goldberg, *BBRC* **47**, 635 (1972).
89. J. A. Beavo, P. J. Bechtel, and E. G. Krebs, *PNAS* **71**, 3580 (1974).
90. J. Hoppe, W. Freist, R. Marutzky, and S. Shaltiel, *EJB* **90**, 427 (1978).
91. J. Hoppe, R. Marutzky, and K. G. Wagner, *EJB* **80**, 369 (1977).
92. J. Hoppe and W. Freist, *EJB* **93**, 141 (1979).
92a. J. Hoppe, R. Lawaczek, E. Rieke, and K. G. Wagner, *EJB* **90**, 585 (1978).
93. P. J. Bechtel, J. A. Beavo, F. Hofmann, W. L. Dills, and E. G. Krebs, *FP* **34**, 617 (1975).
94. J. A. Todhunter and D. A. Purich, *BBA* **485**, 87 (1977).
95. R. Rangel-Aldao and O. M. Rosen, *JBC* **251**, 3375 (1976).
96. O. M. Rosen, R. Rangel-Aldao, and J. Erlichman, *Curr. Top. Cell. Regul.* **12**, 39 (1977).
97. R. A. Steinberg, P. H. O'Farrel, U. Freidrich, and P. Coffino, *Cell* **10**, 381 (1977).

98. R. L. Geahlen and E. G. Krebs, *JBC* **255**, 1164 (1980).
99. R. L. Geahlen and E. G. Krebs, *JBC* **255**, 9375 (1980).
100. B. E. Kemp, D. B. Bylund, T. S. Huang, and E. G. Krebs, *PNAS* **72**, 3448 (1975).
101. T. A. Langan, *Ann. N. Y. Acad. Sci.* **185**, 166 (1971).
102. S. V. Shlyapnikov, A. A. Arutyunyan, S. N. Kurochkin, S. N. Memolova, M. V. Nesterova, L. P. Saschenko, and E. S. Severin, *FEBS Lett.* **53**, 316 (1975).
103. E. Hashimoto, M. Takeda, and Y. Nishizuka, *BBRC* **66**, 547 (1975).
104. A. Farago, T. Rombanyi, F. Antoni, A. Takats, and F. Fabian, *Nature* **254**, 88 (1975).
105. S. Shenolikar and P. Cohen, *FEBS Lett.* **86**, 92 (1978).
106. S. J. Yeaman, P. Cohen, D. C. Watson, and G. H. Dixon, *BJ* **162**, 411 (1977).
107. C. G. Proud, D. M. Rylat, S. J. Yeaman, and P. Cohen, *FEBS Lett.* **80**, 435 (1977).
108. T. S. Huang and E. G. Krebs, *BBRC* **75**, 643 (1977).
109. B. Edlund, J. Anderson, V. L. Titanji, V. Dahlquist, P. Ekman, O. Zetterqvist, and L. Engstrom, *BBRC* **67**, 1516 (1975).
110. P. Cohen, D. C. Watson, and G. H. Dixon, *EJB* **51**, 79 (1975).
111. D. B. Bylund and E. G. Krebs, *JBC* **250**, 6355 (1975).
112. E. Humble, L. Berglund, V. Titanji, O. Ljungstrom, B. Edlund, O. Zetterqvist, and L. Engstrom, *BBRC* **66**, 614 (1975).
113. P. Daile and P. R. Carnegie, *BBRC* **61**, 852 (1974).
115. B. E. Kemp, D. J. Graves, E. Benjamini, and E. G. Krebs, *JBC* **252**, 4888 (1977).
116. P. Daile, P. R. Carnegie, and D. Young, *Nature* **257**, 416 (1975).
117. O. Zetterqvist, U. Ragnarson, E. Humble, L. Berglund, and L. Engstrom, *BBRC* **70**, 696 (1976).
118. A. H. Pomerantz, V. G. Allfrey, R. B. Merrifield, and E. M. Johnson, *PNAS* **74**, 4261 (1977).
119. B. E. Kemp, *JBC* **254**, 2638 (1979).
120. D. Small, P. Y. Chou, and G. D. Fasman, *BBRC* **79**, 341 (1977).
121. J. R. Feramisco, D. B. Glass, and E. G. Krebs, *JBC* **255**, 4240 (1980).
122. M. Matsuo, C. H. Huang, and L. C. Huang, *BJ* **173**, 441 (1978).
123. J. R. Ogez and I. H. Segel, *JBC* **251**, 4551 (1976).
124. K. Schwechheimer and F. Hofmann, *JBC* **252**, 7690 (1977).
125. J. Hoppe, E. Rieke, and K. G. Wagner, *EJB* **83**, 411 (1978).
126. J. M. Boeynaemes and J. F. Dumont, *Mol. Cell. Endocrinol.* **7**, 275 (1977).
127. V. Chau, L. C. Huang, G. Romero, R. L. Biltonen, and C. Huang, *Bchem* **19**, 924 (1980).
128. R. N. Armstrong and E. T. Kaiser, *Bchem* **17**, 2840 (1978).
129. J. Tsuzuki and J. A. Kiger, *Bchem* **17**, 2961 (1978).
130. D. A. Walsh, C. D. Ashby, C. Gonzalez, D. Calkins, E. H. Fischer, and E. G. Krebs, *JBC* **246**, 1977 (1971).
131. J. G. Demaille, K. A. Peters, and E. H. Fischer, *Bchem* **16**, 3030 (1977).
132. H. Weber and O. M. Rosen, *J. Cyclic Nucleotide Res.* **3**, 415 (1977).
133. C. D. Ashby and D. A. Walsh, *JBC* **247**, 6637 (1972).
134. D. A. Walsh and C. D. Ashby, *Recent Prog. Horm. Res.* **29**, 329 (1973).
135. J. F. Kuo, *BBRC* **65**, 1214 (1975).
136. M. Costa, *BBRC* **78**, 1311 (1977).
137. E. G. Beal, J. R. Dedman, and A. R. Means, *JBC* **252**, 6322 (1977).
138. A. Szmigielski, A. Guidotti, and E. Costa, *JBC* **252**, 3848 (1977).
139. J. F. Kuo and P. Greengard, *JBC* **245**, 2493 (1970).
140. J. F. Kuo, G. R. Wyatt, and P. Greengard, *JBC* **246**, 7159 (1971).
141. F. Hofmann and G. Sold, *BBRC* **49**, 1100 (1972).

142. J. F. Kuo, *PNAS* **71**, 4037 (1974).
143. J. F. Kuo, *PNAS* **72**, 2256 (1975).
144. T. M. Lincoln, C. L. Hall, C. R. Park, and J. D. Cobin, *PNAS* **73**, 2559 (1976).
145. G. N. Gill, G. M. Walton, and P. J. Sperry, *JBC* **252**, 6443 (1977).
146. T. M. Lincoln, W. L. Dills, and J. D. Corbin, *JBC* **252**, 4269 (1977).
147. H. R. DeJonge and O. M. Rosen, *JBC* **252**, 2780 (1977).
148. V. Flockerzi, N. Speichermann, and F. Hofmann, *JBC* **253**, 3395 (1978).
149. Y. Takai, K. Nishiyama, H. Yamamura, and Y. Nishizuka, *JBC* **250**, 4690 (1975).
150. G. N. Gill and R. W. McCune, *Curr. Top. Cell. Regul.* **15**, 1 (1979).
151. K. Nakazawa and M. Sano, *JBC* **250**, 7415 (1975).
152. Y. Takai, S. Nakaya, M. Inoue, A. Kishimoto, K. Nishiyama, H. Yamamura, and Y. Nishizuka, *JBC* **251**, 1481 (1976).
153. H. Ahrens and R. K. Sharma, *J. Steroid Biochem.* **11**, 1099 (1979).
154. E. Miyamoto, G. L. Petzold, J. F. Kuo, and P. Greengard, *JBC* **248**, 179 (1973).
155. J. F. Kuo, E. Miyamoto, and P. L. Reyes, *Biochem. Pharmacol.* **23**, 2011 (1974).
156. J. F. Kuo, J. G. Patrick, and V. L. Sperry, *BBRC* **72**, 996 (1976).
157. J. F. Kuo, *Metabolism* **24**, 321 (1975).
158. M. Van-Leemput Coutrez, J. Camus, and J. Christophe, *BBRC* **54**, 182 (1973).
159. R. Kobayashi and V. S. Fang, *BBRC* **69**, 1080 (1976).
160. M. Inoue, A. Kishimoto, Y. Takai, and Y. Nishizuka, *JBC* **251**, 4476 (1976).
161. T. M. Lincoln, D. A. Flockhart, and J. D. Corbin, *JBC* **253**, 6002 (1978).
162. C. E. Monken and G. N. Gill, *JBC* **255**, 7067 (1980).
163. R. W. McCune and G. N. Gill, *JBC* **254**, 5083 (1979).
163a. E. Hashimoto, M. Takeda, Y. Nishizuka, K. Hamana, and K. Iwai, *JBC* **251**, 6287 (1976).
164. D. B. Glass and E. G. Krebs, *FP* **37**, Abstract 1329 (1978).
165. D. B. Glass and E. G. Krebs, *JBC* **254**, 9728 (1979).
166. D. K. Blumenthal, J. T. Stull, and G. N. Gill, *JBC* **253**, 334 (1978).
167. T. M. Lincoln and J. D. Corbin, *JBC* **253**, 337 (1978).
168. T. M. Lincoln and J. D. Corbin, *PNAS* **74**, 3239 (1977).
169. J. C. Khoo, P. J. Sperry, G. N. Gill, and D. Steinberg, *PNAS* **74**, 4843 (1977).
170. J. P. Riou, T. H. Claus, D. A. Flockhart, J. D. Corbin, and S. J. Pilkis, *PNAS* **74**, 4615 (1977).
171. B. Edlund, O. Zetterqvist, U. Ragnarsson, and L. Engstrom, *BBRC* **79**, 139 (1977).
172. D. Schlichter, J. E. Casnellie, and P. Greengard, *Nature* **273**, 61 (1978).
173. J. E. Casnellie and P. Greengard, *PNAS* **71**, 1891 (1974).
174. H. R. DeJonge, *Nature* **262**, 590 (1976).
174a. T. E. Donnelly, Jr., J. F. Kuo, E. Miyamoto, and P. Greengard, *JBC* **248**, 199 (1973).
174b. T. E. Donnelly Jr., J. F. Kuo, P. L. Reyes, Y.-P. Liu, and P. Greengard, *JBC* **248**, 190 (1973).
175. M. Shoji, N. L. Brackett, J. Tse, R. Shapira, and J. F. Kuo, *JBC* **253**, 3427 (1978).
176. W.-N. Kuo and J. F. Kuo, *JBC* **251**, 4283 (1976).
177. J. F. Kuo, E. J. Malveaux, J. G. Patrick, C. W. Davis, W.-N. Kuo, and A. W. Pruitt, *BBA* **497**, 785 (1977).
178. M. Shoji, J. G. Patrick, J. Tse, and J. F. Kuo, *JBC* **252**, 4347 (1977).
179. G. N. Gill, K. E. Holdy, G. M. Walton, and C. B. Kanstein, *PNAS* **73**, 3918 (1976).
180. C. L. Kapoor, J. A. Beavo, and A. L. Steiner, *JBC* **254**, 12427 (1979).
181. U. Walter, P. Miller, F. Wilson, D. Menkes, and P. Greengard, *JBC* **255**, 3757 (1980).
182. T. M. Lincoln and J. D. Corbin, *J. Cyclic Nucleotide Res.* **4**, 3 (1978).

183. B. Hartley, *in* "Evolution in the Microbial World" (M. S. Carlile and J. S. Skehel, eds.), pp. 151–182. Cambridge Univ. Press, London, 1974.

184. K. Nishiyama, H. Katakami, H. Yamamura, Y. Takai, R. Shimoura, and Y. Nishizuka, *JBC* **250**, 1297 (1975).

185. J. Monod, J. Wyman, and J. P. Changeux, *JMB* **12**, 88 (1965).

186. D. Wallach, P. J. A. Davies, and I. Pastan, *JBC* **253**, 4739 (1978).

187. J.-P. Perchellet and R. K. Sharma, *Science* **203**, 1259 (1979).

188. J. F. Kuo and P. Greengard, *PNAS* **64**, 1349 (1969).

189. E. G. Krebs, *Endocrinol. Proc. Int. Congr. 4th, 1973*, pp. 17–29 (1974).

191. P. Cohen, *Curr. Top. Cell. Regul.* **14**, 117 (1978).

192. T. Hayakawa, J. P. Perkins, D. A. Walsh, and E. G. Krebs, *Bchem* **12**, 567 (1973).

193. H. P. Jennisen and L. M. G. Heilmeyer, *FEBS Lett.* **42**, 77 (1974).

194. H. P. Jennisen and L. M. G. Heilmeyer, *Bchem* **14**, 754 (1975).

195. P. Cohen, A. Burchell, J. G. Foulkes, P. T. W. Cohen, T. C. Vanaman, and A. C. Nairn, *FEBS Lett.* **92**, 287 (1978).

196. W. Y. Cheung, *BBRC* **38**, 353 (1970).

197. W. Y. Cheung, *JBC* **246**, 2859 (1971).

197a. E. G. Krebs, D. J. Graves, and E. H. Fischer, *JBC* **234**, 2867 (1959).

198. E. G. Krebs, D. S. Love, G. E. Bratvold, K. A. Trayser, W. L. Meyer, and E. H. Fischer, *Bchem* **3**, 1022 (1964).

199. R. J. DeLange, R. G. Kemp, W. D. Riley, R. A. Cooper, and E. G. Krebs, *JBC* **243**, 2200 (1968).

200. T. R. Soderling, J. P. Hickenbottom, E. M. Reimann, F. L. Hunkeler, D. A. Walsh, and E. G. Krebs, *JBC* **245**, 6317 (1970).

200a. D. A. Walsh and C. D. Ashby, *Rec. Prog. Horm. Res.* **29**, 329 (1973).

201. J. B. Posner, R. Stern, and E. G. Krebs, *JBC* **240**, 982 (1965).

202. G. I. Drummond, J. P. Harwood, and C. A. Powell, *JBC* **244**, 4235 (1969).

203. S. J. Yeaman and P. Cohen, *EJB* **51**, 93 (1975).

204. T. Hayakawa, J. P. Perkins, and E. G. Krebs, *Bchem* **12**, 574 (1973).

205. P. Cohen and J. F. Antoniw, *FEBS Lett.* **34**, 43 (1973).

206. J. F. Antoniw and P. Cohen, *EJB* **68**, 45 (1976).

207. S. Shenolikar, P. T. W. Cohen, P. Cohen, A. C. Nairn, and S. V. Perry, *EJB* **100**, 329 (1979).

208. A. D. Cherrington, F. D. Assimacopoulos, S. C. Harper, J. D. Corbin, C. R. Park, and J. H. Exton, *JBC* **251**, 5209 (1976).

209. M. J. Birnbaum and J. N. Fain, *JBC* **252**, 528 (1977).

210. S. Keppens, J. R. Vendenheede, and H. de Wulf, *BBA* **496**, 448 (1977).

211. J. H. Exton, A. D. Cherrington, N. J. Hutson, and F. D. Assimacopoulos-Jeannet, *in* "Glucagon: Its Role in Physiology and Clinical Medicine" (P. Foa, J. Bajaj and N. L. Foa, eds.), pp. 321–348. Springer-Verlag, Berlin and New York, 1977.

212. K. K. Schlender and E. M. Reimann, *PNAS* **72**, 2197 (1975).

213. K. P. Huang, F. L. Huang, W. H. Glinsmann, and J. C. Robison, *BBRC* **65**, 1163 (1975).

214. H. G. Nimmo, C. G. Proud, and P. Cohen, *EJB* **68**, 31 (1976).

215. T. R. Soderling, *Mol. Cell. Endocrinol.* **16**, 157 (1979).

216. P. J. Roach and J. Larner, *Mol. Cell. Biochem.* **15**, 179 (1977).

217. T. R. Soderling and C. R. Park, *Adv. Cyclic Nucleotide Res.* **4**, 283 (1974).

218. T. R. Soderling, A. K. Srivastava, M. A. Bass, and B. S. Khatra, *PNAS* **76**, 2536 (1979).

219. P. J. Roach, A. A. Roach-DePaoli, and J. Larner, *J. Cyclic Nucleotide Res.* **4**, 245 (1978).
220. A. A. Roach, P. J. Roach, and J. Larner, *JBC* **254**, 4212 (1979).
221. K. X. Walsh, D. M. Milikin, K. K. Schlender, and E. M. Reimann, *JBC* **254**, 6611 (1979).
222. M. E. Payne and T. R. Soderling, *JBC* **255**, 8054 (1980).
223. N. J. Hutson, F. T. Brumley, F. D. Assimacopoulas, S. C. Harper, and J. H. Exton, *JBC* **251**, 5200 (1976).
223a. N. J. Hutson, B. S. Khatra, and T. R. Soderling, *JBC* **253**, 2540 (1978).
224. J. C. Garrison, M. K. Borland, V. A. Florio, and D. A. Twible, *JBC* **254**, 7147 (1979).
225. I. D. K. Halkerston, *Adv. Cyclic Nucleotide Res.* **6**, 99 (1975).
226. G. Sayers, R. J. Beall, and S. Seelig, *Int. Rev. Biochem.* **8**, 20 (1974).
227. D. Schulster, *Adv. Steroid Biochem. Pharmacol.* **4**, 233 (1974).
228. B. P. Schimmer, *Adv. Cyclic Nucleotide Res.* **13**, 181 (1980).
229. R. K. Sharma, *Prog. Cancer Res. Ther.* **9**, 13 (1978).
230. R. C. Haynes, *JBC* **233**, 1220 (1958).
231. D. G. Grahme-Smith, R. W. Butcher, R. L. Ney, and E. W. Sutherland, *JBC* **242**, 5535 (1967).
232. R. J. Beall and G. Sayers, *ABB* **148**, 70 (1972).
233. C. A. Harrington, D. C. Fenimore, and R. W. Farmer, *BBRC* **85**, 55 (1978).
234. W. R. Moyle, Y. C. Kong, and J. Ramchandran, *JBC* **248**, 2409 (1973).
235. M. Nakamura, M. Ide, T. Okabuyashi, and A. Tanaka, *Endocrinol. Jpn.* **19**, 443 (1972).
236. R. K. Sharma, N. K. Ahmed, L. S. Sutliff, and J. S. Brush, *FEBS. Lett.* **45**, 107 (1974).
237. S. Shima, Y. Kawashima, and M. Hirai, *Acta. Endocrinol.* **90**, 139 (1979).
238. K. Yanagibashi, N. Kamiya, G. Lin, and M. Matsuka, *Endocrinol. Jpn.* **25**, 545 (1978).
239. R. K. Sharma, N. K. Ahmed, and G. Shanker, *EJB* **70**, 427 (1976).
240. I. D. K. Halkerston, M. Feinstein, and O. Hechter, *PSEBM* **122**, 896 (1966).
241. A. E. Kitabchi, D. B. Wilson, and R. K. Sharma, *BBRC* **44**, 898 (1971).
242. A. Peytreman, W. E. Nicholson, G. W. Liddle, J. G. Hardman, and E. W. Sutherland, *Endocrinology* **92**, 525 (1973).
243. R. K. Sharma, *FEBS Lett.* **38**, 197 (1974).
243a. R. S. Sawhney and R. K. Sharma, *FEBS Lett.* **70**, 163 (1976).
244. G. B. Sala, K. Hayashi, K. J. Catt, and M. L. Dufau, *JBC* **254**, 3861 (1979).
245. E. J. Podesta, A. Milani, H. Steffen, and R. Neher, *BJ* **180**, 355 (1979).
246. R. S. Sawhney, K. Hirai, and R. K. Sharma, *Endocrine Soc. 61st Annu. Meet. Soc. Washington, D.C.* (Abstract 573) 1980.
247. P. Nambi and R. K. Sharma, *Endocrinology* **108**, 2025 (1981).
247a. P. Nambi and R. K. Sharma, *BBRC* **100**, 508 (1981). (Erratum, Ibid **101**, 330.)
248. W. V. Zucker and H. M. Schulman, *PNAS* **59**, 582 (1968).
249. M. Rabinowitz, M. L. Freedman, J. M. Fisher, and C. R. Maxwell, *CSHSQB* **34**, 567 (1969).
250. T. Hunt, G. Vanderhoff, and I. M. London, *JMB* **66**, 471 (1972).
251. E. Ehrenfeld and T. Hunt, *PNAS* **68**, 1075 (1971).
252. N. S. Kosower, G. A. Vanderhoff, and E. M. Kosower, *BBA* **272**, 623 (1972).
253. D. H. Levin, R. S. Ranu, V. Ernst, and I. M. London, *PNAS* **73**, 3112 (1976).
254. G. Kramer, M. Cimadivella, and B. Hardesty, *PNAS* **73**, 3078 (1976).

255. R. S. Ranu and I. M. London, *PNAS* **73**, 4349 (1976).
256. P. Farrell, J. Balkow, T. Hunt, R. J. Jackson, and H. Trachsel, *Cell* **11**, 187 (1977).
257. M. Gross and J. Mendelewski, *BBRC* **74**, 559 (1977).
258. D. H. Levin and I. M. London, *PNAS* **75**, 1121 (1978).
259. V. Ernst, D. H. Levin, and I. M. London, *PNAS* **75**, 4110 (1978).
260. C. DeHaro, A. Datta, and S. Ochoa, *PNAS* **75**, 243 (1978).
261. R. S. Ranu, I. M. London, A. Das, A. Dasgupta, A. Majumdar, R. Ralston, R. Roy, and N. K. Gupta, *PNAS* **75**, 745 (1978).
262. C. De Haro and S. Ochoa, *PNAS* **75**, 2713 (1978).
263. C. De Haro and S. Ochoa, *PNAS* **76**, 1741 (1979).
264. R. S. Ranu and I. M. London, *PNAS* **76**, 1079 (1979).
265. A. Das, R. O. Ralston, M. Grace, R. Roy, P. Ghosh-Dastidar, H. K. Das, B. Yaghami, S. Palmieri, and N. K. Gupta, *PNAS* **76**, 5076 (1979).
266. A. Datta, C. DeHaro, J. M. Sierra, and S. Ochoa, *PNAS* **74**, 1463 (1977).
267. A. Datta, C. De Haro, J. M. Sierra, and S. Ochoa, *PNAS* **74**, 3326 (1977).
268. S. Ochoa and S. De Haro, *ARB* **48**, 549 (1979).
270. H. Trachsel, R. S. Ranu, and I. M. London, *PNAS* **75**, 3654 (1978).
271. V. Ernst, D. H. Levin, and I. M. London, *PNAS* **76**, 2118 (1979).
272. T. S. Lundak and J. A. Traugh, *in* "Protein Phosphorylation and BioRegulation" (G. Thomas, E. J. Podesta, and J. Gordon, eds.), pp. 154–161. Karger, Basel, 1980.
273. M. Gross and J. Mendelweski, *BBA* **520**, 650 (1978).
274. D. H. Levin, R. Petryshyn, and I. M. London, *PNAS* **77**, 832 (1980).
275. V. Ernst, D. H. Levin, A. L. Leroux, and I. M. London, *PNAS* **77**, 1286 (1980).
276. R. Petryshyn, H. Trachsel, and I. M. London, *PNAS* **76**, 1579 (1978).
277. D. H. Levin, V. Ernst, and I. M. London, *JBC* **254**, 7935 (1979).
278. Y. Kuroda and R. K. Sharma, *BBRC* **96**, 601 (1980).
279. Y. Kuroda, W. Merrick, and R. K. Sharma, *ABB*, in press.
280. G. C. Sen, H. Taira and P. Lengyel, *JBC* **253**, 5915 (1978).
280a. R. E. Moore and R. K. Sharma, *Science* **210**, 1137 (1980).
281. E. Costa, A. Kurosawa, and A. Guidotti, *PNAS* **73**, 1058 (1976).
281a. A. F. Bristow, C. Gleed, J.-L. Fauchere, R. Schwyzer, and D. Schulster, *BJ* **186**, 599 (1980).
282. R. A. Jungman, P. C. Hiestand, and J. S. Schweppe, *Endocrinology* **94**, 168 (1974).
283. W. K. Palmer, M. Castagna, and D. A. Walsh, *BJ* **142**, 469 (1974).
284. M. Castagna, W. K. Palmer, and D. A. Walsh, *EJB* **55**, 193 (1975).
285. G. P. Georgiev, *Annu. Rev. Genet.* **3**, 155 (1969).
286. R. J. DeLange and E. L. Smith, *ARB* **40**, 279 (1971).
287. M. O. J. Olson and H. Busch, *in* "The Cell Nucleus" (H. Busch, ed.), Vol. 3, pp. 212–268. Academic Press, New York, 1974.
288. L. J. Kleinsmith, *J. Cell. Physiol.* **85**, 459 (1975).
289. G. S. Stein, T. C. Spelsberg, and L. J. Kleinsmith, *Science* **183**, 817 (1974).
290. L. J. Kleinsmith, J. Stein, and G. Stein, *PNAS* **73**, 1174 (1976).
291. R. A. Jungman, S. Lee, and A. B. DeAngelo, *Adv. Cyclic Nucleotide Res.* **5**, 218 (1975).
292. R. A. Jungman and E. G. Kranias, *Int. J. Biochem.* **8**, 819 (1977).
293. R. A. Jungman and D. H. Russel, *Life Sci.* **20**, 1787 (1977).
294. Y. S. Cho-Chung, *Life Sci.* **24**, 1231 (1979).

295. T. A. Langan, *PNAS* **64**, 1276 (1969).
296. T. A. Langan, *JBC* **244**, 5763 (1969).
297. A. B. DeAngelo, J. S. Schwepe, R. A. Jungman, P. Huber, and U. Eppenberger, *Endocrinology* **97**, 1509 (1975).
298. A. M. Spielvogel, M. I. Mendieks, U. Eppenberger, and R. A. Jungman, *EJB* **73**, 199 (1977).
299. D. M. Chuang and E. Costa, *Mol. Pharmacol.* **12**, 514 (1976).
300. D. M. Chuang, R. Hollenbeck, and E. Costa, *Science* **193**, 60 (1976).
301. A. Kurosowa, A. Guidotti, and E. Costa, *Science* **193**, 691 (1976).
302. A. Kurosowa, A. Guidotti, and E. Costa, *Mol. Pharmacol.* **12**, 420 (1976).
303. C. V. Byus and D. H. Russel, *Biochem. Pharmacol.* **25**, 1595 (1976).
304. C. V. Byus, W. D. Wicks, and D. H. Russel, *J. Cyclic Nucleotide Res.* **2**, 241 (1976).
305. L. J. Kleinsmith, V. G. Allfrey, and A. W. Mirsky, *PNAS* **55**, 1182 (1966).
306. L. J. Kleinsmith and V. G. Allfrey, *BBA* **175**, 123 (1969).
307. M. Kamiyama and B. Dastuge, *BBRC* **44**, 29 (1971).
308. Y. S. Cho-Chung, D. Archibald, and T. Clair, *Science* **205**, 1390 (1979).
309. Y. S. Cho-Chung, *J. Cyclic Nucleotide Res.* **6**, 163 (1980).
310. W. J. George, J. B. Polson, A. G. O'Toole, and N. D. Goldberg, *PNAS* **66**, 398 (1970).
311. N. D. Goldberg, M. K. Haddox, S. E. Nicol, D. B. Glass, C. H. Sanford, F. A. Kuehl, Jr., and R. Estensen, *Adv. Cyclic Nucleotide Res.* **5**, 307 (1975).
312. N. D. Goldberg and M. K. Haddox, *ARB* **46**, 823 (1977).
313. F. Murad, W. P. Arnold, C. K. Mittal, and J. M. Braughler, *Adv. Cyclic Nucleotide Res.* **11**, 175 (1979).
314. H. Rasmussen and D. B. P. Goodman, *Physiol. Rev.* **57**, 421 (1977).
315. F. E. Bloom, *Rev. Physiol. Pharmacol.* **74**, 1 (1975).
316. P. Greengard, *Nature* **260**, 101 (1976).
317. J. A. Nathanson, *Physiol. Rev.* **57**, 157 (1977).
318. T. P. Lee, J. F. Kuo, and P. Greengard, *PNAS* **69**, 3287 (1972).
319. G. Schultz, J. G. Hardman, K. Schultz, J. W. Davis, and E. W. Sutherland, *PNAS* **70**, 1721 (1973).
320. H. E. Ives, J. E. Casnellie, P. Greengard, and J. Jamieson, *J. Cell. Biol* **75**, 325a (1977).
321. J. E. Casnellie, H. E. Ives, J. D. Jamieson, and P. Greengard, *JBC* **255**, 3770 (1980).
322. H. R. DeJonge, *Nature* **262**, 590 (1976).
323. C. A. Harrington, D. C. Fenimore, and R. W. Farmer, *Endocrine Soc. 59th Annu. Meet. Chicago* (Abstract 170), 1977.
324. G. Neri, A. M. Gambino, G. Mazzochi, and G. G. Nussdorfer, *Experientia* **34**, 815 (1978).
325. G. C. Nussdorfer, G. Neri, and G. Mazzochi, *3rd Int. Conf. Cyclic Nucleotides,* New Orleans (Abstract THA-226) 1977.
326. K. V. Honn and W. Chavin, *in* "Evolution of Vertebrate Endocrines" (P. K. T. Pang and A. Epple, eds.), pp. 133–162. Texas Tech Press, 1980.
327. K. V. Honn and W. Chavin, *Gen. Comp. Endocrinol.* **26**, 374 (1975).
328. K. V. Honn and W. Chavin, *Gen. Comp. Endocrinol.* **36**, 161 (1978).
329. R. P. Rubin, S. G. Laychock, and D. W. End, *BBA* **496**, 329 (1977).
330. J.-P. Perchellet, G. Shanker, and R. K. Sharma, *Science* **199**, 311 (1978).

331. W. H. Glinsman, E. P. Hern, L. G. Linareli, and R. V. Farese, *Endocrinology* **85,** 711 (1969).

332. D. Mahaffee and R. L.Ney, *Metabolism* **19,** 1104 (1970).

333. A. E. Kitabchi and R. K. Sharma, *Endocrinology* **88,** 1109 (1971).

334. I. Rivkin and M. Chasin, *Endocrinology* **88,** 664 (1971).

335. R. K. Sharma and R. S. Sawhney, *Bchem* **17,** 316 (1978).

Index

Contents of Previous Volumes